TRANSVERSAL MAPPINGS
AND
FLOWS

TRANSVERSAL MAPPINGS AND FLOWS

Ralph Abraham
Princeton University

Joel Robbin
University of Wisconsin

W. A. Benjamin, Inc. *New York* *Amsterdam* *1967*

Transversal Mappings and Flows

Library of Congress Catalog Card Number 67–22211
Manufactured in the United States of America

*The manuscript was put into production on 27 July 1966;
this volume was published on 22 July 1967*

*The publisher is pleased to acknowledge the assistance
of H. Petard, who designed the text and cover*

W. A. Benjamin, Inc.
New York, New York 10016

PREFACE

In 1880, Poincaré introduced revolutionary new ideas in the study of ordinary differential equations. Since then, these have evolved into a vast subject known as the *qualitative theory*. By the 1930's the subject had become explicitly global, and its goal was the study of the qualitative features of vectorfields defined on manifolds. In the 1950's, the qualitative theory and differential topology began to infuse each other, most notably in the work of Reeb, Peixoto, Smale, and Thom. Due to this influence, the qualitative theory of systems of ordinary differential equations and their integrals, or more precisely, of vectorfields and their flows on manifolds, has assumed a form which, although very closely conforming to the original ideas of Poincaré, may appear somewhat foreign to the classical workers of the early twentieth century. An exposition of this form, which up to now is accessible only in recent research papers, is one of the goals of this book.

One of the main themes of the recent work in the qualitative theory is the search for *generic,* or typical, properties of vectorfields. This theme, which occurs in the earliest work of Poincaré, achieved its definitive modern form in the papers of Smale in the period 1960–1962. The last of these presents a difficult theorem, in which three important qualitative features of vectorfields, now known as properties *G*1, *G*2 and *G*3, are proved to be generic in a very precise sense. This result, proved independently and simultaneously by Kupka, is an explicit goal of this book, and is proved here by a new method.

The new method is a general technique for establishing generic properties of vectorfields, mappings, partial differential equations, and so on. Called *transversality theory,* it has evolved from basic ideas introduced by Thom in 1954. The first half of this book is a complete exposition of the foundations of the transversality technique, and the second half is devoted to the applications to flows.

The first chapter is a review of differential theory, and can be omitted by those who are already familiar with Banach manifolds, jet bundles, and so on. The only original result in this chapter is the *converse of Taylor's Theorem,* in Section 2. This is a very useful criterion for the smoothness of mappings defined on Banach spaces, and is used several times in later sections.

The second chapter is devoted to the topologies of spaces of vector bundle sections, in terms of which the notion of a generic property can be precisely defined. Here also is an easy proof, using the criterion for smoothness of Section 2, of the *smoothness of the evaluation map* (originally announced in Abraham [*2*]*). This is a basic tool in the transversality technique.

---

*Numbers in square brackets refer to the bibliography.

The third chapter consists of a complete proof of another cornerstone of transversality theory, Smale's Density Theorem for regular values of Fredholm mappings. This is derived from Sard's Density Theorem by an easy trick due to Smale. The proof of Sard's Theorem follows Metivier's, based on the Rough Composition Theorem of Kneser and Glaeser. This in turn is obtained from Whitney's Extension Theorem for smooth mappings of closed subsets, which is proved in Appendix A.

Chapter 4 is devoted to three main results on transversality, the Openness, Density, and Isotopy Theorems. These are all based on prototypes due to Thom. The Density Theorem was announced in Abraham [*1*], but the proof given here, based on Smale's Density Theorem, is much simpler. The Isotopy Theorem is announced here for the first time. All are expressed in the context of *representations of manifolds,* which provides exactly the level of generality needed for the applications to generic properties of flows.

Chapter 5 introduces some of the basic ideas of the recent qualitative theory of vectorfields and flows. These are all expressed both traditionally and equivalently in terms of transversality theory. Here also are the first applications of transversality theory; the Period Bounding Lemma, and the Γ Finiteness and Stability Theorems. Together, these express the basic properties of *flows which are transversal to the diagonal.*

Chapter 6 gives a complete proof of the Global Stable Manifold Theorem, originally due to Smale. This is obtained easily, by a device similar to the one used by Smale, from an analogous local theorem. The local version has evolved gradually since Poincaré, and a complete proof of a very strong and general theorem is given in Appendix C. This is an original research article by Al Kelley, and is published here for the first time.

Chapter 7 presents the new proof of the theorem of Kupka and Smale on the genericity of properties *G*1, *G*2, and *G*3 for flows on a compact manifold. One of the main requirements for this proof is the *structure of semialgebraic sets,* including the theorems of Tarski-Seidenberg and Whitney. These are explained in Appendix B. Another important tool in this approach is the *perturbation theory for vectorfields,* which is given in Section 32. With these prerequisites out of the way, the proof of the Kupka-Smale Theorem becomes a direct application of transversality theory. The most difficult point is sidestepped by a clever induction idea due to Peixoto,which is based on the Period Bounding Lemma of Chapter 5.

This book originated in a series of lectures by one of us (R.A.), given at Princeton University in the fall of 1965. The other (J.R.) prepared a preliminary manuscript which extended and reorganized the material of the lectures considerably. We revised this to the present form with two goals in mind. The first is the publication of the new results from the lectures; the Transversality Theorems in the present form and the new proof of the Kupka-Smale Theorem appear here for the first time.* The second goal is to make the results and methods more accessible than they would be in a journal article, and to this end we have made the exposition as complete and self-contained as possible. Beyond modern differential theory (for example, that of Lang [*1*]), all the main results are proved in detail. We hope that beginning graduate students in mathematics as well as technical specialists in dynamical systems will find the material more understandable in this format. For the former, we might suggest for an introductory course in global analysis: Dieudonné [*1*], Lang [*1*], Chapters 1 through 4 of this book, and the elementary applications of transversality, such as the Whitney Embedding Theorem, which are found in Abraham

---

*In connection with these results, R.A. is grateful to Stephen Smale and René Thom for introducing him to these problems in 1961, to Mauricio Peixoto for a key idea for the *G*2 Density Theorem in 1965, and to many colleagues at Berkeley, Columbia, and Princeton for helpful conversations in the past.

[*2*]. For the latter group, a brief look through Chapter 4 will be ample preparation for the technical applications of transversality to flows in Chapters 5 to 7.

We are indebted to Al Kelley for contributing his article to our book, to the National Science Foundation, Office of Naval Research, NATO, and the Institut des Hautes Etudes Scientifiques, for financial support, and to Mrs. Caroline Browne for her excellent skill and cooperation in the preparation of the manuscript.

Ralph Abraham
Joel Robbin

Bures-sur-Yvette
Amsterdam
February 1967

CONTENTS

CHAPTER 5. FLOWS ON MANIFOLDS

CHAPTER 6. STABLE MANIFOLDS

CHAPTER 7. GENERIC PROPERTIES OF FLOWS

APPENDICES

1

DIFFERENTIAL THEORY

Even in ordinary differential calculus there are changes and new developments. The transversality theory of mappings and flows, like other topics in global analysis, requires a new calculus which extends the classical "advanced calculus" in two ways: the underlying spaces must be infinite-dimensional (Banach spaces), and global (manifolds). These two generalizations are treated thoroughly in Dieudonné [*1*] and Lang [*1*], respectively. In this chapter we review those topics of generalized calculus which will be needed in the transversality theory. Some of these are covered in Lang [*1*]. We use his notations as much as possible, and give references more often than proofs. Several other topics, all concerning higher-order derivatives in one way or another, are not readily accessible in the literature so we give a full discussion.

§1. Review of Calculus

In this section we outline the basic theory of local differential calculus in Banach spaces. We refer frequently to Dieudonné [*1*], the best reference for the basic material, proofs, and additional details.

The symbols $\boldsymbol{E}, \boldsymbol{F}, \boldsymbol{G}$, etc. are used to denote Banach spaces; $L(\boldsymbol{E}, \boldsymbol{F})$ denotes the Banach space of continuous linear maps from $\boldsymbol{E}$ to $\boldsymbol{F}$; $L^k(\boldsymbol{E}, \boldsymbol{F})$ denotes the Banach space of continuous k-multilinear maps from $\boldsymbol{E}$ to $\boldsymbol{F}$ (i.e., $L^0(\boldsymbol{E}, \boldsymbol{F}) = \boldsymbol{F}$; $L^{k+1}(\boldsymbol{E}, \boldsymbol{F}) = L(\boldsymbol{E}, L^k(\boldsymbol{E}, \boldsymbol{F}))$); $L^k_s(\boldsymbol{E}, \boldsymbol{F})$ denotes the Banach space of symmetric k-multilinear maps from $\boldsymbol{E}$ to $\boldsymbol{F}$.

Let $\boldsymbol{E}$ and $\boldsymbol{F}$ be Banach spaces, $U \subset \boldsymbol{E}$ open and $f: U \to \boldsymbol{F}$. Then f is said to be **differentiable** at a point $x \in U$, if there is a (necessarily unique) linear map $Df(x) \in L(\boldsymbol{E}, \boldsymbol{F})$ such that

$$\frac{\|f(x+h) - f(x) - Df(x)h\|}{\|h\|} \to 0$$

as $h \to 0$ ($h \in \mathbf{E}$). f is **class $\mathbf{C}^1$,** in symbols: $f \in \mathscr{C}^1(U, \mathbf{F})$, iff f is differentiable at each $x \in U$ and the map

$$Df\colon U \to L(\mathbf{E}, \mathbf{F})$$

is continuous. More generally, we say f is **class $\mathbf{C}^0$,** in symbols: $f \in \mathscr{C}^0(U, \mathbf{F})$, if f is continuous, and (assuming C^k and $D^k f\colon U \to L^k(\mathbf{E}, \mathbf{F})$ have been defined) we say f is **class $\mathbf{C}^{k+1}$,** in symbols: $f \in \mathscr{C}^{k+1}(U, \mathbf{F})$, iff $D^k f$ is differentiable at each $x \in U$ and the map

$$D^{k+1}f = DD^k f\colon U \to L(\mathbf{E}, L^k(\mathbf{E}, \mathbf{F})) = L^{k+1}(\mathbf{E}, \mathbf{F})$$

is continuous. Finally, f is **class $\mathbf{C}^\infty$,** in symbols: $f \in \mathscr{C}^\infty(U, \mathbf{F})$ iff f is C^r for every $r = 0, 1, 2, \ldots$.

The following proposition is a version of the classical theorem about interchanging the order of partial differentiation.

1.1. PROPOSITION. If $f \in \mathscr{C}^k(U, \mathbf{F})$, then

$$D^k f(x) \in L^k_s(\mathbf{E}, \mathbf{F}) \quad \textbf{for } x \in U$$

(See Dieudonné [*1*; p. 175].)

1.2. CHAIN RULE. Let E, F, G be Banach spaces, $U \subset \mathbf{E}$, $V \subset \mathbf{F}$ open sets, and $g\colon U \to V$, $f\colon V \to \mathbf{G}$. Then if f and g are class $\mathbf{C}^k$, so is $f \circ g\colon U \to \mathbf{G}$ and for $x \in U$

$$D(f \circ g)(x) = Df(g(x)) \circ Dg(x)$$

(See Dieudonné [*1*; p. 178].)

We will have occasion to use a rather general version of Leibnitz' rule, for which some special abbreviations are helpful. Recall that $L^k(\mathbf{F}_1, \ldots, \mathbf{F}_k; \mathbf{G})$ is the Banach space of k-multilinear maps from $\mathbf{F}_1 \times \cdots \times \mathbf{F}_k$ to $\mathbf{G}$; i.e., $L^1(\mathbf{F}_1; \mathbf{G}) = L(\mathbf{F}_1, \mathbf{G})$ and

$$L^{k+1}(\mathbf{F}_1, \ldots, \mathbf{F}_{k+1}; \mathbf{G}) = L(\mathbf{F}_1, L^k(\mathbf{F}_2, \ldots, \mathbf{F}_{k+1}; \mathbf{G}))$$

The following notation is convenient: For $A \in L^k(\mathbf{E}, \mathbf{F})$ and $h_1, \ldots, h_k \in \mathbf{E}$, then $Ah_1 \cdots h_k \in \mathbf{F}$ is the value of A at arguments $h_1, \ldots, h_k$. For $h \in \mathbf{E}$, h^k is an abbreviation for $h \cdots h$ (k terms), so that $Ah^k \in \mathbf{F}$ is the value of A when each of its arguments is h.

For $B \in L^k(\mathbf{F}_1, \ldots, \mathbf{F}_k; \mathbf{G})$, $A_j \in L^{i_j}(\mathbf{E}, \mathbf{F}_j)$ ($j = 1, \ldots, k$) and $p = i_1 + \cdots + i_k$, the map $BA_1 \cdots A_k \in L^p(\mathbf{E}, \mathbf{G})$ is defined by

$$BA_1 \cdots A_k h_1 \cdots h_p = B(A_1 h_1 \cdots h_{i_1})(A_2 \cdots) \cdots (A_k \cdots h_p)$$

for $h_1, \ldots, h_p \in \mathbf{E}$. In particular if a map $\mathbf{F}_1 \times \mathbf{F}_2 \to \mathbf{G}$ given by $(u, v) \rightsquigarrow uv$ ($u \in \mathbf{F}_1$, $v \in \mathbf{F}_2$) is an element of $L^2(\mathbf{F}_1, \mathbf{F}_2; \mathbf{G})$ and if $A \in L^p(\mathbf{E}, \mathbf{F})$ and $B \in L^q(\mathbf{E}, \mathbf{F})$, then $AB \in L^{p+q}(\mathbf{E}, \mathbf{G})$.

With these notations, the generalized rule for the derivatives of a "product" is the following.

1.3. LEIBNITZ' RULE. Let $\mathbf{F}_1 \times \mathbf{F}_2 \to \mathbf{G}$ be a continuous bilinear map (i.e., an element of $L^2(\mathbf{F}_1, \mathbf{F}_2; \mathbf{G})$ given by $(u, v) \rightsquigarrow uv$ for $u \in \mathbf{F}_1$ and $v \in \mathbf{F}_2$. Let $U \in \mathbf{E}$ be open and $\alpha\colon U \to \mathbf{F}_1$ and $\beta\colon U \to \mathbf{F}_2$ be of class C^r. Let $\alpha\beta\colon U \to \mathbf{G}$

be defined by $\alpha\beta(x) = \alpha(x)\beta(x)$ for $x \in U$. Then $\alpha\beta$ is class C^r and for $k \leq r$, $x \in U$

$$D^k\alpha\beta(x) = \sum_{0 \leq q \leq k} \binom{k}{q} D^q\alpha(x) D^{k-q}\beta(x)$$

Proof. The case $k = 1$ is

$$D\alpha\beta(x) = \alpha(x)\, D\beta(x) + (D\alpha(x))\, \beta(x)$$

This follows by the chain rule and the formula for differentiating a bilinear map; i.e., for $A \in L^2(\mathbf{F}_1, \mathbf{F}_2; \mathbf{G})$,

$$DA(u, v)h_1h_2 = A(u, h_2) + A(h_1, v)$$

for $u, h_1 \in \mathbf{F}_1$, $v, h_2 \in \mathbf{F}_2$. The general case follows by induction on k. ∎

In defining the k-jet bundle (§4) and in the Glaeser Rough Composition Theorem (§10) it will be useful to have an explicit formula for the higher derivatives of a composite function. Hence we state and prove the following formula.

1.4. COMPOSITE MAPPING FORMULA. Let $\mathbf{E}, \mathbf{F}, \mathbf{G}$ be Banach spaces; $U \subset \mathbf{E}$, $V \subset \mathbf{F}$ open sets; $g: U \to V$, $f: V \to \mathbf{G}$ maps of class C^r. Then $f \circ g$ is class C^r and for $k = 0, 1, \ldots, r$, and $x \in U$, we have

$$D^k(f \circ g)(x) = \sum_{1 \leq q \leq k} \sum \sigma_k D^q f(g(x)) D^{i_1}g(x) \cdots D^{i_q}g(x)$$

where the second sum is over all q-tuples of positive integers $(i_1, \ldots, i_q)$ with $i_1 + \cdots + i_q = k$ and where $\sigma_k = \sigma_k(i_1, \ldots, i_q)$ is the integer defined below.

Proof. The case $k = 1$ is the chain rule; take $\sigma_1(1) = 1$. The general case is established by induction. By the chain rule

$$D(f \circ g)(x) = (Df) \circ g(x)\; Dg(x)$$

where juxtaposition denotes composition of linear maps. Composition is a continuous bilinear map from $L(\mathbf{F}, \mathbf{G}) \times L(\mathbf{E}, \mathbf{F})$ to $L(\mathbf{E}, \mathbf{F})$. Hence by Leibnitz' rule

(*) $$D^{k+1}(f \circ g)(x) = D^k\{(Df) \circ g\; Dg\}(x) = \sum_{0 \leq q \leq k} \binom{k}{q} D^q\{(Df) \circ g\}(x)\; D^{k-q+1}\, g(x)$$

by the induction hypothesis for $q = 1, \ldots, k$

(**) $$D^q\{(Df) \circ g\}(x) = \sum_{1 \leq j \leq q} \sum \sigma_q\, D^{j+1}f(g(x))\, D^{i_1}g(x) \cdots D^{i_j}(x)$$

where $\sigma_q = \sigma_q\,(i_1, \ldots, i_j)$ has been defined and the second sum is over j-tuples of positive integers $(i_1, \ldots, i_j)$ with $i_1 + \cdots + i_j = q$. We define σ_{k+1} by $\sigma_{k+1}(k+1) = 1$ and

$$\sigma_{k+1}(i_1, \ldots, i_j, k - q + 1) = \binom{k}{q} \sigma_k(i_1, \ldots, i_j)$$

Substituting (**) in (*) we obtain the formula for $D^{k+1}(f \circ g)(x)$. ∎

The following classical theorem states that a C^r map can be approximated by a polynomial of degree r.

1.5. TAYLOR'S THEOREM. Let E, F be Banach spaces, $U \subset E$ an open set, $f: U \to F$, $x \in U$, and $h \in E$ so small that the line segment $\{x + th \mid 0 \leqslant t \leqslant 1\}$ lies in U. Then, if f is class C^r,

$$f(x+h) = \sum_{k=0}^{r} \frac{D^k f(x) h^k}{k!} + R(x, h)h^r$$

where $R(x, h) \in L_s^r(E\ F)$ is defined by

$$R(x, h) = \int_0^1 \frac{(1-t)^{r-1}}{(r-1)!} \{D^r f(x+th) - D^r f(x)\}\, dt$$

Hence R is continuous and $R(x, 0) = 0$.

An easy corollary of 1.5 is the familiar Mean Value Theorem.

1.6. MEAN VALUE THEOREM. Let E, F be Banach spaces, $U \subset E$ open, $f: U \to F$ class C^1, $x, y \in U$. Suppose the segment $(1-t)x + ty$ $(0 \leqslant t \leqslant 1)$ lies in U. Then

$$\|f(y) - f(x)\| \leqslant M\|y - x\|$$

where

$$M = \sup \{\|Df((1-t)x + ty)\| : 0 \leqslant t \leqslant 1\}$$

For proofs of 1.5 and 1.6 as well as the definition of the integral, see Lang [*1*; pp. 9–11].

Recall the Inverse Function Theorem (see Lang [*1*; p. 12]. The Local Representative Theorem below is a more general formulation of the Inverse Function Theorem, and, like the Inverse Function Theorem, it says that in a sufficiently small neighborhood of a point, a C^r function looks like its derivative at that point.

Recall that a map $A \in L(E, F)$ is called **double splitting** iff the kernel of A is a closed subspace of E with closed complement and the image of A is a closed subspace of F with closed complement.

1.7. LOCAL REPRESENTATIVE THEOREM. Let E, F be Banach spaces, f a C^r $(r \geqslant 1)$ map from an open subset of E to F, and x a point in the domain of f. Suppose $Df(x)$ is double splitting. Then there exist Banach spaces E_1, E_2, F_1; open neighborhoods U of x in E and V of $f(x)$ in F; and C^r maps $\alpha: U \to E_1 \times E_2$ and $\beta: V \to F_1 \times E_1$ such that:

(I) $\alpha(x) = (0, 0) \in E_1 \times E_2$; $U \subset$ domain of f; α maps U C^r-diffeomorphically onto $B_1 \times B_2$, where B_1 and B_2 are the open unit balls in E_1 amd E_2 respectively;

(II) $\beta(f(x)) = (0, 0) \in F_1 \times E_1$; $f(U) \subset V$; β maps V C^r-diffeomorphically onto an open subset of $F_1 \times E_1$;

(III) The local representative

$$\beta \circ f \circ \alpha^{-1}: \alpha(U) \to \beta(V)$$

of f has the form

$$\beta \circ f \circ \alpha^{-1}(u, v) = (\eta(u, v), u)$$

for $u \in B_1$, $v \in B_2$, **where**

$$D\eta(0, 0) = 0$$

Proof. By the closed graph theorem (see Lang [*1*; p. 4]) we may assume that $\mathbf{E} = \mathbf{E}_1 \times \mathbf{E}_2$ and $\mathbf{F} = \mathbf{F}_1 \times \mathbf{E}_1$, where $\mathbf{E}_2$ is the kernel of $Df(x)$, $\mathbf{E}_1$ is a closed complement (in $\mathbf{E}$) to $\mathbf{E}_2$, and $\mathbf{F}_1$ is a closed complement (in $\mathbf{F}$) to the image of $Df(x)$. We may also assume, without loss of generality, that $x = (0, 0)$ and $f(x) = (0, 0)$. Then f has the form

$$f(u, v) = (g(u, v), h(u, v))$$

for $u \in \mathbf{E}_1$, $v \in \mathbf{E}_2$, $(u, v) \in$ domain of f, and where $g(u, v) \in \mathbf{E}_1$, $h(u, v) \in \mathbf{F}_1$, $Dh(0, 0)$ is split-surjective with kernel $\mathbf{E}_2$ and $Dg(0, 0) = 0$. Let k be the map defined on the domain of f and with values in $\mathbf{E}$ and given by

$$k(u, v) = (h(u, v), v)$$

Then $Dk(0, 0)$ is a toplinear isomorphism. By the Inverse Function Theorem, choose a neighborhood U of $(0, 0)$ and a C^r diffeomorphism α defined on U so that $k \circ \alpha^{-1}$ is the identity. Then clearly $h \circ \alpha^{-1}(u, v) = u$ for $(u, v) \in U$. Take V to be any neighborhood of $(0, 0) \in \mathbf{F}_1 \times \mathbf{E}_1$ and β to be the identity on V. Then define $\eta = \beta \circ g \circ \alpha^{-1}$. By making routine adjustments in α, β, U, and V we can satisfy the conclusions of the theorem. ∎

Remark. The appearance of β in the statement of the theorem may seem superfluous; we insert it to suggest the obvious generalization of the theorem to manifolds. The manifold version of the theorem would assert the existence of charts (U, α) and (V, β) having the desired properties.

Since every linear map between finite-dimensional Banach spaces is double splitting, the Local Representative Theorem has a somewhat simpler formulation in the finite-dimensional case.

1.8. COROLLARY. Let f **be a** C^r **map from an open subset of** $\mathbf{R}^n$ **to** $\mathbf{R}^p$**, and let** x **be a point in the domain of** f**. Suppose** $Df(x)$ **has rank** q**. Then there exist open neighborhoods** U **of** x **in** $\mathbf{R}^n$ **and** V **of** $f(x)$ **in** $\mathbf{R}^p$ **and** C^r **maps** $\alpha\colon U \to \mathbf{R}^n = \mathbf{R}^q \times \mathbf{R}^{n-q}$ **and** $\beta\colon V \to \mathbf{R}^p = \mathbf{R}^{p-q} \times \mathbf{R}^q$ **such that:**

(I) $\alpha(x) = (0, 0)$, $U \subset$ **domain of** f, α **maps** U C^r**-diffeomorphically onto** $B_1 \times B_2$, **where** B_1 **and** B_2 **are the open unit balls in** $\mathbf{R}^q$ **and** $\mathbf{R}^{n-q}$ **respectively;**

(II) $\beta(f(x)) = (0, 0)$, $f(U) \subset V$, **and** β **maps** V C^r**-diffeomorphically onto an open subset of** $\mathbf{R}^p$**;**

(III) The local representative

$$\beta \circ f \circ \alpha^{-1}\colon \alpha(U) \to \beta(V)$$

of f **has the form**

$$\beta \circ f \circ \alpha^{-1}(u, v) = (\eta(u, v), u)$$

for $u \in B_1$, $v \in B_2$, **where** $\eta\colon \mathbf{R}^n \to \mathbf{R}^{p-q}$ **and** $D\eta(0, 0) = 0$**.**

§2. A Criterion for Smoothness

In this section we prove the converse of Taylor's Theorem; if a mapping has a Taylor formula at each point in its domain with continuous coefficients, it is smooth. In the one-dimensional case this criterion goes back to Marcinkiewicz and Zymund [*1*].

Let $\boldsymbol{E}$ and $\boldsymbol{F}$ be Banach spaces, $U \subset \boldsymbol{E}$ an open subset, and $f: U \to \boldsymbol{F}$ a C^r map. By Taylor's Theorem (1.5) we may write f in the form

$$f(x+h) = \sum_{k=0}^{r} \frac{\varphi_k(x)h^k}{k!} + \rho(x, h)$$

for $x \in U$ and suitable $h \in \boldsymbol{E}$. Here

$$\varphi_k(x) = D^k f(x) \qquad (k = 0, 1, \ldots, r)$$

and

$$\rho(x, h) = R(x, h)h^r$$

where $R(x, h) \in L_s^r(\boldsymbol{E}, \boldsymbol{F})$ is continuous x and h and satisfies $R(x, \boldsymbol{0}) = \boldsymbol{0}$. We see that each φ_k is continuous (in x) and the remainder ρ satisfies the condition

$$\frac{\|\rho(x, h)\|}{\|h\|^r} \to 0$$

as $(x, h) \to (y, \boldsymbol{0})$. Thus it is reasonable to expect to be able to prove 2.1.

2.1. CONVERSE TO TAYLOR'S THEOREM. Let E, F be Banach spaces, $U \subset E$ an open convex set, $f: U \to F$, $\varphi_k: U \to L_s^k(E, F)$ for $k = 0, 1, \ldots, r$ $(r \geq 0)$. For $x \in U$ and $h \in E$ small enough so that $x + h \in U$ define $\rho(x, h) \in F$ by

$$f(x+h) = \sum_{k=0}^{r} \frac{\varphi_k(x)h^k}{k!} + \rho(x, h)$$

Suppose that:

(1) Each φ_k is continuous $(k = 0, 1, \ldots, r)$;

(2) $\|\rho(x, h)\|/\|h\|^r \to 0$ as $(x, h) \to (x_0, \boldsymbol{0})$.

Then f is class C^r and $D^k f = \varphi_k$ for $k = 0, 1, \ldots, r$.

Remark. Before proving 2.1 we point out that it provides an extremely useful technique for proving that a map is C^r. We simply write down the "formal" Taylor formula (without regard for whether the derivatives exist) and verify (1) and (2) above. Often $\rho(x, h)$ is already known to have the form $R(x, h)h^r$; in this case the problem of verifying (2) reduces to showing that R is continuous and $R(x, 0) = 0$.

In §11 we give a different, much easier, converse to Taylor's Theorem. There the hypothesis that each φ_k be continuous is dropped, but the hypothesis on the remainder is strengthened; namely, the condition (2) on ρ is to hold for each ρ_k $(k = 0, 1, \ldots, r)$, where ρ_k is defined by

$$\varphi_k(x+h) = \sum_{j=0}^{r-k} \frac{\varphi_{k+j}(x)h^j}{j!} + \rho_k(x, h)$$

To prove 2.1 we reduce to the special case $\boldsymbol{E} = \boldsymbol{R}^n$ and $\boldsymbol{F} = \boldsymbol{R}$. Our proof in this case is due to Glaeser [*1*], and requires the following lemma.

A **polynomial of degree** $\leqslant p$ **from** $\boldsymbol{R}^n$ **to** $\boldsymbol{R}$ is a map $P: \boldsymbol{R}^n \to \boldsymbol{R}$ of the form

$$P(\mathbf{y}) = \sum_{k=0}^{p} A_k \mathbf{y}^k$$

for $\mathbf{y} \in \boldsymbol{R}^n$. Here $A_k \in L_s^k(\boldsymbol{R}^n, \boldsymbol{R})$ for $k = 0, 1, \ldots, p$.

2.2. INTERPOLATION LEMMA. There exist points $\mathbf{a}_j \in \boldsymbol{R}^n$ and polynomials Q_j from $\boldsymbol{R}^n$ to $\boldsymbol{R}$ ($j = 1, 2, \ldots, (r+1)^n$), such that, for every polynomial P of degree $\leqslant r$, we have

(I)
$$DP(\mathbf{y}) = \sum_j \frac{1}{t} P(\mathbf{y} + t\mathbf{a}_j)\, DQ_j(\mathbf{0})$$

for all $\mathbf{y} \in \boldsymbol{R}^n$ and $t \in \boldsymbol{R}$, $t \neq 0$.

Proof. Let A be any set of $r+1$ distinct real numbers. For each $a \in A$ there is a unique polynomial Q_a of degree $\leqslant r$ from $\boldsymbol{R}$ to $\boldsymbol{R}$, such that, $Q_a(y) = 1$ if $y = a$, 0 if $y \in A$ but $y \neq a$, the **Lagrange interpolation polynomial** for a and A.

For $\mathbf{a}_j = (a_{j1}, \ldots, a_{jn}) \in A^n$, define a polynomial Q_j from $\boldsymbol{R}^n$ to $\boldsymbol{R}$ by

$$Q_j(\mathbf{y}) = Q_{a_{j1}}(y_1) Q_{a_{j2}}(y_2) \ldots Q_{a_{jn}}(y_n)$$

for $\mathbf{y} = (y_1, \ldots, y_n) \in \boldsymbol{R}^n$. Then $Q_j(\mathbf{a}_i) = 1$ for $i = j$, 0 for $i \neq j$.

Note that $Q_j(y_1, \ldots, y_n)$ is of degree $\leqslant r$ in each y_i, and two polynomials of degree $\leqslant r$ from $\boldsymbol{R}$ to $\boldsymbol{R}$ which agree at $r+1$ distinct points must be identical. Hence, by induction on n

$$P(\mathbf{y}) = \sum_j P(\mathbf{a}_j) Q_j(\mathbf{y})$$

for all $\mathbf{y} \in \boldsymbol{R}^n$ and all polynomials P of degree $\leqslant r$ from $\boldsymbol{R}^n$ to $\boldsymbol{R}$.

Differentiating this identity yields

(II)
$$DP(\mathbf{y}) = \sum_j P(\mathbf{a}_j)\, DQ_j(\mathbf{y})$$

for all $\mathbf{y} \in \boldsymbol{R}^n$ (and all appropriate P).

We reduce the proof of (I) to a series of special cases.

Case 1. $\mathbf{y} = \mathbf{0}$ and $P \in L(\boldsymbol{R}^n, \boldsymbol{R})$. Then $\frac{1}{t} P(\mathbf{y} + t\mathbf{a}_j) = P(\mathbf{a}_j)$ so (I) is (II).

Case 2. $\mathbf{y} = \mathbf{0}$ and $P(\mathbf{y}) = A\mathbf{y}^k$, where $A \in L_s^k(\boldsymbol{R}^n, \boldsymbol{R})$ and $k \neq 1$. The left side of (II) is zero; (I) results from (II) by dividing by t^{k+1}.

Case 3. $\mathbf{y} = \mathbf{0}$. As (I) is linear in P, this case follows from Case 1 and Case 2.

The general case is proved by applying Case 3 to the polynomial $\mathbf{x} \rightsquigarrow P(\mathbf{y} + \mathbf{x})$. ∎

Proof of 2.1. We shall show that for $k = 0, \ldots, r-1$, $x \in U$, and h sufficiently small,

$$\varphi_k(x+h) - \varphi_k(x) = \int_0^1 [\varphi_{k+1}(x+th)h]\, dt \tag{3}$$

from which 2.1 follows immediately. For (3) implies that φ_k is differentiable and $D\varphi_k(x) = \varphi_{k+1}(x)$ for all $x \in U$. But obviously $\varphi_0 = f$, so f is differentiable and $Df = \varphi_1$, which is continuous by hypothesis. Similarly, by induction, f is C^r with $D^k f = \varphi_k$ for $k = 0, \ldots, r$.

To prove (3), we prove 2.1 first in the special case $\mathbf{E} = \mathbf{R}^n$ and $\mathbf{F} = \mathbf{R}$. We shall show in this case that the coefficient φ_1 has a Taylor formula of order $r-1$,

$$\varphi_1(x+h) = \sum_{k=0}^{r-1} \frac{\varphi_{k+1}(x)h^k}{k!} + \sigma(x, h)$$

where

$$\|\sigma(x, h)\|/\|h\|^{r-1} \to 0 \quad \text{as } (x, h) \to (x_0, \mathbf{0}) \tag{4}$$

From this, it follows easily by induction on r that f is C^r and thus (3) holds in this special case.

To prove (4), we use the following notations. For $x \in U$, let P_x be the polynomial defined by

$$P_x(y) = \sum_{k=0}^{r} \frac{\varphi_k(x)(y-x)^k}{k!}$$

Then in 2.1, the remainder term becomes $\rho(x, h) = P_y(y) - P_x(y)$ where $y = x + h$, so hypothesis (2) becomes

$$\frac{\|P_y(y) - P_x(y)\|}{\|y - x\|^r} \to 0 \quad \text{as } y, x \to x_0. \tag{2'}$$

Similarly, as the derivative of P_x is given by $DP_x(y) = \sum_{k=0}^{r-1} \frac{\varphi_{k+1}(x)(y-x)^k}{k!}$, the remainder term for φ_1 is $\sigma(x, h) = DP_y(y) - DP_x(y)$ and so condition (4), which we wish to establish, becomes

$$\frac{\|DP_y(y) - DP_x(y)\|}{\|y - x\|^{r-1}} \to 0 \quad \text{as } y, x \to x_0 \tag{4'}$$

To prove (4′), we apply the Interpolation Lemma 2.2(I) to the polynomial $z \rightsquigarrow P_y(z) - P_x(z)$. Thus, for $z = y$,

$$DP_y(y) - DP_x(y) = \sum_j \frac{1}{t}[P_y(v_j) - P_x(v_j)]\, DQ_j(\mathbf{0}) \tag{5}$$

where $v_j = y + t\mathbf{a}_j$. Let $M = \sum_j \|DQ_j(\mathbf{0})\|$, $S = \max_j \{\|\mathbf{a}_j\|\}$, and $t = \dfrac{\|y - x\|}{S}$.

Then $\|t\mathbf{a}_j\| \leqslant \|y - x\|$ so $y, x \to x_0$ implies $v_j \to x_0$.

Choose $\epsilon > 0$. For y and x sufficiently near x_0, we obtain from (2′)

$$\begin{aligned} \|P_y(v_j) - P_x(v_j)\| &\leqslant \|P_y(v_j) - P_{v_j}(v_j)\| + \|P_{v_j}(v_j) - P_x(v_j)\| \\ &\leqslant \frac{\epsilon}{3MS}\|t\mathbf{a}_j\|^r + \frac{\epsilon}{3MS}\|y - x\|^r + \frac{\epsilon}{3MS}\|t\mathbf{a}_j\|^r \leqslant \frac{\epsilon}{MS}\|y - x\|^r = \frac{\epsilon t}{M}\|y - x\|^{r-1} \end{aligned} \tag{6}$$

Hence by (5), (6), the definition of M, and the triangle inequality we obtain

$$\|DP_y(y) - DP_x(y)\| \leqslant \epsilon \|y - x\|^{r-1}$$

This proves (4′), and thus (3) in the special case.

We now prove (3) in the general case by contradiction. If (3) fails for some k, x, and h, there exist points $h_1, \ldots, h_k \in \mathbf{E}$ and (by the Hahn-Banach Theorem) a continuous linear functional $\lambda \in \mathbf{F}^*$ such that

$$[\lambda \circ \varphi_k(x+h) - \lambda \circ \varphi_k(x)]h_1 \cdots h_k \neq \int_0^1 [\lambda \circ \varphi_{k+1}(x+th)hh_1 \cdots h_k]\, dt \tag{7}$$

Let $\mathbf{E}_0$ be a finite dimensional subspace of $\mathbf{E}$ containing $x, h, h_1, \ldots, h_k$; $V = \mathbf{E}_0 \cap U$, $g = \lambda \circ f \mid V$, and $\psi_j \colon V \to L_s^j(\mathbf{E}_0, \mathbf{R})$ be defined by $\psi_j(x)\mathbf{e}_1 \cdots \mathbf{e}_j = \lambda[\varphi_j(x)\mathbf{e}_1 \cdots \mathbf{e}_j]$.

Choosing some isomorphism, we identify $\mathbf{E}_0$ with $\mathbf{R}^n$ for the appropriate n. Then clearly

$$g(x+h) = \sum_{j=1}^{r} \frac{\psi_j(x)h^j}{j!} + \lambda \circ \rho(x, h)$$

where ψ_j and $\lambda \circ \rho$ satisfy (1) and (2) of 2.1 in the special case treated above, so by (3)

$$\psi_k(x+h) - \psi_k(x) = \int_0^1 [\psi_{k+1}(x+th)h]\, dt$$

which contradicts (7). This completes the proof of (3) in the general case. ∎

§3. Manifolds

Here we review the category of C^r manifolds and mappings. Our treatment is essentially the same as in Lang [*1*].

A **local manifold** is an open set in a Banach space. A **C^r local manifold morphism** is a C^r map between local manifolds. These form a category. In a category a morphism f is called an **isomorphism** iff there is a morphism g such that g is both left and right inverse to f. Hence a C^r local manifold isomorphism is a C^r diffeomorphism.

Let X be a Hausdorff space. A **manifold chart** (or simply a **chart**) on X is a pair (U, α) when U is an open subset of X and α is a homeomorphism from U into a local manifold. Two local charts (U, α) and (V, β) are **C^r compatible** iff the composition

$$\beta \circ \alpha^{-1} \colon \alpha(U \cap V) \to \beta(U \cap V)$$

is a local C^r manifold isomorphism. A **C^r atlas** on X is a collection of charts $\{(U, \alpha)\}$ any two of which are C^r compatible and such that the U's cover X. An atlas is **maximal** iff it contains each chart which is compatible with all of its members. Clearly, every atlas extends uniquely to a maximal atlas. A **C^r manifold** is a Hausdorff space X together with a maximal atlas on X. In the sequel we suppress notation for the maximal atlas on X; we simply let X refer ambiguously to both the underlying topological space and the maximal atlas. Instead of saying that a chart (U, α) is a member of the maximal atlas we say that (U, α) is an **admissible chart** on X.

Let X and Y be C^r manifolds and $f \colon X \to Y$ a map. For charts (U, α) and (V, β) admissible on X and Y respectively and such that $f(U) \subset V$ we define $f_{\alpha\beta}$, the **local representative** of f (with respect to the two charts), to be the map

$$f_{\alpha\beta} \colon \alpha(U) \to \beta(V)$$

given by

$$f_{\alpha\beta} = \beta \circ f \circ \alpha^{-1}$$

The map f is a C^r **manifold morphism** iff for every $x \in X$ and every admissible chart (V, β) on Y with $f(x) \in V$, there exists an admissible chart (U, α) on X such that $x \in U$, $f(U) \subset V$, and $f_{\alpha\beta}$ is a C^r local manifold morphism. The reader will note the similarity between this definition of C^r morphism and the definition of a continuous map.

§4. Orientation

In this section we give a definition of orientation analogous to our definition of manifold. The reader should compare our definitions with other definitions (see for example, Abraham-Marsden [*1*, §11]).

Let $\boldsymbol{E}$ be a finite-dimensional Banach space and $A: \boldsymbol{E} \to \boldsymbol{E}$ a toplinear isomorphism. For each choice of a vector space basis of $\boldsymbol{E}$, A has a representation as a square matrix $\tilde{A}$; and if $\tilde{B}$ is the representation with respect to another basis, then $\tilde{B} = P\tilde{A}P^{-1}$ where P is some nonsingular square matrix. The determinant is a multiplicative function of square matrices, and so we see that the sign of the determinant of $\tilde{A}$ is independent of the choice of the matrix representation (i.e., basis for E). We say that A is **orientation preserving** (resp. **orientation reversing**) iff this sign is positive (resp. negative).

Now let X be a finite-dimensional C^r manifold ($r \geq 1$) and (U, α) and (V, β) be two admissible charts on X with $\alpha(U), \beta(V) \subset \boldsymbol{R}^n$. We say that (U, α) and (V, β) are **orientation compatible** iff for each $x \in U \cap V$ the toplinear isomorphism $D(\beta \circ \alpha^{-1})(\alpha(x))$ is orientation preserving. An **oriented atlas** on X is an atlas such that each two of its charts are orientation compatible. If X has such an atlas, we say X is **orientable;** otherwise, X is **nonorientable.** An **orientation** of X is a maximal oriented atlas, i.e., an oriented atlas which contains every chart orientation compatible with each of its members. The reader may verify that a connected orientable manifold has exactly two orientations. Given an orientation on X, we call its members **admissible oriented charts** (with respect to the given orientation).

Let X be an orientable manifold and $\boldsymbol{O}$ be one of its two orientations. A diffeomorphism $f: X \to X$ is called **orientation preserving** iff for each $x \in X$ and each suitable pair (U, α) and (V, β) of admissible oriented charts with respect to $\boldsymbol{O}$ at x and $f(x)$ respectively, the linear map $Df_{\alpha\beta}(\alpha(x)): \boldsymbol{R}^n \to \boldsymbol{R}^n$ is orientation preserving (here $f_{\alpha\beta} = \beta \circ f \circ \alpha^{-1}$ is the local representative of f). Note that the definition is independent of the choice of the orientation $\boldsymbol{O}$.

We recall that a C^r diffeomorphism $f: X \to X$ is **C^r isotopic to the identity** iff there is a C^r map

$$F: X \times \boldsymbol{R} \to X$$

such that:

(1) for each $t \in R$, the map $F_t: X \to X$ defined by $F_t(x) = F(x, t)$ for $x \in X$, is a C^r diffeomorphism;

(2) F_0 is the identity map on X and $F_1 = f$.

The following proposition is left as an exercise for the reader.

4.1. PROPOSITION. Let X be an orientable C^r manifold ($r \geq 1$) and $f: X \to X$ a C^r diffeomorphism which is C^r isotopic to the identity. Then f is orientation preserving.

Let X be a finite-dimensional C^r manifold ($r \geq 1$). We will define a C^r manifold X^* and a C^r map $p: X^* \to X$ called the **double covering** of X. We consider triples (U, α, x) where (U, α) is an admissible manifold chart on X with $\alpha(U) \subset$

$\boldsymbol{R}^n$ and $x \in U$. Define an equivalence relation $\equiv$ on such triples by stipulating that $(U, \alpha, x) \equiv (V, \beta, y)$ iff $x = y$ and $D(\beta \circ \alpha^{-1})(\alpha(x))\colon \boldsymbol{R}^n \to \boldsymbol{R}^n$ is orientation preserving. Let $[U, \alpha, x]$ denote the equivalence class of the triple (U, α, x) and define X^* as the set of all the equivalence classes, and $p\colon X^* \to X$ by the equation

$$p([U, \alpha, x]) = x$$

Now let $\rho\colon \boldsymbol{R}^n \to \boldsymbol{R}^n$ be a fixed orientation reversing toplinear isomorphism (reflection through a hyperplane, for example). Given an admissible chart (U, α) on X, we define two charts (U_1^*, α_1^*) and (U_2^*, α_2^*) on X^* as follows:

$$U_1^* = \{[U, \alpha, x] \mid x \in U\}$$

$$U_2^* = \{[U, \rho \circ \alpha, x] \mid x \in U\}$$

and for $x \in U$,

$$\alpha_1^*([U, \alpha, x]) = \alpha(x)$$

$$\alpha_2^*([U, \rho \circ \alpha, x]) = \rho \circ \alpha(x)$$

4.2. PROPOSITION. (I) The set of all (U_i^*, α_i^*) $i = 1, 2$ as (U, α) ranges over the admissible charts on X is an oriented C^r atlas on X^*; hence X^* (together with the unique maximal atlas extending this atlas) is an orientable manifold.

(II) The map $p\colon X^* \to X$ is a local C^r diffeomorphism; i.e., for $x^* \in X^*$ there is an open neighborhood U^* of x^* in X^* such that $p|U^*$ is a C^r diffeomorphism onto an open subset of X.

(III) For $x \in X$, $p^{-1}(x)$ contains exactly two points.

(IV) If X is compact, so is X^*.

(V) If X is connected and nonorientable, then X^* is connected; if X is connected and orientable, then X^* consists of exactly two components, each of which is diffeomorphic (under p) to X.

We leave the proof as an exercise for the reader.

4.3. PATH LIFTING THEOREMS. Let X be a C^r manifold ($r \geq 1$), $p\colon X^* \to X$ its double covering, $c\colon [0, 1] \to X$ a continuous curve and $x^* \in p^{-1}(c(0))$. Then,

(I) there exists a unique continuous curve $c_1\colon [0, 1] \to X^*$ such that $c_1(0) = x^*$ and $c = p \circ c_1$ (c_1 may be called the *lift* of c to X^* at x^*), and

(II) if c is a closed curve (i.e., $c(0) = c(1)$) but $c_1(0) \neq c_1(1)$, and if $c_2\colon [0, 1] \to X$ is the lift of c to X^* at $c_1(1)$, then the curve $c^*\colon [0, 2] \to X^*$ defined by

$$c^*(s) = \begin{cases} c_1(s) & 0 \leq s \leq 1; \\ c_2(s_{-1}) & 1 \leq s \leq 2 \end{cases}$$

is a closed curve and $p \circ c^*(s) = p \circ c^*(1 + s) = c(s)$ for $0 \leq s \leq 1$.

The proof is left to the reader. See also Hocking-Young [*1;* p. 188].

§5. Vector Bundles

Intuitively speaking, manifolds are constructed (§3) by "patching" together local manifolds by means of local isomorphisms. Mappings are defined similarly by patching together local mappings. With this process we obtain an enlargement of the category of local manifolds and mappings. The patching process can be abstracted to any category satisfying appropriate axioms (a local category, see Eilenberg and Cartan [*1*]) giving a universal construction for defining global objects and morphisms from local ones.

We now use this process to define vector bundles and their morphisms. In this we depart somewhat from Lang [*1*] but the results are identical. Thus we begin by defining local vector bundles and morphisms, then patch them together.

A **local vector bundle** is a map $\pi: U \times \mathbf{F} \to U$ where U is a local manifold, $\mathbf{F}$ is a Banach space, and π is the projection onto the first factor. Let $\pi: U \times \mathbf{F} \to U$ and $\pi': U' \times \mathbf{F}' \to U'$ be local vector bundles. A pair (f, f_0) where $f: U \times \mathbf{F} \to U' \times \mathbf{F}'$ and $f_0: U \to U'$ is a $\boldsymbol{C^r}$ **local vector bundle morphism** iff:

LVBM 1. The diagram

$$\begin{array}{ccc} U \times \mathbf{F} & \xrightarrow{\quad f \quad} & U' \times \mathbf{F}' \\ \downarrow \pi & & \downarrow \pi' \\ U & \xrightarrow{\quad f_0 \quad} & U' \end{array}$$

commutes;

LVBM 2. For each $x \in U$ the map

$$f^{\#}(x): \mathbf{F} \to \mathbf{F}'$$

defined by

$$f(x, v) = (f_0(x), f^{\#}(x)v)$$

for $v \in \mathbf{F}$ is continuous linear;

LVBM 3. The maps $f_0: U \to U'$ and $f^{\#}: U \to L(\mathbf{F}, \mathbf{F}')$ are class C^r.

The local vector bundles and C^r local vector bundle morphisms form a category (with $(f, f_0) \circ (g, g_0)$ defined by $(f \circ g, f_0 \circ g_0)$). Hence we have a notion of isomorphism; i.e., (f, f_0) is a $\boldsymbol{C^r}$ **local vector bundle isomorphism** iff it is a C^r local vector bundle morphism and there is a C^r local vector bundle morphism such that $f \circ g$, $g \circ f$, $f_0 \circ g_0$, and $g_0 \circ f_0$ are the identities.

5.1. PROPOSITION. (I) For C^r local vector bundle morphisms the condition

LVBM 4. $$f: U \times \mathbf{F} \to U' \times \mathbf{F}' \text{ is } C^r$$

holds. Furthermore, if $\mathbf{F}$ is finite dimensional, condition LVBM 4 may replace condition LVBM 3 in the definition of C^r local vector bundle morphism.

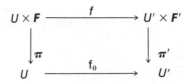

(II) A C^r local vector bundle morphism (f, f_0) is a C^r local vector bundle isomorphism iff f_0 is a C^r diffeomorphism and for each $x \in U$, $f^{\#}(x)$ is a toplinear isomorphism.

Proof. See Lang [*1;* pp. 8, 15].

Let E be a set, X a C^r manifold and $\pi: E \to X$ a surjective map. A **C^r vector bundle chart** on π, for short a **C^r VB chart,** is a triple (α, α_0, U) where (U, α_0) is an admissible C^r chart on X, $\alpha: \pi^{-1}(U) \to \alpha_0(U) \times \mathbf{F}_\alpha$ (where $\mathbf{F}_\alpha$ is a Banach space not necessarily the ambient space of $\alpha_0(U)$) is a bijection, and the diagram

$$\begin{array}{ccc} \pi^{-1}(U) & \xrightarrow{\quad\alpha\quad} & \alpha_0(U) \times \mathbf{F}_\alpha \\ \downarrow & & \downarrow \\ U & \xrightarrow{\quad\alpha_0\quad} & \alpha_0(U) \end{array}$$

commutes. (The right-hand map is the natural projection.) Two C^r VB charts (α, α_0, U) and (β, β_0, V) are **C^r compatible** iff the pair $(\beta \circ \alpha^{-1}, \beta_0 \circ \alpha_0^{-1})$ is a C^r local vector bundle isomorphism from the local vector bundle $\alpha(U \cap V) \times \mathbf{F}_\alpha \to \alpha(U \cap V)$ to the local vector bundle $\beta(U \cap V) \times \mathbf{F}_\beta \to \beta(U \cap V)$. A **$C^r$ vector bundle atlas** on π, for short, a **C^r VB atlas,** is a collection $\{(\alpha, \alpha_0, U)\}$ of VB charts on π any two of which are C^r compatible and such that the U's cover X. A C^r VB atlas is **maximal** iff it contains each C^r VB chart which is C^r compatible with all of its members. As before, every VB atlas extends uniquely to a maximal VB atlas. A **C^r vector bundle** is a surjective map $\pi: E \to X$ where E is a set and X is a C^r manifold together with a maximal C^r VB atlas on π. In the sequel, we suppress notation for the maximal VB atlas, denote the vector bundle by π, and refer to the VB charts of the maximal VB atlas as **admissible C^r VB charts** on π. Note that the pairs $(\pi^{-1}(U), \alpha)$ form a C^r manifold atlas (albeit not a maximal one) on E. Hence the vector bundle structure on π determines a manifold structure on E. ▮

Let $\pi: E \to X$ and $\pi': E' \to X'$ be C^r vector bundles, $f: E \to E'$ and $f_0: X \to X'$ a pair of maps, and (α, α_0, U) and (β, β_0, V) admissible C^r VB charts on π and π' respectively with $f_0(U) \subset V$ and $f(\pi^{-1}(U)) \subset \pi'^{-1}(V)$. Then $(f, f_0)_{\alpha\beta} = (f_{\alpha\beta}, f_{\alpha\beta_0})$, the **local representative** of (f, f_0) (with respect to the charts) is defined by $f_{\alpha\beta} = \beta \circ f \circ \alpha^{-1}$ and $f_{\alpha\beta_0} = \beta_0 \circ f_0 \circ \alpha_0^{-1}$. We say that (f, f_0) is a **C^r vector bundle morphism from π to π'**, for short a **C^r VB morphism,** iff for every $x \in X$ and every admissible VB chart (β, β_0, V) on π' with $f_0(x) \in V$ there is an admissible VB chart (α, α_0, U) on π with $x \in U$, $f_0(U) \subset V$, $f(\pi^{-1}(U)) \subset \pi'^{-1}(V)$, and such that $(f, f_0)_{\alpha\beta}$ is a C^r local vector bundle morphism.

Let $\pi: E \to X$ be a C^r vector bundle. For $x \in X$ the set E_x defined by

$$E_x = \pi^{-1}(x)$$

has the structure of a Banach(able) space. (Each VB chart (α, α_0, U) puts E_x in one-to-one correspondence with the Banach space $\mathbf{F}_\alpha$ and for different charts the "transition" map is a toplinear isomorphism.) A **C^r section** of π is a C^r (manifold) morphism

$$\xi: X \to E$$

such that $\pi \circ \xi$ is the identity on X. Thus, a section ξ assigns to each $x \in X$ a vector $\xi(x) \in E_x$. If ξ is a C^r section and (α, α_0, U) is a C^r VB chart, then the local representative

$$\alpha \circ \xi \circ \alpha_0^{-1}: \alpha_0(U) \to \alpha_0(U) \times \mathbf{F}_\alpha$$

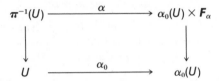

has the form

$$\alpha \circ \xi \circ \alpha_0^{-1}(x) = (x, \xi_\alpha(x))$$

for $x \in \alpha_0(U)$. The map ξ_α: $\alpha_0(U) \to \boldsymbol{F}_\alpha$ is called the **principal part of the local representative** of ξ (with respect to the VB chart).

We let $\Gamma^r(\boldsymbol{\pi})$ denote the set of C^r sections of $\boldsymbol{\pi}$. Then $\Gamma^r(\boldsymbol{\pi})$ has a linear structure in the obvious way, for $a, b \in \boldsymbol{R}$, $\xi, \zeta \in \Gamma^r(\boldsymbol{\pi})$, $a\xi + b\zeta$ is defined by

$$(a\xi + b\zeta)(x) = a\xi(x) + b\zeta(x)$$

for $x \in X$. The reader can easily verify that $\Gamma^r(\boldsymbol{\pi})$ is closed under these linear operations and hence $\Gamma^r(\boldsymbol{\pi})$ is a vector space. We will show in §12 that under certain conditions (namely that X be compact and E_x, the fiber over x, be finite dimensional for each $x \in X$), $\Gamma^r(\boldsymbol{\pi})$ can be made into a Banach space.

In addition it is obvious that if $\xi \in \Gamma^r(\boldsymbol{\pi})$ and (α, α_0, U) is an admissible C^r VB chart on $\boldsymbol{\pi}$, then $\xi_\alpha \in \mathscr{C}^r(\alpha_0(U), \boldsymbol{F}_\alpha)$. Also the map

$$\Gamma^r(\boldsymbol{\pi}) \to \mathscr{C}^r(\alpha_0(U), \boldsymbol{F}_\alpha)$$

given by

$$\xi \rightsquigarrow \xi_\alpha$$

for $\xi \in \Gamma^r(\boldsymbol{\pi})$ is linear.

If X is a C^r manifold, $\boldsymbol{E}$ a Banach space, and $\boldsymbol{\pi}$: $X \times \boldsymbol{E} \to X$ is the projection on the first factor, we may define a C^r VB atlas on $\boldsymbol{\pi}$ as follows. For each admissible manifold chart (U, α_0) on $\boldsymbol{\pi}$ we define

$$\alpha: U \times \boldsymbol{E} \to \alpha_0(U) \times \boldsymbol{E}$$

by

$$\alpha(x, \boldsymbol{e}) = (\alpha_0(x), \boldsymbol{e})$$

for $x \in U$, $\boldsymbol{e} \in \boldsymbol{E}$. We call $\boldsymbol{\pi}$ a **product bundle.** A C^r vector bundle is called **trivial** iff it is C^r vector bundle isomorphic to a product bundle.

§6. Tangents

The most direct global generalization of the derivative of a local morphism is the tangent of a morphism. This is actually a functor from manifolds of class C^{r+1} to vector bundles of class C^r. As in the last section, our treatment differs slightly from Lang [*1*].

Let X be a C^{r+1} manifold ($r \geqslant 0$). A $\boldsymbol{C^{r+1}}$ **curve** in X is a C^{r+1} map from an open interval in $\boldsymbol{R}$ containing 0 to X. Curves c_1 and c_2 are **tangent at a point** $x \in X$ iff $c_1(0) = c_2(0) = x$ and for some (and hence every) admissible chart (U, α) at x

$$(\alpha \circ c_1)'(0) = (\alpha \circ c_2)'(0)$$

Here $(\alpha \circ c)'(0)$ is defined by

$$(\alpha \circ c)'(0) = \lim_{h \to 0} \frac{1}{h} \{\alpha \circ c(h) - \alpha \circ c(0)\}$$

$$= D\alpha(0)\,1$$

A curve c is called a **curve at** x iff $c(0) = x$. Among the curves c at x, tangency (at x) is an equivalence relation and we define T_xX to be the set of equivalence classes, T_xX is called the **tangent space to** X **at** x. We define

$$T(X) = \bigcup_{x \in X} T_xX$$

and

$$\tau_X\colon T(X) \to X$$

by

$$\tau_X(\dot{x}) = x \qquad \text{for } \dot{x} \in T_xX$$

Note τ_X is a candidate for a vector bundle with fiber over the point $x \in X$ being T_xX.

Let (U, α) be an (admissible) chart on X with $\alpha(U)$ an open set of the Banach space $\mathbf{E}_\alpha$. We define

$$T\alpha\colon \tau_X^{-1}(U) \to \alpha(U) \times \mathbf{E}_\alpha$$

by setting

$$T\alpha(\dot{x}) = (\alpha(\tau_X(\dot{x})), \mathbf{e})$$

where $\mathbf{e} \in \mathbf{E}_\alpha$ is the unique point of $\mathbf{E}_\alpha$ such that the curve at $\tau(\dot{x})$ defined (for sufficiently small t) by $c(t) = \alpha^{-1}(t\mathbf{e})$ is an element of the equivalence class $\dot{x}$. Then $(T\alpha, \alpha, U)$ is a local VB chart on τ_X; it may be called the **natural chart** associated with the manifold chart (U, α). The set of all such natural charts (as (U, α) ranges over the admissible charts on X) is called the **natural atlas** on τ_X.

6.1. PROPOSITION. Where X is a C^{r+1} manifold, the natural atlas on τ_X is a C^r VB atlas; hence τ_X (together with the unique maximal VB atlas which extends the natural atlas) is a C^r vector bundle.

Proof. For two natural charts $(T\alpha, \alpha, U)$ and $(T\beta, \beta, V)$ the transition map

$$(T\beta) \circ (T\alpha)^{-1}\colon \alpha(U \cap V) \times \mathbf{E}_\alpha \to \beta(U \cap V) \times \mathbf{E}_\beta$$

is given by

$$(T\beta) \circ (T\alpha)^{-1}(x, \mathbf{e}) = (\beta \circ \alpha^{-1}(x), D(\beta \circ \alpha^{-1})(x)\mathbf{e})$$

for $x \in \alpha(U \cap V)$, $\mathbf{e} \in \mathbf{E}_\alpha$. ∎

Now let X and Y be C^{r+1} manifolds and $f\colon X \to Y$ a C^{r+1} (manifold) morphism. Note that if c_1 and c_2 are curves in

X, which are tangent at a point $x \in X$, then $f \circ c_1$ and $f \circ c_2$ are curves in Y which are tangent at the point $f(x) \in Y$. Hence f induces a map

$$Tf: T(X) \to T(Y)$$

defined by

$$Tf(\dot{x}) = \dot{y}$$

where $\dot{y}$ is the equivalence class of the curve $f \circ c$, c being any member of the equivalence class $\dot{x}$. We define for $x \in X$

$$T_x f: T_x X \to T_{f(x)} Y$$

by

$$T_x f = Tf | T_x X$$

6.2. PROPOSITION. For $r \geqslant 0$, T is a covariant functor from the category of C^{r+1} manifolds (and C^{r+1} manifold morphisms) to the category of C^r vector bundles (and C^r VB morphisms); that is:

(I) If $f: X \to Y$ is a C^{r+1} map between C^{r+1} manifolds ($r \geqslant 0$), then the pair $\tau_f = (Tf, f)$ is a C^r VB morphism from τ_X to τ_Y;

(II) If $id_X: X \to X$ is the identity map on the C^{r+1} manifold X, then $T\, id_X = id_{T(X)}$, the identity map on the C^r vector bundle τ_X;

(III) If $f: X \to Y$ and $g: Y \to Z$ are C^{r+1} maps between C^{r+1} manifolds, then $T(g \circ f) = Tg \circ Tf$.

We leave the details of 6.2 to the reader. He should also show that τ_X by our definition is VB isomorphic to the bundle τ_X defined in Lang [*1*]. In the course of verifying 6.2 the reader will discover that, if $f: X \to Y$ is a C^{r+1} map between C^{r+1} manifolds X and Y, (U, α) and (V, β) are suitable admissible charts on X and Y respectively, and $f_{\alpha\beta}$ is the local representative of f with respect to these charts, then the local representative of Tf with respect to the natural VB charts $(T\alpha, \alpha, U)$ and $(T\beta, \beta, V)$ is given by

$$(x, \mathbf{e}) \rightsquigarrow (f_{\alpha\beta}(x), Df_{\alpha\beta}(x)\mathbf{e})$$

for $x \in \alpha(U)$, $\mathbf{e} \in \mathbf{E}_\alpha$. The tangent mapping Tf may be alternatively constructed by patching together these local tangent mappings, in the spirit of Eilenberg-Cartan [*1*].

§7. Double Tangents

Upon iteration of the tangent functor defined in the last section, we obtain the double tangent functor T^2, whose values lie in a category of diagrams of vector bundles called *rhombics.* If X is a manifold, the rhombic T^2X has a special symmetry which is important in the study of ordinary differential equations. In this section we develop the structure of these double tangent rhombics.

Let X be a C^{r+1} manifold ($r \geqslant 1$). Then $T(X)$ is a C^r manifold, and we may form its tangent bundle

$$\tau_{T(X)}: T(T(X)) \to T(X)$$

We will write $T^2(X)$ instead of $T(T(X))$. Hence

$$\tau_{T(X)}: T^2(X) \to T(X)$$

Corresponding to each chart (U, α) on X there is a natural (manifold) chart $(\tau_X^{-1}(U), T\alpha)$ on $T(X)$ and hence a **natural-natural** C^{r-1} VB chart $(T^2\alpha, T\alpha, \tau_X^{-1}(U))$ on $\tau_{T(X)}$; here we write $T^2\alpha$ instead of $TT\alpha$. An easy computation (left to the reader) establishes the following proposition.

7.1. PROPOSITION. Let X be a C^{r+1} manifold ($r \geq 1$), (U, α) and (V, β) admissible charts on X, and E_α and E_β the ambient spaces of $\alpha(U)$ and $\beta(V)$ respectively. Then the transition map

$$(T^2\beta) \circ (T^2\alpha)^{-1}: \alpha(U \cap V) \times \mathbf{E}_\alpha^3 \to \beta(U \cap V) \times \mathbf{E}_\beta^3$$

is given by

$$(T^2\beta) \circ (T^2\alpha)^{-1}(x, \mathbf{e}_2, \mathbf{e}_3, \mathbf{e}_4) = (\beta \circ \alpha^{-1}(x), D\beta \circ \alpha^{-1}(x)\mathbf{e}_2, D\beta \circ \alpha^{-1}(x)\mathbf{e}_3, D^2\beta \circ \alpha^{-1}(x)\mathbf{e}_2\mathbf{e}_3 + D\beta \circ \alpha^{-1}(x)\mathbf{e}_4)$$

for $(x, \mathbf{e}_2, \mathbf{e}_3, \mathbf{e}_4) \in \alpha(U \cap V) \times \mathbf{E}_\alpha^3$.

The natural natural VB chart $(T^2\alpha, T\alpha, \tau_X^{-1}(U))$ on $\tau_{T(X)}$ arising from a manifold chart (U, α) on X gives a natural natural manifold chart $(\tau_X^{-1}(U), T^2\alpha)$ on $T^2(X)$. We define a map

$$\omega: T^2(X) \to T^2(X)$$

by defining its local representative ω_α with respect to such a manifold chart on $T^2(X)$ by

$$\omega_\alpha(x, \mathbf{e}_2, \mathbf{e}_3, \mathbf{e}_4) = (x, \mathbf{e}_3, \mathbf{e}_2, \mathbf{e}_4)$$

ω_α interchanges the second and third coordinates. By 7.1 we see that this defines a map $\omega: T^2(X) \to T^2(X)$ independently of the choice of the charts (U, α) on X. (We need the fact that $D^2(\beta \circ \alpha^{-1})(x)$ is symmetric bilinear!) Clearly ω is a C^r diffeomorphism and $\omega \circ \omega$ is the identity map of $T^2(X)$.

The map $\omega: T^2(X) \to T^2(X)$ defined above is called the **canonical involution** on $T^2(X)$.

We will examine ω more closely. Let X be a C^{r+1} manifold ($r \geq 1$). Then the tangent bundle $\tau_X: T(X) \to X$ is a C^r manifold morphism. It has a tangent $T\tau_X: T^2(X) \to T(X)$ which (by 6.2) makes the following diagram commute:

$$\begin{array}{ccc} T^2(X) & \xrightarrow{T\tau_X} & T(X) \\ \downarrow{\scriptstyle \tau_{T(X)}} & & \downarrow{\scriptstyle \tau_X} \\ T(X) & \xrightarrow{\tau_X} & X \end{array}$$

We rotate the diagram above as follows:

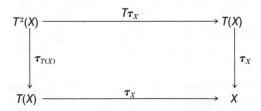

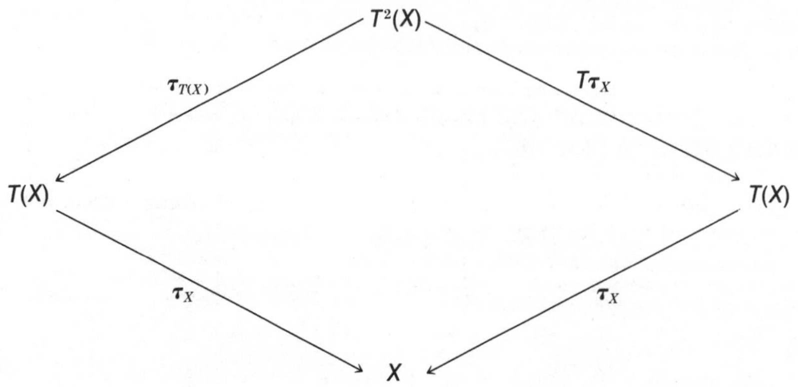

This diagram is called a **rhombic** and it commutes.

The surjection $T\tau_X \circ \tau_X = \tau_{T(X)} \circ \tau_X$: $T^2(X) \to X$ has the structure of a fiber bundle over X (see 7.1). It is *not* a vector bundle because of the presence of a term $D^2\beta \circ \alpha^{-1}(x)\mathbf{e}_2\mathbf{e}_3$ in the fourth factor of the transition map (see 7.1).

If we restrict attention to the top half of the rhombic, we see that $T^2(X)$ is a vector bundle over $T(X)$ in two ways, namely

$$T\tau_X\colon T^2(X) \to T(X)$$

and

$$\tau_{T(X)}\colon T^2(X) \to T(X)$$

In natural-natural coordinates the first vector bundle corresponds to projection on the first and third coordinates; the second bundle corresponds to projection on the first and second coordinates. The triangular diagram

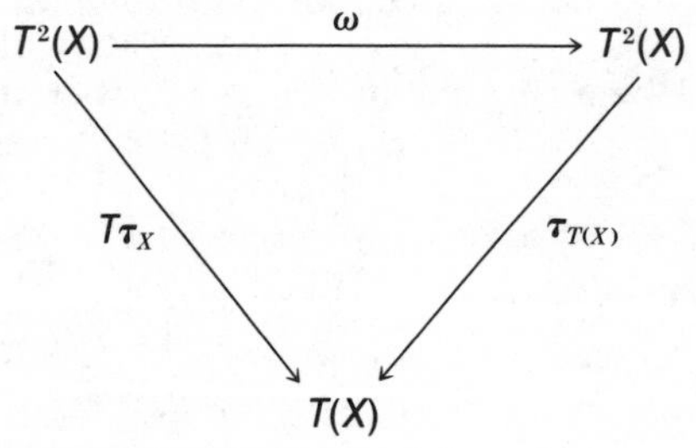

commutes. Using this diagram, the functoriality of T (Proposition 6.2), Proposition 7.1, and the definition of ω, one easily proves the following proposition.

7.2. PROPOSITION. Let X be a C^{r+1} manifold ($r \geq 1$).

(I) The diagram

$$\begin{array}{ccc} T^2(X) & \xrightarrow{\ \ \omega\ \ } & T^2(X) \\ {\scriptstyle T\tau_X}\downarrow & & \downarrow{\scriptstyle \tau_{T(X)}} \\ T(X) & \xrightarrow[id_{T(X)}]{} & T(X) \end{array}$$

defines a C^{r-1} vector bundle isomorphism between $T\tau_X$ and $\tau_{T(X)}$.

(II) If $\xi \in \Gamma^r(\tau_X)$, then $T\xi \in \Gamma^{r-1}(T\tau_X)$ and $\omega \circ T\xi \in \Gamma^{r-1}(\tau_{T(X)})$.

(III) The maps T: $\Gamma^r(\tau_X) \to \Gamma^{r-1}(T\tau_X)$ and $\omega \circ T$: $\Gamma^r(\tau_X) \to \Gamma^{r-1}(\tau_{T(X)})$ are R-linear; i.e., for $\xi, \zeta \in \Gamma^r(\tau_X)$ and $a, b \in R$

$$T(a\xi + b\zeta) = aT\xi + bT\zeta$$

and

$$\omega \circ T(a\xi + b\zeta) = a\omega \circ T\xi + b\omega \circ T\zeta$$

A map η: $T(X) \to T^2(X)$ which is a section of both the bundles $T\tau_X$ and $\tau_{T(X)}$ is called a **second-order differential equation** on X. (Compare with Lang [*1*; p. 67].) According to 7.2 (II), $\xi' = \omega \circ T\xi$ is thus a second-order equation, called the **equation of first variation** of ξ.

§8. Jets

In the applications of differential theory it is frequently necessary to put restrictions on the higher-order derivatives of mappings. This may be accomplished most easily in terms of Ehresmann's notion of jets, which globalizes the higher-order derivatives of the local theory. In this section we define a special case of this general notion which applies to sections of a vector bundle only. This is basic to many of the constructions in the sequel.

Let $\mathbf{E}$ and $\mathbf{F}$ be Banach spaces. For each nonnegative integer k define $P^k(\mathbf{E}, \mathbf{F})$, the (Banach) **space of polynomials of degree k defined on $\mathbf{E}$ with values in $\mathbf{F}$,** by

$$P^k(\mathbf{E}, \mathbf{F}) = \mathbf{F} \times L(\mathbf{E}, \mathbf{F}) \times L_s^2(\mathbf{E}, \mathbf{F}) \times \cdots \times L_s^k(\mathbf{E}, \mathbf{F})$$

Let $U \subset \mathbf{E}$ open, $x \in U$, ξ: $U \to \mathbf{F}$ a C^r map, and k a nonnegative integer $\leqslant r$. We define $P^k\xi(x) \in P^k(\mathbf{E}, \mathbf{F})$ by

$$P^k\xi(x) = (\xi(x), D\xi(x), D^2\xi(x), \ldots, D^k\xi(x))$$

Let π: $E \to X$ be a C^r vector bundle and $k \leqslant r$ a nonnegative integer. We will define a C^{r-k} vector bundle π^k: $J^k(\pi) \to X$ called the **k-jet bundle of sections** of π. For this purpose we define a **partial section** of π to be a map ξ defined on an open subset of X (but not necessarily on all of X) with values in E and satisfying $\pi \circ \xi(x) = x$ whenever x is in the domain of definition of ξ. In case X admits bump functions, every partial section defined at a point x can be restricted to a neighborhood of x and then extended to the whole of X; when this happens, the jet bundle can be defined without recourse to the notion of a partial section.

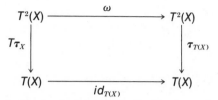

Let $x_1, x_2 \in X$, (α, α_0, U) be a VB chart on π with $x_1, x_2 \in U$, and ξ_1, ξ_2 partial sections defined on U. Let $\xi_{1\alpha}$ and $\xi_{2\alpha}$ be the principal parts of local representatives of ξ_1 and ξ_2 respectively. Then $\alpha_0: U \to \alpha_0(U)$, $\alpha: \pi^{-1}(U) \to \alpha_0(U) \times \mathbf{F}_\alpha$, and $\xi_{1\alpha}, \xi_{2\alpha}: \alpha_0(U) \to \mathbf{F}_\alpha$. We say $(\xi_1, x_1) \equiv^k (\xi_2, x_2)$ iff $x_1 = x_2$ and $P^k\xi_{1\alpha}(\alpha_0(x_1)) = P^k\xi_{2\alpha}(\alpha_0(x_2))$. This definition is independent of the choice of the VB chart (α, α_0, U); if (β, T_0, V) is another suitable VB chart on π, we may express $P^k\xi_\beta(\beta_0(x))$ in terms of $\xi_\alpha(\alpha_0(x))$, $D\xi_\alpha(\alpha_0(x)), \ldots, D^k\xi_\alpha(\alpha_0(x))$, and various factors independent of ξ. One simply writes

$$\xi_\beta(\beta_0(x)) = (\beta \circ \alpha^{-1})^\#(\alpha_0 \circ \beta_0^{-1}(\bar{x}))\xi_\alpha(\alpha_0 \circ \beta_0^{-1}(\bar{x}))$$

where $\bar{x} = \beta_0(x)$. To compute $P^k\xi_\beta(\beta_0(x))$ one computes the first k derivatives of the expression on the right (with respect to $\bar{x}$). Since $\alpha_0 \circ \beta_0^{-1}(\bar{x}) = \alpha_0(x)$, this will depend only on the charts and $P^k\xi_\alpha(\alpha_0(x))$. Also, $\equiv^k$ is clearly an equivalence relation. We let $j^k\xi(x)$ denote the equivalence class of the pair (ξ, x). Let $J^k(\pi)$ be the set of all $j^k\xi(x)$. For each C^r section $\xi: X \to E$ the map

$$j^k\xi: X \to J^k(\pi)$$

given by

$$x \rightsquigarrow j^k\xi(x)$$

is called the **k-jet extension of** ξ. The map

$$\pi^k: J^k(\pi) \to X$$

given by

$$\pi^k(j^k\xi(x)) = x$$

is called the **k-jet projection.** We also call

$$\pi^k: J^k(\pi) \to X$$

the **k-jet bundle of sections of π.**

For each VB chart (α, α_0, U) on π define the corresponding **natural k-jet chart** on π^k by

$$\alpha^k(j^k\xi(x)) = (\alpha_0(x), P^k\xi_\alpha(\alpha_0(x)))$$

It is a bijection; it is injective by definition and is surjective since we can always find a partial section ξ having a prescribed value for $P^k\xi_\alpha(x)$. (Indeed if X admits bump functions we can find such a ξ defined on all of X.) The set of all such natural k-jet charts (as (α, α_0, U) ranges over the admissible VB charts on π) is called the **natural k-jet atlas on π^k.**

8.1. PROPOSITION. The natural k-jet atlas on π^k is a C^{r-k} VB atlas; hence π^k (together with the unique maximal atlas which extends the natural k-jet atlas) is a C^{r-k} vector bundle. Furthermore, if $\xi: X \to E$ is a C^r section of π, then $j^k\xi: X \to J^k(\pi)$ is a C^{r-k} section of π^k.

Proof. Choose VB charts (α, α_0, U) and (β, β_0, V) on π and let (α^k, α_0, U) and (β^k, β_0, V) be the corresponding natural k-jet charts respectively. Let $\mathbf{E}_\alpha$ be the ambient space of $\alpha_0(U)$, i.e., $\alpha_0(U) \subset \mathbf{E}_\alpha$; $\mathbf{E}_\beta$ be the ambient space of $\beta_0(V)$; $\alpha: \pi^{-1}(U) \to \alpha_0(U) \times \mathbf{F}_\alpha$; $\beta: \pi^{-1}(V) \to \beta_0(V) \times \mathbf{F}_\beta$. It suffices to show that

(I) $(\beta^k \circ (\alpha^k)^{-1})^\#(x)$ is continuous linear for $x \in \alpha_0(U \cap V)$ and

(II) the map

$$(\beta^k \circ (\alpha^k)^{-1})^{\#}: \alpha_0(U \cap V) \to L(P^k(\mathbf{E}_\alpha, \mathbf{F}_\alpha), P^k(\mathbf{E}_\beta, \mathbf{F}_\beta))$$

is class C^{r-k}.

Choose $(x, p) \in \alpha_0(U \cap V) \times P^k(\mathbf{E}_\alpha, \mathbf{F}_\alpha)$. To compute $(\beta^k \circ (\alpha^k)^{-1})^{\#}(x)p$, we choose a partial section ξ defined at $\alpha_0^{-1}(x)$ such that $P^k\xi_\alpha(x) = p$. Then

(1) $$(\beta^k \circ (\alpha^k)^{-1})^{\#}(x)p = P^k\xi_\beta(\beta_0 \circ \alpha_0^{-1}(x))$$

Now

(2) $$\xi_\beta(\beta_0 \circ \alpha_0^{-1}(x)) = (\beta \circ \alpha^{-1})^{\#}(x)\xi_\alpha(\beta_0 \circ \alpha_0^{-1}(x))$$

In the term on the right, concatenation denotes a continuous bilinear map, namely, the evaluation map

$$L(\mathbf{F}_\alpha, \mathbf{F}_\beta) \times \mathbf{F}_\alpha \to \mathbf{F}_\beta$$

Compute $D^j\xi_\beta(\beta_0 \circ \alpha_0^{-1}(x))$ $j \leq k$, in terms of ξ_α using (2), Leibnitz' rule, and the composite mapping formula. The result will be a sum of terms of form

(3) $$D^l(\beta \circ \alpha^{-1})^{\#}(x)\ D^q\xi_\alpha(\beta_0 \circ \alpha_0^{-1}(x))D^{i_1}\beta_0 \circ \alpha_0^{-1}(x) \cdots D^{i_q}\beta_0 \circ \alpha_0^{-1}(x)$$

The result is clearly linear in $P^k\xi_\alpha(\beta_0 \circ \alpha_0^{-1}(x))$; thus the left-hand side of (1) is linear in p. Since it is a sum of the terms of form (3), it is continuous in p. This proves (I). Since in each term (3), $l, i_1, \ldots, i_q \leq k$, it follows that these terms are class C^{r-k} in x. This proves (II).

The second part of the proposition is trivial, for if ξ_α is the principal part of a local representative of some C^r section ξ of π, then $P^k\xi_\alpha$ is the corresponding principal part of $j^k\xi_\alpha$. ▮

§9. Linear Map Bundles

In this section we consider vector bundles with spaces of linear mappings as fibers. This is an example of a tensor bundle (Abraham-Marsden [*1;* §6] and Lang [*1;* Ch. III, §4]) and includes the fiber bundle of 1-jets of mappings (Abraham [*2;* §15]). Our treatment is similar to Lang [*1*].

Let $\pi: E \to X$ and $\pi': E' \to X'$ be two C^r vector bundles. Recall that for $x \in X$, E_x denotes the fiber over x. Define the set $L(E, E')$ by

$$L(E, E') = \bigcup L(E_x, E'_{x'})$$

where the union is over all pairs $(x, x') \in X \times X'$. One has a natural projection

$$L(\pi, \pi'): L(E, E') \to X \times X'$$

given by

$$L(\pi, \pi')(\lambda) = (x, x')$$

where

$$\lambda \in L(E_x, E'_{x'})$$

Given VB charts (α, α_0, U) and (α', α_0', U') on π and π' respectively, one defines a **natural chart** $(L_{\alpha\alpha'}, \alpha_0 \times \alpha_0', U \times U')$ on $L(\pi, \pi')$ as follows.

Let $\mathbf{E}$ and $\mathbf{E}'$ be the ambient spaces of $\alpha_0(U)$ and $\alpha_0'(U')$ respectively; i.e., $\alpha_0(U) \subset \mathbf{E}$ and $\alpha_0'(U') \subset \mathbf{E}'$. Suppose $\alpha(\pi^{-1}(U)) = \alpha_0(U) \times \mathbf{F}_\alpha$ and $\alpha'(\pi'^{-1}(U)) = \alpha_0'(U') \times \mathbf{F}'_{\alpha'}$. Then for $x \in U$, $x' \in U'$, and $\lambda \in L(\mathbf{E}_x, \mathbf{E}'_{x'})$ define

$$L_{\alpha\alpha'}(\lambda) \in \alpha_0(U) \times \alpha_0'(U') \times L(\mathbf{F}_\alpha, \mathbf{F}'_\alpha)$$

by

$$L_{\alpha\alpha'}(\lambda) = (\alpha_0(x), \alpha_0'(x'), \lambda_{\alpha\alpha'}(x))$$

where $\lambda_{\alpha\alpha'}(x) \in L(\mathbf{F}_\alpha, \mathbf{F}'_{\alpha'})$ is defined by

$$\lambda_{\alpha\alpha'}(x)\mathbf{v} = pr_2 \circ \alpha' \circ \lambda \circ \alpha^{-1}(\alpha_0(x), \mathbf{v})$$

for $\mathbf{v} \in \mathbf{F}_\alpha$ and where $pr_2\colon \alpha_0'(U') \times \mathbf{F}'_{\alpha'} \to \mathbf{F}'_{\alpha'}$ is the natural projection on the second factor. The set of all such natural charts (as (α, α_0, U) and (α', α_0', U') range over the admissible VB charts on π and π' respectively) is called the **natural atlas** for $L(\pi, \pi')$.

The reader will note that if (β, β_0, V) and (β', β_0', V') are VB charts on π and π' at $\alpha_0^{-1}(x)$ and $\alpha_0'^{-1}(x')$ respectively, the transition map

$$(L_{\beta\beta'} \circ L_{\alpha\alpha'}^{-1})^{\#}(x, x')\colon L(F_\alpha, F'_{\alpha'}) \to L(F_\beta, F'_{\beta'})$$

is given by

$$(L_{\beta\beta'} \circ L_{\alpha\alpha'})^{\#}(x, x')\lambda = \mu' \circ \lambda \circ \mu^{-1}$$

for $\lambda \in L(F_\alpha, F'_{\alpha'})$ and where

$$\mu' = (\beta' \circ \alpha'^{-1})^{\#}(x')$$

and

$$\mu = (\beta \circ \alpha^{-1})^{\#}(x)$$

9.1. PROPOSITION. The natural atlas on $L(\pi, \pi')$ is a C^r VB atlas; hence $L(\pi, \pi')$ (together with the unique maximal VB atlas which extends the natural atlas) is a C^r vector bundle.

The vector bundle of 9.1 is called the **linear map bundle** of π and π'.

2
SPACES OF SECTIONS

If X and Y are C^r manifolds, the set $\mathscr{C}^r(X, Y)$ of C^r morphisms from X to Y, with an appropriate topology, is a space of mappings which generalizes the familiar notion of a function space.

If X is compact, this space becomes a differentiable manifold which is very useful in global nonlinear analysis, especially in the elementary applications of transversality theory (see Abraham [*2*]). In this chapter we consider spaces of sections of a vector bundle from this point of view. The most important result concerns the differentiability of the *evaluation map.*

§10. Local Mappings

In this section we consider the local analogue of the space of smooth sections of a vector bundle and prove the differentiability of the evaluation mapping. This result is one of the most important in differential theory for the applications of the transversality technique. Our proof is much simpler than the original one (Abraham [*2;* §11]), because we make use of the simple criterion of differentiability of §2.

Let $\boldsymbol{E}$ and $\boldsymbol{F}$ be Banach spaces and $U \subset \boldsymbol{E}$ be convex and open. Recall that for a nonnegative integer r, $P^r(\boldsymbol{E}, \boldsymbol{F})$ is the Banach space of polynomials from $\boldsymbol{E}$ to $\boldsymbol{F}$; i.e.,

$$P^r(\boldsymbol{E}, \boldsymbol{F}) = \boldsymbol{F} \times L(\boldsymbol{E}, \boldsymbol{F}) \times L_s^2(\boldsymbol{E}, \boldsymbol{F}) \times \cdots \times L_s^r(\boldsymbol{E}, \boldsymbol{F})$$

Recall that $\mathscr{C}^r(U, \mathbf{F})$ is the (vector) space of C^r maps from U to $\mathbf{F}$ and that, for $\xi \in \mathscr{C}^r(U, \mathbf{F})$ and $x \in U$, $P^r\xi(x)$ is the point of $P^r(\mathbf{E}, \mathbf{F})$ given by

$$P^r\xi(x) = (\xi(x), D\xi(x), D^2\xi(x), \ldots, D^r\xi(x))$$

Choose a norm $\| \quad \|$ on $P^r(\mathbf{E}, \mathbf{F})$. For $\xi \in \mathscr{C}^r(U, \mathbf{F})$ define

$$\|\xi\|_r = \sup \{\|P^r\xi(x)\|: x \in U\},$$

and define

$$\mathscr{B}^r(U, \mathbf{F}) = \{\xi \in \mathscr{C}^r(U, \mathbf{F}): \|\xi\|_r < \infty\}$$

That is, $\mathscr{B}^r(U, \mathbf{F})$ is the set of all C^r maps from U to $\mathbf{F}$ whose first r derivatives are bounded. The set $\mathscr{C}^r(U, \mathbf{F})$ has a structure of real vector space in the obvious way. For $\xi, \zeta \in \mathscr{C}^r(U, \mathbf{F})$ and $a, b \in \mathbf{R}$ define $a\xi + b\zeta$ in $\mathscr{C}^r(U, \mathbf{F})$ by

$$(a\xi + b\zeta)(x) = a\xi(x) + b\zeta(x)$$

10.1. PROPOSITION. (I) $\mathscr{B}^r(U, \mathbf{F})$ is a (linear) subspace of $\mathscr{C}^r(U, \mathbf{F})$ and hence is itself a vector space.

(II) $\| \quad \|_r$ is a norm on $\mathscr{B}^r(U, \mathbf{F})$.

(III) The topology on $\mathscr{B}^r(u, \mathbf{F})$ induced by $\| \quad \|_r$ is independent of the choice of norm $\| \quad \|$ on $P^r(\mathbf{E}, \mathbf{F})$ used in defining $\| \quad \|_r$.

We omit the proof.

10.2. THEOREM. $\mathscr{B}^r(U, \mathbf{F})$ with the norm $\| \quad \|_r$ is a Banach space.

Proof. Let $\{\xi_n\}_n$ be a Cauchy sequence in $\mathscr{B}^r(U, \mathbf{F})$. Since $\mathbf{F}$ is complete, we have for each $x \in U$ a point $\xi(x) \in \mathbf{F}$ such that $\xi_n(x) \to \xi(x)$ as $n \to \infty$. We must show:

(1) $\xi \in \mathscr{B}^r(U, \mathbf{F})$;

(2) $\xi_n \to \xi$ in the norm $\| \quad \|_r$.

For each $x \in U$ and each $k = 0, 1, \ldots, r$ we have $\varphi_k(x) \in L^k_s(\mathbf{E}, \mathbf{F})$ such that

(*) $$D^k\xi_n(x) \to \varphi_k(x)$$

as $n \to \infty$. In fact, the convergence (*) is uniform so that each $\varphi_k: U \to L^k_s(\mathbf{E}, \mathbf{F})$ is continuous.

Now choose $x \in U$ and $h \in \mathbf{E}$ so small that the line segment $x + th$ $(0 \leq t \leq 1)$ lies in U. By Taylor's formula (1.5) we have for $n = 0, 1, 2, 3, \ldots$

$$\xi_n(x + h) = \sum_{k=0}^{r} \frac{D^k\xi_n(x)}{k!} h^k + R_n(x, h)h^r$$

where

$$R_n(x, h) = \int_0^1 \frac{(1 - t)^{r-1}}{(r - 1)!} \{Dr\xi_n(x + th) - D^r\xi_n(x)\}\, dt$$

By uniformity, integral and limit commute; hence, letting $n \to \infty$ we get

$$\xi(x+h) = \sum_{k=0}^{r} \frac{\varphi_k(x)h^k}{k!} + R(x, h)h^r$$

where

$$R(x, h) = \int_0^1 \frac{(1-t)^{r-1}}{(r-1)!} \{\varphi_r(x+th) - \varphi_r(x)\}\, dt$$

Clearly $R(x, h)$ is continuous in x and h and $R(x, \mathbf{0}) = \mathbf{0}$. Hence, by the converse to Taylor's Theorem (2.1), it follows that $\xi: U \to \mathbf{F}$ is of class C^r and $D^k\xi = \varphi_k$ for $k = 0, 1, \ldots, r$.

We have shown that $\xi \in \mathscr{C}^r(U, \mathbf{F})$. Since $\xi_n \to \xi$ pointwise and $\{\xi_n\}_n$ is a Cauchy sequence in the norm $\|\ \|_r$, it follows that $\xi \in \mathscr{B}^r(U, \mathbf{F})$ and $\xi_n \to \xi$ in the norm $\|\ \|_r$. This completes the proof of 10.2. ∎

10.3. THEOREM. The evaluation map

$$ev: \mathscr{B}^r(U, \mathbf{F}) \times U \to \mathbf{F}$$

given by

$$ev(\xi, x) = \xi(x)$$

for $\xi \in \mathscr{B}^r(U, \mathbf{F})$ and $x \in U$ is a C^r map. In fact,

$$D^k ev(\xi, x)(\eta, h)^k = kD^{k-1}\eta(x)h^{k-1} + D^k\xi(x)h^k$$

for $(\xi, x) \in \mathscr{B}^r(U, \mathbf{F}) \times U$ and $(\eta, h) \in \mathscr{B}^r(U, \mathbf{F}) \times \mathbf{E}$ and for $k = 1, \ldots, r$.

Remark. Setting $k = 1$ in the above formula we obtain

(*) $$Dev(\xi, x)(\eta, h) = \eta(x) + D\xi(x)h$$

This formula (*) is not at all mysterious, for ev is a function of two variables; if it is differentiable, we may compute its derivative by the partial derivative rule

(i) $$Dev(\xi, x)(\eta, h) = D_1 ev(\xi, x)\eta + D_2 ev(\xi, x)h$$

For fixed ξ, the map $x \rightsquigarrow ev(\xi, x)$ is simply ξ. Hence

(ii) $$D_2 ev(\xi, x)h = D\xi(x)h$$

For fixed x, the map $\xi \rightsquigarrow ev(\xi, x)$ is simply the map $\xi \rightsquigarrow \xi(x)$. This map is linear and is therefore its own derivative. Hence

(iii) $$D_1 ev(\xi, x)\eta = \eta(x)$$

On substituting (ii) and (iii) in (i), we get (*).

Proof of 10.3. Choose $(\xi, x) \in \mathscr{B}^r(U, \mathbf{F}) \times U$ and $(\eta, h) \in \mathscr{B}^r(U, \mathbf{F}) \times \mathbf{E}$ with h so small that the line segment $x + th$

$(0 \leq t \leq 1)$ lies in U. By Taylor's formula (§1.5) we have

$$\begin{aligned} ev(\xi+\eta, x+h) &= \xi(x+h)+\eta(x+h) \\ &= \sum_{k=0}^{r} \frac{D^k\xi(x)}{k!} h^k + R_\xi(x, h)h^r + \sum_{k=0}^{r} \frac{D^k\eta(x)}{k!} h^k + R_\eta(x, h)h^r \\ &= \sum_{k=0}^{r} \frac{\varphi_k(\xi, x)}{k!} (\eta, h)^k + \rho(\xi, x, \eta, h) \end{aligned}$$

where

(1) $R_\xi(x, h) = \int_0^1 \frac{(1-t)^{r-1}}{(r-1)!} \{D^r\xi(x+th) - D^r\xi(x)\}\, dt;$

(2) $R_\eta(x, h) = \int_0^1 \frac{(1-t)^{r-1}}{(r-1)!} \{D^r\eta(x+th) - D^r\eta(x)\}\, dt;$

(3) For $k = 0, 1, \ldots, r$,

$$\varphi_k(\xi, x) \in L_s^k(\mathscr{B}^r(U, \mathbf{F}) \times \mathbf{E}, \mathbf{F})$$

is defined by

$$\varphi_k(\xi, x)(\eta_1, h_1)(\eta_2, h_2) \cdots (\eta_k, h_k) = D^k\xi(x)h_1 \cdots h_k + \sum_{i=1}^{k} D^{k-1}\eta_i(x)h_1 \cdots h_{i-1}h_{i+1} \cdots h_k$$

(4) $\rho(\xi, x, \eta, h) = R_\xi(x, h) + R_\eta(x, h) + \dfrac{D^r\eta(x)h^r}{r!}$

The reader may show that for each $k = 0, 1, \ldots, r$ the map

$$\varphi_k\colon \mathscr{B}^r(U, \mathbf{F}) \times U \to L_s^k(\mathscr{B}^r(U, \mathbf{F}) \times \mathbf{E}, \mathbf{F})$$

is continuous. (Hint: this will require the triangle inequality and the Mean Value Theorem (1.6).)

We may define a norm on $\mathscr{B}^r(U, \mathbf{F}) \times U$ by

$$\|(\eta, h)\| = \max \{\|\eta\|_r, \|h\|\}$$

where $h \rightsquigarrow \|h\|$ is a norm on $\mathbf{E}$. Using this norm, one easily sees that

$$\frac{\|\rho(\xi, x, \eta, h)\|}{\|(\eta, h)\|^r} \to 0$$

as $(\eta, h) \to (0, \mathbf{0})$. Now 10.3 follows immediately from the converse to Taylor's formula (2.1). This completes the proof of 10.3 ∎

Recall from §6 the definition of $P^k(\mathbf{E}, \mathbf{F})$, the space of polynomials from $\mathbf{E}$ to $\mathbf{F}$, and also the definition of $P^k\xi(x)$.

10.4. THEOREM. Suppose k is an integer with $0 \leqslant k \leqslant r$. Let

$$ev_k\colon \mathscr{B}^r(U, \mathbf{F}) \times U \to U \times P^k(\mathbf{E}, \mathbf{F})$$

be defined by

$$ev_k(\xi, x) = (x, P^k\xi(x))$$

for $x \in U$, $\xi \in \mathscr{B}^r(U, \mathbf{F})$. Then,

(I) ev_k is a C^{r-k} map, and

(II) For $(\xi, x) \in \mathscr{B}^r(U, \mathbf{F}) \times U$, the linear map $D\, ev_k(\xi, x)$ is split surjective.

Proof. The map

$$P^k\colon \mathscr{B}^r(U, \mathbf{F}) \to \mathscr{B}^{r-k}(U, P^k(\mathbf{E}, \mathbf{F}))$$

given by

$$\xi \rightsquigarrow P^k\xi$$

for $\xi \in \mathscr{B}^r(U, \mathbf{F})$ is continuous linear. The evaluation map

$$ev\colon \mathscr{B}^{r-k}(U, P^k(\mathbf{E}, \mathbf{F})) \times U \to P^k(\mathbf{E}, \mathbf{F})$$

given by

$$ev(f, x) = f(x)$$

for $f \in \mathscr{B}^{r-k}(U, P^k(\mathbf{E}, \mathbf{F}))$ and $x \in U$ is class C^{r-k} by the last theorem. But for $\xi \in \mathscr{B}^r(U, \mathbf{F})$ and $x \in U$

$$ev_k(\xi, x) = (x, ev(P^k\xi, x))$$

and hence by the chain rule, ev_k is class C^{r-k}. This proves (I).

Now, for $\xi \in \mathscr{B}^r(U, \mathbf{F})$, $x \in U$,

$$ev_k(\xi, x) = (x, \xi(x), D\xi(x), \ldots, D^k\xi(x))$$

and hence by the last theorem

$$D\, ev_k(\xi, x)(\zeta, h) = (h, \zeta(x) + D\xi(x)h, D\zeta(x) + D^2\zeta(x)h, \ldots, D^{k-1}\xi(x) + D^k\xi(x)h)$$

for $\zeta \in \mathscr{B}^r(U, \mathbf{F})$, $h \in \mathbf{E}$. Since we can find ζ with any prescribed values for $\zeta(x), D\zeta(x), \ldots, D^k\zeta(x)$; it follows that $D\, ev_k(\xi, x)$ is surjective.

Now define

$$\mathbf{K}_1 = \{\zeta \in \mathscr{B}^r(U, \mathbf{F}) \mid D^i\zeta(x) = \mathbf{0},\ i = 0, \ldots, k\}$$

and

$$\mathbf{K}_2 = \{\zeta \in \mathscr{B}^r(U, \mathbf{F}) \mid D^i\zeta \equiv \mathbf{0},\ i = k+1, \ldots, r\}$$

Clearly

$$\mathscr{B}^r(U, \boldsymbol{F}) = \boldsymbol{K}_1 \oplus \boldsymbol{K}_2$$

where the sum is direct and each summand is closed. Thus we have the splitting decomposition

$$\mathscr{B}^r(U, \boldsymbol{F}) \times \boldsymbol{E} = (\boldsymbol{K}_1 \times \{0\}) \oplus (\boldsymbol{K}_2 \times \boldsymbol{E})$$

whence, since the left summand is the kernel of $D\, ev_k(\xi, x)$, it follows that $D\, ev_k(\xi, x)$ is kernel splitting. This completes the proof of (II) and of the theorem. ∎

§11. Continuous Sections

Let $\pi: E \to X$ be a C^r vector bundle. Recall that $\Gamma^k(\pi)$, $k = 0, 1, \ldots, r$ is the vector space of C^k sections of π. Our aim in this section is to make $\Gamma^0(\pi)$ into a Banach space. We will do this only in case X is compact (and hence finite dimensional) and $\boldsymbol{F}$, the model space of the fiber is finite dimensional. These two conditions imply that E is finite dimensional (as a manifold).

For each $x \in X$ the fiber $E_x = \pi^{-1}(x)$ has the structure of a Banach space since a choice of VB coordinates at x puts E_x in one-to-one correspondence with a Banach space $\boldsymbol{F}$, and a change of coordinates induces a toplinear isomorphism from $\boldsymbol{F}$ to $\boldsymbol{F}$. Unfortunately, there is no "preferred" norm on E_x. To remedy this we make the following definition.

Let $\pi: E \to X$ be a vector bundle. A continuous map $\varphi: E \to \boldsymbol{R}$ is called a **Finsler** on π, iff for each $x \in X$, $\varphi | E_x$ is an admissible norm for E_x; i.e., if (α, α_0, U) is a VB chart at x and $\alpha(\pi^{-1}(U)) = \alpha_0(U) \times \boldsymbol{F}$, then the composite map

$$\boldsymbol{F} \to \{\alpha_0(x)\} \times \boldsymbol{F} \xrightarrow{\alpha^{-1}} E_x \xrightarrow{\varphi} \boldsymbol{R}$$

(where the map on the left is the natural injection) is a norm for $\boldsymbol{F}$.

The trivial bundle $U \times \boldsymbol{F} \to U$ has a **trivial Finsler** $\varphi: U \times \boldsymbol{F} \to \boldsymbol{R}$ given by

$$\varphi(x, \boldsymbol{v}) = \|\boldsymbol{v}\|$$

where $x \in U$, $\boldsymbol{v} \in \boldsymbol{F}$ and $\| \ \|$ is a norm on $\boldsymbol{F}$.

11.1. PROPOSITION. Let $\pi: E \to X$ be a vector bundle. If X admits C^0 partitions of unity, there is a Finsler on π.

Proof. Simply take a trivial Finsler on each VB chart and add them up via partitions of unity. We omit the details. ∎

Let $\pi: E \to X$ be a vector bundle and $\varphi: E \to \boldsymbol{R}$ be a Finsler on π. Define for each $\xi \in \Gamma^0(\pi)$

$$\|\xi\|_\varphi = \sup \{\varphi(\xi(x)) \mid x \in X\}$$

Note that if X is compact, $\|\xi\|_\varphi < \infty$.

A VB chart (α, α_0, U) on a vector bundle π is called **pseudocompact** iff

(1) $\bar{U}$ is compact, and

(2) there is a VB chart (β, β_0, V) on π with $\bar{U} \subset V$, $\alpha_0 = \beta_0 | U$, and $\alpha = \beta | \pi^{-1}(U)$.

11.2. THEOREM. Let $\pi\colon E \to X$ be a vector bundle with finite-dimensional fiber and with X compact. Let φ be a Finsler on π. Then,

(I) $\| \ \|_\varphi$ is a norm on $\Gamma^0(\pi)$;

(II) The topology on $\Gamma^0(\pi)$ determined by $\| \ \|_\varphi$ is independent of the choice of φ;

(III) In this topology $\Gamma^0(\pi)$ is a separable (and hence second-countable) Banach space.

The first conclusion is immediate from the definitions. For (II) we need the following result.

11.3. LEMMA. If ψ is another Finsler on π, then there exist positive real numbers A and B such that

$$A\psi(e) \leqslant \varphi(e) \leqslant B\psi(e)$$

for $e \in E$.

For the proof of this we need another lemma.

11.4. LEMMA. Let ψ be a Finsler on π and (α, α_0, U) be a pseudocompact VB chart on π. Suppose F models the fiber of π; i.e., $\alpha(\pi^{-1}(U)) = \alpha_0(U) \times F$ and $\| \ \|$ is a norm on F. Then there are positive real numbers $A_{\alpha\psi}$ and $B_{\alpha\psi}$ such that

$$A_{\alpha\psi}\|v\| \leqslant \psi(e) \leqslant B_{\alpha\psi}\|v\|$$

for all $e \in \pi^{-1}(U)$. Here $v \in F$ is defined by $\alpha(e) = (\alpha_0(\pi e), v)$.

Proof. Let S be the unit sphere of F; i.e.,

$$S = \{v \in F \mid \|v\| = 1\}$$

Then $\alpha_0(\bar{U}) \times S$ is compact and $\varphi(e) > 0$ for $e \in E, \alpha(e) \in \alpha_0(\bar{U}) \times S$. By continuity there exist positive real numbers $A_{\alpha\psi}$ and $B_{\alpha\psi}$ so that

$$A_{\alpha\psi} \leqslant \psi(e) \leqslant B_{\alpha\psi}$$

for $e \in E$, $\alpha(e) \in \alpha_0(\bar{U}) \times S$. The lemma follows, as ψ is a Finsler. ∎

Proof of 11.3. Cover π with finitely many pseudocompact VB charts (α, α_0, U). Take A to be the smallest of the (finitely many) numbers $A_{\alpha\varphi}/B_{\alpha\psi}$. Take B to be the largest of the numbers $B_{\alpha\varphi}/A_{\alpha\psi}$. An easy computation completes the proof. ∎

Proof of 11.2 (II). By 11.3

$$A\|\xi\|_\psi \leqslant \|\xi\|_\varphi \leqslant B\|\xi\|_\psi$$

for $\xi \in \Gamma^0(\pi)$. This says that $\| \ \|_\psi$ and $\| \ \|_\varphi$ are equivalent norms. ∎

Lemma 11.3 fails in case F is not finite dimensional. For example, take $X = [0, 1]$, $F = l_2$ and $\pi\colon X \times F \to X$ the trivial bundle. Take a sequence of continuous functions f_n: $[0, 1] \to \mathbf{R}$ such that

(1) $\sup_n f_n(x) < \infty$ for each $x \in [0, 1]$, but

(2) $\sup_{n,x} f_n(x) = \infty$.

Assume also that $f_n(x) \geqslant 1$ for all x and all n.

Recall that a point of l_2 is a sequence $a = \langle a_1, a_2, \ldots \rangle$ such that

$$\|a\| = \sum_n a_n^2 < \infty$$

We define the Finsler φ by

$$\varphi(x, a) = \sum_n f_n(x) a_n^2$$

This Finsler is not equivalent to the trivial Finsler in the sense of Lemma 11.3. The example is due to E. Stein.

Proof of 11.2 (III). Let $\{\xi_n\}_n$ be a Cauchy sequence in $\Gamma^0(\boldsymbol{\pi})$. Let (α, α_0, U) be a pseudocompact VB chart on $\boldsymbol{\pi}$ with $\alpha(\boldsymbol{\pi}^{-1}(U)) = \alpha_0(U) \times \mathbf{F}$. By 11.4 the map

$$\Gamma^0(\boldsymbol{\pi}) \to \mathscr{B}^0(U, \mathbf{F})$$

given by

$$\xi \rightsquigarrow \xi_\alpha$$

is continuous linear. Hence, the sequence $\{\xi_{n\alpha}\}_n$ is a Cauchy sequence in $\mathscr{B}^0(U, \mathbf{F})$. Hence, by 10.1 there is a $\xi^{(\alpha)} \in \mathscr{B}^0(U, \mathbf{F})$ such that $\xi_{n\alpha} \to \xi^{(\alpha)}$ in the norm $\| \quad \|_0$ (sup norm). Cover $\boldsymbol{\pi}$ with pseudocompact VB charts. Then the $\xi^{(\alpha)}$'s define a section $\xi \in \Gamma^0(\boldsymbol{\pi})$; i.e., $\xi_\alpha = \xi^{(\alpha)}$ for each (α, α_0, U) in the covering. Since $\xi_{n\alpha} \to \xi_\alpha$ for each (α, α_0, U) in the covering, it follows that $\xi_n \to \xi$ pointwise, and hence (since ξ_n is Cauchy in $\| \quad \|_\varphi$) $\xi_n \to \xi$ in $\| \quad \|_\varphi$. This shows that $\Gamma^0(\boldsymbol{\pi})$ is complete.

To complete our proof of (III) we must show that $\Gamma^0(\boldsymbol{\pi})$ is separable. We need the Stone-Weierstrass Theorem (Kelley [*1*] page 244). Using that theorem we prove the following. Let $K \subset \mathbf{R}^n$ be a compact set. Then $C^0(K, \mathbf{R}^r)$, the space of continuous maps from K to $\mathbf{R}^p$, has a countable dense subset. ($C^0(K, \mathbf{R}^p)$, of course, has the sup norm topology.) This can be proved by noting that the polynomial maps are dense (by Stone-Weierstrass) and the polynomial maps with rational coefficients are dense in the polynomial maps.

Now take a partition of unity on X consisting of finitely many functions φ_α with the support of each φ_α compact and contained in the domain U of a VB chart (α, α_0, U) on $\boldsymbol{\pi}$. Let K_α be the image under α_0 of the closure of the support of φ_α. Take a countable dense subset Q_α of each $C^0(K_\alpha, \mathbf{F})$. We obtain a countable dense subset of $\Gamma^0(\boldsymbol{\pi})$ by adding up elements of the sets Q_α via the partition of unity. We omit details. This completes our proof of (III) and hence of 11.2. ∎

§12. Smooth Sections

In this section we globalize the space $\mathscr{B}^r(U, \mathbf{F})$ of §10.

Let $\pi: E \to X$ be a C^r vector bundle with X compact. Let $\pi^r: J^r(\pi) \to X$ be the r-jet bundle of sections of π. Then π^r is a C^0 vector bundle. We take the Banach space $\mathbf{E}$ as the model of X and the Banach space $\mathbf{F}$ as the model of the fiber of π. Then $P^r(\mathbf{E}, \mathbf{F})$, the space of degree r polynomials from $\mathbf{E}$ to $\mathbf{F}$, models the fiber of π^r. Recall that for $\xi \in \Gamma^r(\pi)$, $j^r\xi \in \Gamma^0(\pi^r)$; i.e., the r-jet extension of a C^r section of π is a continuous section of π^r. Recall that $\Gamma^0(\pi^r)$ is a Banach space by 11.2.

12.1. THEOREM. The map

$$j^r: \Gamma^r(\pi) \to \Gamma^0(\pi^r)$$

is a linear injection with closed image.

Proof. It is an injection since $j^r\xi(x) = j^r\zeta(x)$ entails $\xi(x) = \zeta(x)$; whence $j^r\xi = j^r\zeta$ entails $\xi = \zeta$. Linearity follows immediately from the fact that if ξ_α is the principal part of the local representative of some section $\xi \in \Gamma^r(\pi)$ with respect to some VB chart (α, α_0, U) on π, then $P^r\xi_\alpha$ is the principal part of the local representative of the section $j^r\xi$ with respect to the corresponding natural VB chart (α^r, α_0, U) on π^r. (P^k is clearly linear.)

We must show that $j^r(\Gamma^r(\pi))$ is closed in $\Gamma^0(\pi^r)$. Choose a sequence $\{\xi_n\}_n$ of elements of $\Gamma^r(\pi)$ so that $j^r\xi_n \to \eta \in \Gamma^0(\pi^r)$. We must show that $\eta = j^r\xi$ for some $\xi \in \Gamma^r(\pi)$. Let (α, α_0, U) be a pseudocompact VB chart on π. Then (α^r, α_0, U) is a pseudocompact VB chart on π^r. By 11.4 $P^r\xi_{n\alpha} \to \eta_\alpha$ in the sup norm. Hence, $\{\xi_{n\alpha}\}_n$ is a Cauchy sequence in $\mathscr{B}^r(\alpha_0(U), \mathbf{F})$; (here $\mathbf{F}$ models the fiber of π). By 10.1 there is a $\xi^{(\alpha)} \in \mathscr{B}^r(\alpha_0(U), \mathbf{F})$ such that $\xi_{n\alpha} \to \xi^{(\alpha)}$ in the norm $\| \ \|_r$. Hence $P^r\xi_{n\alpha} \to P^r\xi^{(\alpha)}$. Hence, $P^r\xi^{(\alpha)} = \eta_\alpha$. Covering π with pseudocompact VB charts (α, α_0, U), we see that the $\xi^{(\alpha)}$'s define a section $\xi \in \Gamma^r(\pi)$; i.e., $\xi_\alpha = \xi^{(\alpha)}$ for each VB chart in the covering. Hence, $P^r\xi_\alpha = \eta_\alpha$ for each α. Hence, since $P^r\xi_\alpha$ is the principal part of the local representative of $j^r\xi$, $j^r\xi = \eta$. ∎

This theorem justifies the following definition. Let $\pi: E \to X$ be a C^r vector bundle with finite-dimensional fiber and X compact. The **C^r topology** on $\Gamma^r(\pi)$ is the topology induced by the injection $j^r: \Gamma^r(\pi) \to \Gamma^0(\pi^r)$; i.e., $N \subset \Gamma^r(\pi)$ is open if and only if $j^r(N) \subset \Gamma^0(\pi^r)$ is open.

12.2 THEOREM. (I) $\Gamma^r(\pi)$ is a separable (and hence second-countable) Banach space.

(II) The map

$$j^r: \Gamma^r(\pi) \to \Gamma^0(\pi^r)$$

is a toplinear injection onto a closed subspace.

The proof of 12.2 is immediate from the definition and 12.1. From now on $\Gamma^r(\pi)$ shall always denote the space of C^r sections of π with the C^r topology.

The following two theorems are global versions of 10.3 and 10.5.

12.3. THEOREM. Let $\pi: E \to X$ be a C^r vector bundle with finite-dimensional fiber and X compact. Then the evaluation map

$$ev: \Gamma^r(\pi) \times X \to E$$

given by

$$ev(\xi, x) = \xi(x)$$

is class C^r.

12.4. THEOREM. Let π, E, and X be as in 12.3. Suppose $0 \leqslant k \leqslant r$. Let

$$ev_k\colon \Gamma^r(\pi) \times X \to J^k(\pi)$$

be given by

$$ev_k(\xi, x) = j^k\xi(x)$$

for $\xi \in \Gamma^r(\pi)$ and $x \in X$. Then,

(I) ev_k is class C^{r-k};

(II) ev_k is a submersion; i.e., for $(\xi, x) \in \Gamma^r(\pi) \times X$ the tangent map $T_{(\xi,x)}ev$ is split surjective.

To prove these theorems reduce to the local case by taking pseudocompact VB charts on π. Note that if (α, α_0, U) is a pseudocompact VB chart, the map $\Gamma^r(\pi) \to \mathscr{B}^r(\alpha_0(U), \mathbf{F}_\alpha)$ given by $\xi \rightsquigarrow \xi_\alpha$ is a continuous linear map. Then use 10.3 and 10.5. We omit details.

3

REGULAR VALUES

The proof of the Transversality Density Theorem follows quite easily from Smale's Theorem on the density of regular values of a smooth mapping. This in turn follows easily from Sard's Density Theorem. In this chapter we give a new proof, essentially due to Metivier [*1*], of this difficult theorem. This will require theorems of Whitney and Kneser-Glaeser, with which we begin.

§13. Extension of Smooth Mappings

In this section we state a basic theorem of Whitney [*1*] on the extension of mappings defined on a closed subset. This can be viewed as a generalization of the following obvious converse of Taylor's Theorem (§1, compare also §2).

13.1. PROPOSITION. Let *E, F* be Banach spaces, $U \subset E$ open, $f\colon U \to F$ and $f_k\colon U \to L_s^k(E, F)$, for $k = 0, 1, \ldots, r$. Define, for $k = 0, 1, \ldots, r$, $R_k\colon U \times U \to L_s^k(E, F)$ by

$$f_k(y) = \sum_{j=0}^{r-k} \frac{f_{k+j}(x)}{j!}(y-x)^j + R_k(x, y)$$

for $x, y \in U$. Then f is class C^r and $D^k f = f_k$, for $k = 0, 1, \ldots, r$, provided that the following condition on the remainders is satisfied.

(R) For $x_0 \in U$ and $k = 0, 1, \ldots, r$,

$$\frac{\|R_k(x_0, y)\|}{\|y - x_0\|^{r-k}} \to 0$$

as $y \to x_0$.

The proof of 13.1 is trivial and is omitted. The Whitney Extension Theorem is a generalization of 13.1.

13.2. WHITNEY EXTENSION THEOREM. Let $A \subset R^n$ be a closed subset, F a Banach space, $f: A \to F$, and $f_k: A \to L_s^k(R^n, F)$, for $k = 0, 1, \ldots, r$. Define, for $k = 0, 1, \ldots, r$, $R_k: A \times A \to L_s^k(R^n, F)$ by

$$f_k(y) = \sum_{j=0}^{r-k} \frac{f_{k+j}(x)}{j!}(y-x)^j + R_k(x, y)$$

for $x, y \in A$. Then f extends to a C^r function $F: R^n \to F$, satisfying $D^kF(x) = f_k(x)$ for $x \in A$ and $k = 0, 1, \ldots, r$, provided that the following condition is satisfied.

(W) For $x_0 \in A$ and $k = 0, 1, \ldots, r$,

$$\frac{\|R_k(x, y)\|}{\|y - x\|^{r-k}} \to 0$$

as $x, y \to x_0$ in A; i.e., for every $\epsilon > 0$ there exists $\delta > 0$ such that

$$\|R_k(x, y)\| < \epsilon \|y - x\|^{r-k}$$

whenever $x, y \in A$ and

$$\|x - x_0\|, \|y - x_0\| < \delta$$

For the proof, see Appendix A. Note that condition (W) in 13.2, which involves three points x, y, and x_0, is stronger than condition (R) in 13.1, which only involves two points x_0 and y. An example is given in Appendix A which shows that (W) cannot be replaced by the weaker analog of (R) in 13.2.

The following trivial theorem will enable us to avoid a lengthy computation in the next section.

13.3. UNIQUENESS OF TAYLOR'S FORMULA. Let E, F be Banach spaces, $U \subset E$ open, $f: U \to F$ of class C^r and $x_0 \in U$. Suppose that

$$f(y) = \sum_{k=0}^{r} \frac{a_k}{k!}(y - x_0)^k + R(y)$$

for $y \in U$, and that

$$\frac{\|R(y)\|}{\|y - x_0\|^r} \to 0$$

as $y \to x_0$. Then

$$D^kf(x_0) = a_k \qquad \text{for } k = 0, 1, \ldots, r$$

Proof. If we subtract the usual Taylor's formula (i.e., the one in 1.6) from the above equation we obtain

$$(*) \qquad 0 = \sum_{k=0}^{r} b_k(y - x_0)^k + S(y)$$

where

$$b_k = \frac{a_k - D^kf(x_0)}{k!}$$

and

$$\frac{\|S(y)\|}{\|y - x_0\|^r} \to 0$$

as $y \to x_0$. We must show that $b_k = 0$ for $k = 0, 1, \ldots, r$. This we do by induction on k. Then $b_0 = 0$ is proved by letting $y \to x_0$ in (*). Suppose we have shown that $b_i = 0$ for $i = 0, 1, \ldots, k$, where $k < r$. Then by (*)

$$-b_{k+1}(y - x_0)^{k+1} = \sum_{j=k+2}^{r} b_j(y - x_0)^j + S(y)$$

Hence,

$$\|b_{k+1}\| \;\; \|y - x_0\|^{k+1} \leq \sum_{j=k+2}^{r} \|b_j\| \;\; \|y - x_0\|^j + \|S(y)\|$$

Dividing through by $\|y - x_0\|^{k+1}$ and letting $y \to x_0$ shows that $b_{k+1} = 0$ and completes the proof. ∎

§14. Composition of Rough Mappings

The Rough Composition Theorem of Kneser [*1*] and Glaeser [*1*] in this section is a preliminary to Sard's Theorem, which we prove in the next section. It tells us that under certain conditions, the composition of a rough map with a smooth map is smooth.

Let f be a C^r map and A be a subset of the domain of definition of f. Then f is **s-flat on** A iff $D^j f(x) = 0$ for $j = 1, \ldots, s$ and $x \in A$.

14.1. KNESER-GLAESER ROUGH COMPOSITION THEOREM. Let $W \subset \mathbf{R}^m$ **and** $V \subset \mathbf{R}^n$ **be open sets;** $A^* \subset W$ **and** $A \subset V$**, with** A **closed relative to** V**;** $f\colon V \to \mathbf{R}^p$ **of class** C^r **on** V **and** s**-flat on** A**;** $g\colon W \to V$ **of class** C^{r-s} **with** $g(A^*) \subset A$**. Then there is a map** $H\colon W \to \mathbf{R}^p$ **satisfying**

(I) H **is** C^r**;**

(II) $H(x) = f(g(x))$ **for** $x \in A^*$**;**

(III) H **is** s**-flat on** A^***.**

Proof. Suppose for the moment that g is C^r and define for $x \in A^*$ and $k = 0, 1, \ldots, r$

$$h_k(x) = D^k(f \circ g)(x)$$

Then, by the composite mapping formula (§1.4) and the hypothesis of the theorem, we have

(*) $$h_k(x) = \sum_{s<q\leq k} \sum \sigma_k \, D^q f(g(x)) \, D^{i_1} g(x) \cdots D^{i_q} g(x)$$

for $x \in A^*$. Here $\sigma_k = \sigma_k(i_1, \ldots, i_q)$ and the second sum is over all q-tuples of integers $i_1, \ldots, i_q$ satisfying

(a) $i_1 + \cdots + i_q = k$;

(b) $1 \leq i_j$ for $j = 1, \ldots, q$.

By (a) and (b) and the fact that the first sum in (*) is over integers q with $s < q \leq k$, we know that $i_j \leq k - q + 1 \leq r - s$ for every i_j appearing in (*); hence (*) defines $h_k(x)$ for $x \in A^*$ even when g is only class C^{r-s}.

Define for $x \in A^*$, $h(x) = f(g(x))$ $(S_0 h = h_0)$. We would like to apply the Whitney Extension Theorem (§13.2) to find a C^r function H such that $D^k H(x) = h_k(x)$ for $x \in A^*$ and $k = 0, 1, \ldots, r$. Once we have done this we are done because of the definition of h_k. Note that the fact that A^* is not necessarily closed but is only closed relative to W

offers no difficulty; we may define F locally and extend to all of W via partitions of unity. Hence we suppose, without loss of generality, that A^* is closed. In order to apply 13.2 we need only verify condition W of its hypothesis.

By Taylor's formula (1.6) we may write

$$D^q f(y') = \sum_{s<q+\alpha\leq r} \frac{D^{q+\alpha}f(y)}{\alpha!}(y'-y)^\alpha + I_q(y, y')(y'-y)^{r-q} \tag{1}$$

for $q = s+1, \ldots, r$; $y \in A$ and $y' \in V$ and

$$I_q: V \times V \to L_s^q(\mathbf{R}^n, \mathbf{R}^p)$$

is given by

$$I_q(y, y') = \int_0^1 \frac{(1-t)^{q-1}}{(q-1)!}\{D^q f(y + t(y'-y)) - D^q f(y)\}\, dt$$

Similarly, for $i \leq r-s$ and $x, x' \in W$,

$$D^i g(x') = \sum_{0\leq i+\beta\leq r-s} \frac{D^{i+\beta}g(x)}{\beta!}(x'-x)^\beta + J_i(x, x')(x'-x)^{r-s-i} \tag{2}$$

where $J_i: W \times W \to L_s^i(R^m, R^n)$ is given by

$$J_i(x, x') = \int_0^1 \frac{(1-t)^{i-1}}{(i-1)!}\{D^i g(x + t(x'-x)) - D^i g(x)\}\, dt$$

We see from the formulas for I_q and J_i that they are locally uniformly continuous in both variables and zero on the diagonal.

Now, take $x_0, x, x' \in A^*$ and let $y = g(x)$ and $y' = g(x')$. By (*) we have

$$h_k(x') = \sum_{s<q\leq k} \sigma_k\, D^q f(y')\, D^{i_1}g(x') \cdots D^{i_q}g(x') \tag{3}$$

Substituting (1) and (2) in (3) we get

$$h_k(x') = \sum_{j=0}^{r-k} a_j^k (x'-x)^j + R_k(x, x') \tag{4}$$

where $R_k(x, x')$ is the sum of all terms T of one of the forms

$$a(x'-x)^j \quad \text{where} \quad j > r-k \tag{5}$$

$$I_q(y, y')(y'-y)^{r-q} \ \ldots \tag{6}$$

$$\ldots\ J_{i_j}(x, x')(x'-x)^{r-s-i_j}\ \ldots \tag{7}$$

We will show that if T is any term in $R_k(x, x')$, then

$$\frac{\|T\|}{\|x-x'\|^{r-k}} \to 0 \qquad \text{as } x, x' \to x_0 \text{ in } A. \tag{8}$$

If T is of form (5) this is immediate. If T has form (6), then since $q \leq k$ in (3), g is continuous, and I_q is locally uniformly continuous and zero on the diagonal, so (8) is again immediate. For any term of form (7), $i_j \leq k-q+1$

where $s+1 \leqslant q$. Hence, $s+i_j \leqslant k$, and $r-s-i_j \geqslant r-k$. Thus by the same reasoning as case (6), we establish (8) in case (7). This yields (8) in all cases and by the triangle inequality, also

$$\frac{\|R_k(x, x')\|}{\|x-x'\|^{r-k}} \to 0 \tag{9}$$

as $x, x' \to x_0$ in A^*.

For each $k=0, 1, \ldots, r$ and $j=0, \ldots, r-k$, we have also

$$j!\,a_j^k = h_{k+j}(x) \tag{10}$$

To see this, suppose for the moment that g is class C^r. Then so is $h = f \circ g$, and (4) is a "Taylor's formula" for $h_k = D^k(f \circ g)$. Then by the uniqueness of Taylor's formula (9.3) and (9) (reading x' for y, x for x_0, a_j^k for a_j, $r-k$ for r, and $R_k(x, x')$ for $R(y)$), we have

$$j!\,a_j^k = D^{k+j}(f \circ g)(x) = h_{k+j}(x)$$

Since (10) is an identity in the derivatives of f and g and points x and x', and since C^r functions can always be found which have prescribed derivatives at any finite set of points, it follows that (10) must hold in general. Thus (4) may be written

$$h_k(x') = \sum_{j=0}^{r-k} \frac{h_{k+j}(x')}{j!}(x'-x)^j + R_k(x, x')$$

This together with (9) constitutes the hypothesis (W) of the Whitney Extension Theorem (13.2). This completes the proof. ∎

§15. Sard's Density Theorem

This section is devoted entirely to the proof of Sard's Theorem on the density of the set of regular values of a smooth mapping, one of the deepest results of differential theory, on which all transversality and general position arguments are based. The theorem has a complicated history and is sometimes associated with the names of earlier authors who obtained preliminary results of the same type, especially Brown [*1*] and A. P. Morse [*1*]. Similar results were rediscovered later by Kneser [*1*] and Thom [*1*], and our proof, which follows Metivier [*1*] closely, has something in common with the arguments of Kneser and Thom.

Let $f\colon U \to \mathbf{F}$ be C^1, where U is an open subset of $\mathbf{E}$ and $\mathbf{E}$ and $\mathbf{F}$ are Banach spaces. A point $x \in U$ is a **critical point** of f iff $Df(x) \in L(E, F)$ is *not* surjective; x is a **regular point** iff it is not a critical point. A point $y \in F$ is a **critical value** of f iff there exists a critical point $x \in U$ with $y = f(x)$; y is a **regular value** of f iff it is not a critical value.

15.1. SARD'S DENSITY THEOREM. Let $f\colon U \to \mathbf{R}^p$ where U is open in $\mathbf{R}^n$. Let f be C^r where $r > \max(0, n-p)$. Then the set of critical values of f has measure zero in $\mathbf{R}^p$.

Recall that a subset of $\mathbf{R}^p$ has measure zero iff for every $\epsilon > 0$ there is a countable covering of the subset by closed cubes (with edges parallel to the coordinate axes) with total volume less than ϵ. The property of having measure zero is a differentiable invariant; more precisely, if $\varphi\colon V \to W^p$ is a C^1 isomorphism (where V and W are open subsets of a finite-dimensional Euclidean space) and $A \subset V$ has measure zero, then $\varphi(A) \subset W$ has measure zero. Indeed, since the countable union of sets of measure zero is again of measure zero, we may suppose $\|D\varphi(x)\| \leq M$ for $x \in V$. Then, if p is the dimension of the ambient space of V and W, it follows by the Mean Value Theorem that the image of a cube of edge e (and volume $v = e^p$) is contained in a cube of edge $eM(p)^{1/2}$ (and volume $v' = v(M(p)^{1/2})^p$. This provides the justification for choosing charts as below.

Milnor [*1*] contains an easy proof of this theorem for the case $r = \infty$. By using the Kneser-Glaeser Rough Composition Theorem in Milnor's Step 2, his proof goes through, *mutatis mutandis,* for the general case. We present here a slightly different argument.

We need a special case of Fubini's Theorem: A measurable set $A \subset \mathbf{R}^p = \mathbf{R}^{p-q} \times \mathbf{R}^q$ has measure zero if $A \cap (\mathbf{R}^{p-q} \times \{t\})$ has $(p-q)$-dimensional measure zero for every $t \in \mathbf{R}^q$ $(1 \leq q < p)$. (See Sternberg [*1*; p. 51].)

Let C be the set of critical points of f, that is,

$$C = \{x \in U \mid \text{rank } Df(x) < p\}$$

We must show that $f(C)$ has measure zero.

Recall that f is s-flat at x iff $D^i f(x) = 0$ for $i = 1, \ldots, s$. For $s = 1, \ldots, r$ define $B_s \subset U$ by

$$B_s = \{x \in U \mid f \text{ is } s\text{-flat at } x\}$$

Let $K = C \setminus B_1$, that is,

$$K = \{x \in U \mid 1 \leq \text{rank } Df(x) < p\}$$

We divide the proof of 15.1 into three steps:

Step 1. $f(B_r)$ has measure zero;

Step 2. $f(B_1)$ has measure zero;

Step 3. $f(K)$ has measure zero.

For Step 1 we need the following lemma.

15.2. LEMMA. If $s \geq 1$ and $s \geq n/p$, then $f(B_s)$ has measure zero.

Proof. Let $J \subset U$ be a closed cube with edges parallel to the coordinate axes. We will show that $f(B_s \cap J)$ has measure zero. Since B_s can be covered by countably many such cubes, this will prove that $f(B_s)$ has measure zero.

By Taylor's Theorem, the compactness of J, and the definition of B_s, we have

$$f(y) = f(x) + R(x, y)$$

where

$$(*) \qquad \|R(x, y)\| \leq M\|y - x\|^{s+1}$$

for $x \in B_s \cap J$ and $y \in J$. Here M is a constant depending only on $D^s f$ and J. Let e be the length of the edge of J. Choose an integer k, subdivide J into k^n cubes with edge e/k, and choose any cube J^* of this subdivision which intersects B_s. For $x \in B_s \cap J^*$ and $y \in J^*$, we have $\|x - y\| \leq \sqrt{n}(e/k)$. By (*), $f(J^*) \subset I$ where I is the cube of edge

Nk^{-s-1} with center $f(x)$; $N = 2M((n)^{1/2}e)^{s+1}$. The volume of I is $N^p k^{-p(s+1)}$. There are at most k^n such cubes; hence, $f(B_s \cap J)$ is contained in a union of cubes whose total volume v satisfies

$$v \leqslant N^p k^{n-p(s+1)}$$

By hypothesis $n \leqslant ps$; hence $n - p(s+1) < 0$, so $v \to 0$ as $k \to \infty$, and $f(B_s \cap J)$ has measure zero. ∎

15.3. STEP 1. $f(B_r)$ **has measure zero.**

Proof. By the hypothesis of Sard's Theorem, $r \geqslant 1$, and $r \geqslant n - p + 1$. Hence as $(r-1)p \geqslant r-1$, $rp \geqslant p+r-1$, $rp \geqslant n$, and $r \geqslant n/p$. The conclusion follows from Lemma 15.2. ∎

The next step uses Rough Composition (§14).

15.4. STEP 2. $f(B_1)$ **has measure zero.**

Proof. We do an induction on n. To start the induction, note that the case $n \leqslant p$ is a corollary of Lemma 15.2; i.e., for $n \leqslant p$, $n/p \leqslant 1$, and hence, taking $s = 1$ in 15.2, $f(B_1)$ has measure zero.

Now assume Step 2 is proved for the case $n - 1$. We will show that $f(B_1)$ has measure zero. But

$$B_1 = (B_1 \setminus B_2) \cup (B_2 \setminus B_3) \cup \cdots \cup (B_{r-1} \setminus B_r) \cup B_r$$

By Step 1, $f(B_r)$ has measure zero. It suffices to show $f(B_s \setminus B_{s+1})$ has measure zero for $s = 1, \ldots, r-1$.

To show $f(B_s \setminus B_{s+1})$ has measure zero, it suffices to show that every $x \in B_s \setminus B_{s+1}$ has a neighborhood V such that $f(B_s \cap V)$ has measure zero; then since $B_s \setminus B_{s+1}$ is covered by countably many such neighborhoods V, it follows that $f(B_s \setminus B_{s+1})$ has measure zero.

Choose $\bar{x} \in B_s \setminus B_{s+1}$. All the partial derivatives of f at $\bar{x}$ of order $\leqslant s$ are zero, but some partial derivative of order $s+1$ is not zero. Hence we may assume

$$\partial_1 w(\bar{x}) \neq 0$$

where

$$w(\bar{x}) = \partial_{i_1} \cdots \partial_{i_s} f(\bar{x}) = 0$$

Define $h\colon U \to \boldsymbol{R}^n$ by

$$h(x) = (w(x), x_2, \ldots, x_n)$$

where $x = (x_1, x_2, \ldots, x_n) \in U \subset \boldsymbol{R}^n$. Clearly $h \in C^{r-s}$ and $Dh(\bar{x})$ is nonsingular; hence there is an open neighborhood V of $\bar{x}$ and an open set $W \subset \boldsymbol{R}^n$ such that

$$h\colon V \to W$$

is a C^{r-s} isomorphism. Let $A = B_s \cap V$, $A^* = h(A)$ and $g = h^{-1}$. By the Kneser-Glaeser Rough Composition Theorem (14.1) there is a function $F\colon W \to \boldsymbol{R}^p$ satisfying:

(I) $F \in C^r$;

(II) $F(x) = f(g(x))$ for $x \in A^*$;

(III) $DF(x) = 0$ for $x \in A^*$.

Define the open set $W_0 \subset \boldsymbol{R}^{n-1}$ by

$$W_0 = \{(x_2, \ldots, x_n) \in \boldsymbol{R}^{n-1} \mid (0, x_2, \ldots, x_n) \in W\}$$

Define F_0: $W_0 \to R^p$ by

$$F_0(x_2, \ldots, x_n) = F(0, x_2, \ldots, x_n)$$

Let B_1^0 be the set of points in W_0 at which F_0 is 1-flat, that is,

$$B_1^0 = \{(x_2, \ldots, x_n) \in W_0 \mid DF_0(x_2, \ldots, x_n) = 0\}$$

By the induction hypothesis, $F_0(B_1^0)$ has measure zero. But $A^* = h(B_s \cap V) \subset 0 \times B_1^0$ since for $x \in A^*$, $DF(x) = 0$ by (III), and since for $x \in B_s \cap V$,

$$\begin{aligned} h(x) &= (w(x), x_2, \ldots, x_n) \\ &= (0, x_2, \ldots, x_n) \end{aligned}$$

because w is an sth derivative of f. Hence

$$f(B_s \cap V) = Fh(B_s \cap V) \subset F(0 \times B_1^0) = F_0(B_1^0)$$

Hence $f(B_s \cap V)$ has measure zero. As $B_s \setminus B_{s+1}$ is covered by countably many such V, $f(B_s \setminus B_{s+1})$ has measure zero ($s = 1, \ldots, r-1$). By Step 1, $f(B_r)$ has measure zero, and

$$B_1 = (B_1 \setminus B_2) \cup (B_2 \setminus B_3) \cup \cdots \cup (B_{r-1} \setminus B_r) \cup B_r$$

so $f(B_1)$ has measure zero. ▮

15.5. STEP 3. $f(K)$ **has measure zero.**

Proof. We write $K = K_1 \cup \cdots \cup K_{p-1}$ where

$$K_q = \{x \in U \mid \text{rank } Df(x) = q\}$$

and it suffices to show that $f(K_q)$ has measure zero for $q = 1, \ldots, p-1$. Since K_q is empty for $q > n$, we may assume $q \leqslant n$. As before it will suffice to show that each point of K_q has a neighborhood V such that $f(V \cap K_q)$ has measure zero.

Choose $\bar{x} \in K_q$. By the Local Representative Theorem (1.8), we may assume that $\bar{x}$ has a neighborhood $V = V_1 \times V_2$ where $V_1 \subset R^{n-q}$ and $V_2 \subset R^q$ are open balls such that for $x \in V_1$ and $t \in V_2$

$$f(x, t) = (\eta(x, t), t).$$

Hence η: $V_1 \times V_2 \to R^{p-q}$ is a C^r map. For $t \in V_2$ define η_t: $V_1 \to R^{p-q}$ by

$$\eta_t(x) = \eta(x, t) \qquad \text{for } x \in V_1.$$

Then for $t \in V_2$

$$K_q \cap (V_1 \times \{t\}) = \{x \in V_1 \mid D\eta_t(x) = 0\} \times \{t\}$$

This is because, for $(x, t) \in V_1 \times V_2$, $Df(x, t)$ is given by the matrix

$$Df(x, t) = \begin{bmatrix} D\eta_t(x) & * \\ 0 & I_q \end{bmatrix}$$

Hence rank $Df(x, t) = q$ iff $D\eta_t(x) = 0$.

Now η_t is C^r and $r \geqslant n - p = (n - q) - (p - q)$. Hence by Step 2, $\eta_t(\{x \in V_1 \mid D\eta_t(x) = 0\})$ has measure zero for each $t \in V_2$. By Fubini's Theorem, $f(K_q \cap V)$ has measure zero. Since K_q is covered by countably many such V, this shows that $f(K_q)$ has measure zero. ∎

Proof of 15.1. As $C = K \cup B_1$, we have $f(C) = f(K) \cup f(B_1)$. As a finite union of sets of measure zero has measure zero, $f(C)$ has measure zero by 15.4 and 15.5. ∎

This completes the proof of Sard's Theorem.

§16. Smale's Density Theorem

In the proof of transversality density (§19) we will need the density of regular values of mappings in an infinite-dimensional context. Sard's Density Theorem is easily extended to this context when the correct generalization is found. This was accomplished very cleverly by Smale [2], who invented Fredholm mappings for this purpose.

Let X and Y be C^1 manifolds and $f: X \to Y$, a C^1 map. A point $x \in X$ is a **regular point** of f iff $T_x f$ is surjective; otherwise, x is a **critical point** of f. If $C \subset X$ is the set of critical points of f, then $f(C) \subset Y$ is the set of **critical values** of f and $Y \setminus f(C)$ is the set of **regular values** of f. The set of regular values is denoted by $\mathscr{R}_f$ or $\mathscr{R}(f)$. In addition, for $A \subset X$ we define $\mathscr{R}_f | A$ by

$$\mathscr{R}_f | A = Y \setminus f(A \cap C)$$

In particular, if $U \subset X$ is open, $\mathscr{R}_f | U = \mathscr{R}(f | U)$.

Before stating the Smale Theorem, we restate Sard's Theorem in the form which generalizes.

A subset of a topological space is **residual** iff it is the countable intersection of open dense sets. Recall that the *Baire Category Theorem* asserts that a residual subset of a complete metric space is dense.

16.1. SARD'S THEOREM (Alternate Form). Let X and Y be finite-dimensional C^r manifolds with dim $(X) = n$, dim $(Y) = p$, and with X Lindelöf. Let $f: X \to Y$ be a C^r map. Then if $r > \max(0, n - p)$, $\mathscr{R}_f$ is residual (and hence dense) in Y.

Proof. Let C be the set of critical points of f. We will show that every $x \in X$ has a neighborhood Z such that $\mathscr{R}_f | \bar{Z}$ is open dense. Then, by the hypothesis that X is Lindelöf (every open cover of X has a countable subcover), we can find a countable cover $\{Z_i\}$ of X such that $\mathscr{R}_f | Z_i$ is open dense. Since $\mathscr{R}_f = \cap_i \mathscr{R}_f | \bar{Z}_i$, it will follow that $\mathscr{R}_f$ is residual.

Choose $x \in X$. We want a neighborhood Z of x such that $\mathscr{R}_f | \bar{Z}$ is open dense. By taking local charts we may assume that X is an open subset of $\mathbf{R}^n$ and $Y = \mathbf{R}^p$. Choose an open neighborhood Z of x such that $\bar{Z}$ is compact. Then $C = \{x \in X | \text{rank } Df(x) < p\}$ is closed, so $\bar{Z} \cap C$ and $f(\bar{Z} \cap C)$ are compact, and $f(\bar{Z} \cap C)$ is closed. But $f(\bar{Z} \cap C)$

is a subset of the set of critical values of f and hence, by Sard's Theorem, (15.1) has measure zero. A closed set of measure zero is nowhere dense; hence, $\mathscr{R}_f|\bar{Z} = \mathbf{R}^p \setminus f(\bar{Z} \cap C)$ is open dense. ∎

Let $\mathbf{E}, \mathbf{F}$ be Banach spaces and $A \in L(\mathbf{E}, \mathbf{F})$. Then A is a **Fredholm operator** iff:

(1) A is double splitting; i.e., both the kernel and the image of A are closed and have closed complement;

(2) the kernel of A is finite dimensional;

(3) the image of A has finite codimension.

In this case, if $n = \dim(\ker A)$ and $p = \text{codim}(\text{im}(A))$, $n - p$ is the **index** of A; in symbols, index $(A) = n - p$. If X and Y are C^1 manifolds and $f\colon X \to Y$ is a C^1 map, then f is a **Fredholm map** iff for every $x \in X$, T_xf is a Fredholm operator.

Note that a finite-dimensional subspace is closed and splits; hence (1) above may be replaced by the weaker condition that the image of A is closed.

16.2. SMALE'S DENSITY THEOREM. Let X and Y be C^r manifolds with X Lindelöf and $f\colon X \to Y$ a C^r Fredholm map. Suppose that $r > \max(0, \text{index } (T_xf))$ for every $x \in X$. Then $\mathscr{R}_f$ is a residual subset of Y.

As in 15.1, it suffices to show that every $x_0 \in X$ has a neighborhood Z such that $\mathscr{R}_f|Z$ is open dense. We require two lemmas.

Let $\mathbf{E}, \mathbf{F}$ be Banach spaces. Then $BL(\mathbf{E}, \mathbf{F})$ denotes the set of toplinear isomorphisms from $\mathbf{E}$ onto $\mathbf{F}$, and $SL(\mathbf{E}, \mathbf{F})$ denotes the set of (linear) **splitting surjections** from $\mathbf{E}$ onto $\mathbf{F}$; i.e., the set of surjective linear maps from $\mathbf{E}$ onto $\mathbf{F}$ whose kernels split (have closed complement).

16.3. LEMMA. The set $SL(\mathbf{E}, \mathbf{F})$ is open in $L(\mathbf{E}, \mathbf{F})$.

Proof. Choose $A \in SL(\mathbf{E}, \mathbf{F})$. Write $\mathbf{E} = \mathbf{F} \oplus \mathbf{K}$ where $\mathbf{K}$ is the kernel of A, and define $A'\colon \mathbf{E} \to \mathbf{F} \times \mathbf{K}$ by $A'(e) = (A(e), p(e))$ where $p\colon \mathbf{E} = \mathbf{F} \oplus \mathbf{K} \to \mathbf{K}$ is the projection. By the Closed Graph Theorem, p is continuous; hence, $A \in BL(\mathbf{E}, \mathbf{F} \times \mathbf{K})$. Consider the map $T\colon L(\mathbf{E}, \mathbf{F} \times \mathbf{K}) \to L(\mathbf{E}, \mathbf{F})$ given by $T(B) = \pi \circ B$ for $B \in L(\mathbf{E}, \mathbf{F} \times \mathbf{K})$ where $\pi\colon \mathbf{F} \times \mathbf{K} \to \mathbf{F}$ is the projection. Then T is continuous ($\|\pi \circ B\| \leq \|\pi\|\,\|B\|$), linear, and surjective; hence, by the open mapping principle, T is an open mapping. But $BL(\mathbf{E}, \mathbf{F} \times \mathbf{K})$ is open in $L(\mathbf{E}, \mathbf{F} \times \mathbf{K})$ (Lang [*1;* p. 5]) so $T(BL(\mathbf{E}, \mathbf{F} \times \mathbf{K}))$ is open in $L(\mathbf{E}, \mathbf{F})$. But $A = TA'$ and $T(BL(\mathbf{E}, \mathbf{F} \times \mathbf{K})) \subset SL(\mathbf{E}, \mathbf{F})$. This shows that $SL(\mathbf{E}, \mathbf{F})$ is open. ∎

A similar argument shows that $IL(\mathbf{E}, \mathbf{F})$, the set of splitting linear injections, is open in $L(\mathbf{E}, \mathbf{F})$; and $\text{Fred}_q(\mathbf{E}, \mathbf{F})$, the set of Fredholm operators with index q, is open in $L(\mathbf{E}, \mathbf{F})$.

A map g between topological spaces is **locally closed** iff every point in the domain of definition of g has an open neighborhood U such that $g|\bar{U}$ is a closed map (i.e., maps closed sets to closed sets).

16.4. LEMMA. A Fredholm map is locally closed.

Proof. By the Local Representative Theorem (1.7) we may suppose our Fredholm map has the form $f\colon B_1 \times B_2 \to \mathbf{R}^p \times \mathbf{E}$ where $B_1 \subset \mathbf{R}^n$ and $B_2 \subset \mathbf{E}$ are open unit balls and for $x \in B_1$, $e \in B_2$

$$f(x, e) = (\eta(x, e), e)$$

Let D_1 and D_2 be open balls so that $\bar{D}_1 \subset B_1$ and $\bar{D}_2 \subset B_2$. Let $U = D_1 \times D_2$ so that $\bar{U} = \bar{D}_1 \times \bar{D}_2$. Then $f|\bar{U}$ is closed. For if $A \subset \bar{U}$ is closed, we see as follows that $f(A)$ is closed. Choose a sequence $\{(y_i, e_i)\}$ such that $(y_i, e_i) \to (y, e)$ as $i \to \infty$ and $(y_i, e_i) \in f(A)$, say

$$(y_i, e_i) = f(x_i, e_i)$$

where $(x_i, e_i) \in A$. Since $x_i \in \bar{D}_1$ and $\bar{D}_1$ is compact, we may assume $x_i \to x \in \bar{D}_1$. Then $(x_i, e_i) \to (x, e)$. Since A is closed, $(x, e) \in A$, and $f(x, e) = (y, e)$, so $(y, e) \in f(A)$. Thus $f(A)$ is closed. ▮

Proof of 16.2. Choose $x_0 \in X$. We shall construct a neighborhood Z of x_0 so that $\mathscr{R}_f|\bar{Z}$ is open dense.

By the Local Representative Theorem we may choose charts (U, α) at x_0 and (V, β) at $f(x_0)$ such that $\alpha(U) \subset R^n \times$ **E**, $\beta(V) \subset R^p \times \mathbf{E}$ and the local representative $f_{\alpha\beta} = \beta \circ f \circ \alpha^{-1}$ of f has the form

$$f_{\alpha\beta}(x, e) = (\eta(x, e), e)$$

for $(x, e) \in \alpha(U)$. (Here $x \in \mathbf{R}^n$, $e \in \mathbf{E}$, and $\eta\colon \alpha(U) \to \mathbf{R}^p$.) The index of $T_{x_0}f$ is $n-p$ and so $r > \max(0, n-p)$ by hypothesis. We now show that $\mathscr{R}(f|U)$ is dense in Y. Indeed it suffices to show that $\mathscr{R}_{f_{\alpha\beta}}$ is dense in $R^p \times E$. For $e \in \mathbf{E}$, $(x, e) \in \alpha(U)$, define $\eta_e(x) = \eta(x, e)$. Then for each e, η_e is a C^r map defined on an open set of $\mathbf{R}^n$. By Sard's Theorem $\mathscr{R}(\eta_e)$ is dense in $\mathbf{R}^n$ for each $e \in \mathbf{E}$. But for $(x, e) \in \alpha(U) \subset \mathbf{R}^n \times \mathbf{E}$, we have

$$Df_{\alpha\beta}(x, e) = \begin{bmatrix} D\eta_e(x) & * \\ 0 & I \end{bmatrix}$$

so $Df_{\alpha\beta}(x, e)$ is surjective iff $D\eta_e(x)$ is surjective. Thus for $e \in \mathbf{E}$

$$\mathscr{R}(\eta_e) \times \{e\} = \mathscr{R}_{f_{\alpha\beta}} \cap (\mathbf{R}^p \times \{e\})$$

Thus $\mathscr{R}_{f_{\alpha\beta}}$ intersects every plane $\mathbf{R}^p \times \{e\}$ in a dense set and is, therefore, dense in $\mathbf{R}^p \times \mathbf{E}$, and $\mathscr{R}(f|U)$ is dense as claimed.

Now by Lemma 16.4, we choose an open neighborhood Z of x_0 such that $\bar{Z} \subset U$ and $f|\bar{Z}$ is closed. By Lemma 16.3 the set C of critical points of f is closed in X. Hence, $f(\bar{Z} \cap C)$ is closed in Y. Hence $\mathscr{R}_f|\bar{Z} = Y \setminus f(\bar{Z} \cap C)$ is open in Y. Since $\mathscr{R}(f|U) \subset \mathscr{R}_f|\bar{Z}$, this latter set is also dense.

We have shown that every point x_0 has an open neighborhood Z such that $\mathscr{R}_f|\bar{Z}$ is open dense. Repeating the argument of 16.1 shows that $\mathscr{R}_f$ is residual (recall that X is Lindelöf). ▮

4

TRANSVERSALITY THEORY

Two manifold morphisms having the same range are transversal, roughly speaking, if their images intersect in general position. If two morphisms have a nontransversal intersection, then it is clear intuitively that one or both can be adjusted slightly so as to make their intersection transversal. This is essentially the content of the original Transversal Density Theorem of Thom [*2*] (see also Levine [*1*]), which initiated this subject in 1954. Thom also established the basic property of transversal intersections; they are stable in the sense that a small perturbation of either of the morphisms preserves the intersection (up to *isotopy*). These two results are very useful because of the fact that a great number of important properties of morphisms can be expressed in terms of transversal intersection. In this chapter we give some new results of this type, expressed in the very general context of *representations of manifolds*. These theorems were inspired by the applications given in the last chapter, and the generality in which they are discussed here is the minimum admitting that application. The original results of Thom can be obtained from these without difficulty (see Abraham [*1*]), and more general theorems are easily obtained by the same methods.

§17. Transversality

In this section we give the definition and basic properties of transversal intersection. For simplicity we consider only the case in which one of the morphisms is a fixed embedding onto a submanifold. The case of two (or more) arbitrary morphisms is easily obtained from this special case (see Abraham [*1, 2*]).

Recall that a subset $W \subset Y$ of a C^r manifold Y is a (C^r) **submanifold** iff at every point $y \in W$ there is an admissible chart (V, β) such that $\beta(V) = V_1 \times V_2$, where V_1 and V_2 are open neighborhoods of the origin in Banach spaces $\boldsymbol{F}_1$ and $\boldsymbol{F}_2$ respectively, $\beta(y) = (\mathbf{0}, \mathbf{0})$, and $\beta(W \cap V) = V_1 \times \{\mathbf{0}\}$. Such a chart (V, β) is said to have the **submanifold**

property for W **in** Y **at** y. A submanifold need not be closed (e.g., an open ray in the plane) but it must be locally closed (see Lang [*1*; p. 19]). Note that for $y \in W$ the tangent space T_yW to W at y is a closed splitting subspace of the tangent space T_yY to Y at y.

Let X and Y be C^1 manifolds, $f: X \to Y$ a C^1 map, and $W \subset Y$ a submanifold. We say that f is **transversal to** W **at a point** $x \in X$, in symbols: $f \pitchfork_x W$, iff, where $y = f(x)$, either $y \notin W$ or $y \in W$ and

(1) the inverse image $(T_xf)^{-1}(T_yW)$ splits, and

(2) the image $(T_xf)(T_xX)$ contains a closed complement to T_yW in T_yY.

We say f is **transversal to** W, in symbols: $f \pitchfork W$, iff $f \pitchfork_x W$ for every $x \in X$.

17.1. LOCAL REPRESENTATION OF TRANSVERSALITY. Let X **and** Y **be** C^r **manifolds** ($r \geqslant 1$), $f: X \to Y$ **a** C^r **map,** $W \subset Y$ **a submanifold, and** $x \in X$ **such that** $y = f(x) \in W$. **A necessary and sufficient condition for** $f \pitchfork_x W$ **is that there exist admissible charts** (U, α) **and** (V, β) **at** x **and** $y = f(x)$ **respectively such that,**

(I) $\alpha(U) = U_1 \times V_2$, $\beta(V) = V_1 \times V_2$, $f(U) \subset V$, $\alpha(x) = (\mathbf{0}, \mathbf{0})$, $\beta(y) = (\mathbf{0}, \mathbf{0})$, $\beta(V \cap W) = V_1 \times \{\mathbf{0}\}$;

(II) for $f_{\alpha\beta} = \beta \circ f \circ \alpha^{-1}: U_1 \times V_2 \to V_1 \times V_2$, **the local representative of** f, **we have**

$$f_{\alpha\beta}(x_1, x_2) = (\eta(x_1, x_2), x_2)$$

for all $x_1 \in U_1$, $x_2 \in V_2$.

Proof. Sufficiency is trivial. To prove necessity, choose admissible charts (U, α) and (V, β) at x and $y = f(x)$ respectively, with the latter chart having the submanifold property and such that $f(U) \subset V$. Then $\alpha(U)$ is an open subset of some Banach space $\mathbf{E}$, $\beta(V) = V_1 \times V_2$ where V_1 and V_2 are open neighborhoods of the origin in Banach spaces $\mathbf{F}_1$ and $\mathbf{F}_2$ respectively, $\beta(y) = (\mathbf{0}, \mathbf{0})$ and $\beta(W \cap V) = V_1 \times \{\mathbf{0}\}$. Consider the composite map

$$\alpha(U) \xrightarrow{\alpha^{-1}} U \xrightarrow{f} V \xrightarrow{\beta} V_1 \times V_2 \xrightarrow{pr} V_2$$

where pr is the projection on the second factor. By the hypothesis that $f \pitchfork_x W$, this composite map has split surjective tangent at $\alpha^{-1}(x)$ (because of the chain rule). Hence by the Local Representative Theorem (1.8) we may modify the charts (U, α) and (V, β) so that $\alpha(U) = U_1 \times V_2$, and the composite $U_1 \times V_2 = \alpha(U) \to V_2$ is the projection on the second factor. For these charts the local representative

$$f_{\alpha\beta} = \beta \circ f \circ \alpha^{-1}: U_1 \times V_2 \to V_1 \times V_2$$

has the desired form. ∎

17.2. COROLLARY. Let X, Y **be** C^r **manifolds** ($r \geqslant 1$), $f: X \to Y$ **a** C^r **map,** $W \subset Y$ **a** C^r **submanifold. Then, if** $f \pitchfork W$:

(I) $f^{-1}(W)$ **is a** C^r **submanifold of** X;

(II) For $x \in f^{-1}(W)$ **and** $y = f(x)$

$$(T_xf)^{-1}T_yW = T_x(f^{-1}(W));$$

(III) W **and** $f^{-1}(W)$ **have the same codimension; more precisely, for** $x \in f^{-1}(W)$, $y = f(x)$ **any closed complement to** $T_x(f^{-1}(W))$ **in** T_xX **is toplinearly isomorphic to any closed complement to** T_yW **in** T_yY;

(IV) If W is closed and X is compact, $f^{-1}(W)$ has only finitely many connected components.

In particular if y is a regular point of f, then $f^{-1}(y)$ is a submanifold of X. We leave the proof of 17.2 as an exercise.

§18. Openness Theorems

The first step toward the stability of transversal intersection is the openness of this condition. That is, if $f \pitchfork W$ and g is close to f, then $g \pitchfork W$. In this section we prove two easy results of this type, in the general context of *representations of manifolds.*

Let $\mathscr{A}$, X, and Y be C^r manifolds, $\mathscr{C}^r(X, Y)$ the set of C^r maps from X to Y, and $\rho: \mathscr{A} \to \mathscr{C}^r(X, Y)$ a map. For $a \in \mathscr{A}$ we write ρ_a instead of $\rho(a)$; i.e., $\rho_a: X \to Y$ is a C^r map. We say ρ is a **C^r representation** iff the evaluation map

$$ev_\rho: \mathscr{A} \times X \to Y$$

given by

$$ev_\rho(a, x) = \rho_a(x)$$

for $a \in \mathscr{A}$ and $x \in X$ is a C^r map from $\mathscr{A} \times X$ to Y.

Now for $k = 1, \ldots, r$ let $T^k(X)$ be the kth iterated tangent space of X; i.e., $T^0(X) = X$ and $T^{k+1}(X) = T(T^k(X))$. If $f: X \to Y$ is a C^r map, let $T^k f: T^k(X) \to T^k(Y)$ be the kth iterated tangent map; i.e., $T^0 f = f$ and $T^{k+1} f = T(T^k f)$. If $\rho: \mathscr{A} \to \mathscr{C}^r(X, Y)$ as any map and $k = 0, 1, \ldots,$ or n, we define the map

$$\rho^{(k)}: \mathscr{A} \to C^{r-k}(T^k(X), T^k(Y))$$

by

$$\rho^{(k)}(a) = T^k \rho_a$$

for $a \in \mathscr{A}$. We say that ρ is a **C^r pseudorepresentation** iff each of the maps $\rho^{(k)}$ $(k = 0, 1, \ldots, r)$ is a C^0 representation; i.e., iff for each $k = 0, 1, \ldots, r$ the map $\mathscr{A} \times T^k(X) \to T^k(Y)$ given by $(a, \dot{x}) \rightsquigarrow T^k \rho_a(\dot{x})$ for $a \in \mathscr{A}$ and $\dot{x} \in T^k(X)$ is continuous.

Clearly every C^r representation is a C^r pseudorepresentation, and for $r = 0$ the concepts are identical. For a simple (but important) example of a C^r representation, let $\pi: E \to X$ be a C^r vector bundle over a compact manifold X and take $\mathscr{A} = \Gamma^r(\pi)$, $Y = E$, and $\rho: \Gamma^r(\pi) \to \mathscr{C}^r(X, E)$ to be the identity injection. Then by 12.3, ρ is a C^r representation.

The first openness property is the following.

18.1. OPENNESS OF NONINTERSECTION. Let $\mathscr{A}$, X, Y be C^0 manifolds, $W \subset Y$ a closed subset of Y (not necessarily a submanifold), $K \subset X$ a compact subset of X, and $\rho: \mathscr{A} \to C^0(X, Y)$ a C^0 representation. Define $\mathscr{A}^0_{KW} \subset \mathscr{A}$ by

$$\mathscr{A}^0_{KW} = \{a \in \mathscr{A} \mid \rho_a(K) \cap W = \varnothing\}$$

Then $\mathscr{A}^0_{KW}$ is an open subset of $\mathscr{A}$.

Proof. Choose $a_0 \in \mathscr{A}^0_{KW}$. We must find an open neighborhood N of a_0, such that $N \subset \mathscr{A}^0_{KW}$. For each $x_0 \in K$ take open neighborhoods N_{x_0} of a_0 in $\mathscr{A}$ and U_{x_0} of x_0 in X so that $\rho_a(x) \notin W$ for $(a, x) \in N_{x_0} \times U_{x_0}$. This is possible since W is closed and the evaluation map is continuous by hypothesis. By compactness, we may cover K by finitely many of the sets U_{x_0}; say $K \subset U_{x_1} \cup \cdots \cup U_{x_n}$. Then $N = N_{x_1} \cap \cdots \cap N_{x_n} \subset \mathscr{A}^0_{KW}$ by construction. ∎

The second openness property is a simple consequence.

18.2. OPENNESS OF TRANSVERSAL INTERSECTION. Let $\mathscr{A}$, X, and Y be C^1 manifolds with X finite dimensional, $W \subset Y$ a closed C^1 submanifold, $K \subset X$ a compact subset of X, and ρ: $\mathscr{A} \to C^1(X, Y)$ a C^1 pseudorepresentation. Then the subset $\mathscr{A}_{KW} \subset \mathscr{A}$ defined by

$$\mathscr{A}_{KW} = \{a \in \mathscr{A} \mid \rho_a \pitchfork_x W \text{ for } x \in K\}$$

is open. This holds even if X is not finite dimensional, provided that ρ is a C^1 representation.

Proof. Recall that the linear map bundle

$$L(\tau_X, \tau_Y)\colon L(T(X), T(Y)) \to X \times Y$$

defined in §9 has, for the fiber over a point (x, y), the Banach space $L(T_xX, T_yY)$ of continuous linear maps from T_xX to T_yY. In other words,

$$L(T(X), T(Y)) = \bigcup_{(x,y)} L(T_xX, T_yY)$$

Define the subset Z of $L(T(X), T(Y))$ as the set of all $A \in L(T(X), T(Y))$ such that if $x \in X$, $y \in Y$, and $A \in L(T_xX, T_yY)$, then either

(1) $y \notin W$, or

(2) $y \in W$, the image of A splits, and $A(T_xX)$ contains a closed complement to T_yW and Y_yY.

Then define $W' = L(T(X), T(Y)) \setminus Z$. Using Lemma 12.3 one easily shows that Z is open in $L(T(X), T(Y))$. Hence W' is closed.

Since ρ is a C^1 pseudorepresentation, the map ρ': $\mathscr{A} \to C^0(X, L(T(X), T(Y))$ defined by $\rho'_a(x) = T_x\rho_a$ for $a \in \mathscr{A}$, and $x \in X$ is a C^0 representation. (This is where we use the finite-dimensionality of X.) By construction, $\rho_a \pitchfork_x W$ if and only if $\rho'_a(x) \notin W'$. Thus 18.2 follows from 18.1. ∎

Note that the definition of a C^r pseudorepresentation makes sense even when $\mathscr{A}$ is only a topological space (and not necessarily a Banach manifold). Theorems 18.1 and 18.2 hold in this more general setting. Also note that 18.1 simply asserts that ρ is continuous, if $C^0(X, Y)$ has the compact-open topology.

§19. Density Theorem

We now prove that, in the context of representations of manifolds with suitable hypothesis, almost every point in the domain is represented by a transversal map. The theorem stated is not the most general possible in this context, but it is adequate for the elementary applications of the transversal approximation technique (Abraham [2]) as well as the application to flows of Chapter 7, and it implies the earlier density theorems (Thom [2], Abraham [*1*]). More general results can be obtained from the proof we give with only trivial modifications (see Abraham [*3*]). The proof is a simple argument based on Smale's Density Theorem for regular values of Fredholm maps, and this is our only application of that theorem.

19.1. TRANSVERSAL DENSITY THEOREM. Let $\mathscr{A}$, X, Y be C^r manifolds, $\rho: \mathscr{A} \to \mathscr{C}^r(X, Y)$ a C^r representation, $W \subset Y$ a submanifold (not necessarily closed), and $ev_\rho: \mathscr{A} \times X \to Y$ the evaluation map. Define $\mathscr{A}_W \subset \mathscr{A}$ by

$$\mathscr{A}_W = \{a \in \mathscr{A} \mid \rho_a \pitchfork W\}$$

Assume that:

(1) **X has finite dimension n and W has finite codimension q in Y;**

(2) **$\mathscr{A}$ and X are second countable;**

(3) $r >$ **max** $(0, n - q)$;

(4) $ev_\rho \pitchfork W$.

Then $\mathscr{A}_W$ is residual (and hence dense) in $\mathscr{A}$.

The proof follows from the next four lemmas. Define $\mathscr{B} = ev_\rho^{-1}(W) \subset \mathscr{A} \times X$. Then by (1), (4) and 17.2, $\mathscr{B}$ is a submanifold of $\mathscr{A} \times X$ of codimension q. Let $\pi_1: \mathscr{A} \times X \to \mathscr{A}$ be the projection on the first factor and let

$$\pi: \mathscr{B} \to \mathscr{A}$$

be given by

$$\pi = \pi_1 | \mathscr{B}$$

Clearly π is a C^r map. Let $\mathscr{R}_\pi$ be the set of regular values of π. (See Figure 19–1.)

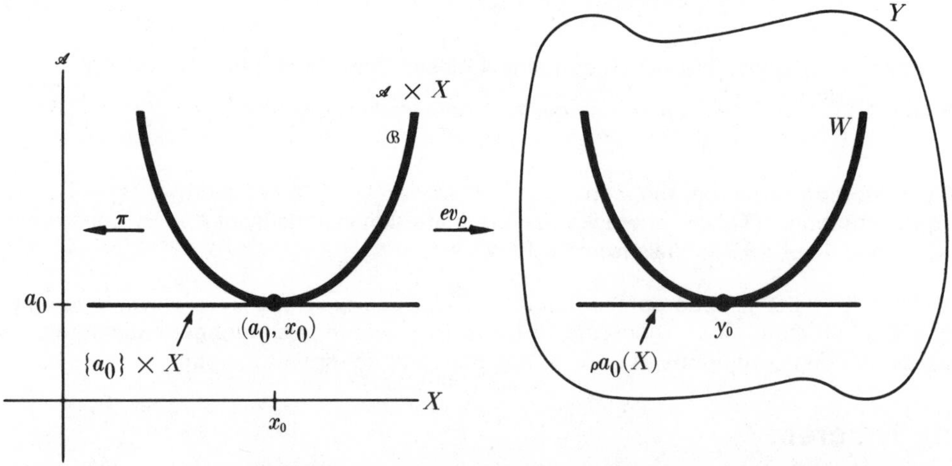

Figure 19–1. **$\mathscr{A}$, X and W are shown as one-dimensional, Y as two-dimensional. The point (a_0, x_0) is a critical point of π (the tangent line to B is vertical). W is the image of B under ev_ρ; $\rho_{a_0}(X)$ the image of the line $a = a_0$. ρ_{a_0} intersects W nontransversally at $y_0 = \rho_{a_0}(x_0)$.**

We will show that $\mathscr{A}_W = \mathscr{R}_\pi$ and π is a Fredholm map of constant index $n - q$.

19.2 LEMMA. Let F and G be Banach spaces, dim $G = n$, $p_1: F \times G \to F$ the projection on the first factor, and $E \subset F \times G$ a closed subspace of codimension q. If $p: E \to F$ is the restriction of p_1 to E, $p = p_1 \mid E$, then p is a Fredholm operator with index $n - q$.

Proof. Let $\mathbf{H} = \mathbf{E} + (\{\mathbf{0}\} \times \mathbf{G})$ and $\mathbf{K} = \mathbf{E} \cap (\{\mathbf{0}\} \times \mathbf{G})$. As $\mathbf{G}$ is finite dimensional and $\mathbf{E}$ is closed, $\mathbf{H}$ is closed (see Dieudonne [*1*, p. 108]). As $\mathbf{E}$ has finite codimension and $\mathbf{E} \subset \mathbf{H}$, $\mathbf{H}$ has finite codimension. Thus, we may choose a finite-dimensional subspace $\mathbf{J} \subset \mathbf{F} \times \{\mathbf{0}\}$ such that $\mathbf{F} \times \mathbf{G} = \mathbf{H} \oplus \mathbf{J}$, where $\oplus$ indicates that the sum is direct. As $\mathbf{G}$ is finite dimensional and $\mathbf{K} \subset \mathbf{G}$, we may choose closed subspaces $\mathbf{E}_0 \subset \mathbf{E}$ and $\mathbf{G}_0 \subset \{\mathbf{0}\} \times \mathbf{G}$ such that $\mathbf{E} = \mathbf{E}_0 \oplus \mathbf{K}$ and $\{\mathbf{0}\} \times \mathbf{G} = \mathbf{K} \oplus \mathbf{G}_0$. Thus, $\mathbf{H} = \mathbf{E}_0 \oplus \mathbf{K} \oplus \mathbf{G}_0$, and

$$\mathbf{F} \times \mathbf{G} = \mathbf{E}_0 \oplus \mathbf{K} \oplus \mathbf{G}_0 \oplus \mathbf{J}$$

Then p_1 restricted to $\mathbf{E}_0 \oplus \mathbf{J}$ is an isomorphism, $\mathbf{K}$ is the kernel of p, and $p_1(\mathbf{J})$ is a complement to the image of p in $\mathbf{F}$. Hence p is a Fredholm operator, and its index is given by

$$\begin{aligned} \text{index}(p) &= \dim(\mathbf{K}) - \dim(\mathbf{J}) \\ &= \dim(\mathbf{K} \oplus \mathbf{G}_0) - \dim(\mathbf{G}_0 \oplus \mathbf{J}) \end{aligned}$$

As $\mathbf{K} \oplus \mathbf{G}_0 \approx \mathbf{G}$ and $\mathbf{G}_0 \oplus \mathbf{J}$ is a complement to $\mathbf{E}$, $\text{index}(p) = n - q$. ▮

19.3. LEMMA. Under the hypotheses of 19.1, the map $\pi: \mathcal{B} \to \mathcal{A}$ is a Fredholm map of constant index $n - q$.

Proof. Choose $(a, x) \in \mathcal{B}$. We must show that the tangent map

$$T_{(a,x)}\pi: T_{(a,x)}\mathcal{B} \to T_a\mathcal{A}$$

is a Fredholm map with index $n - q$. In Lemma 19.2 read T_xX for $\mathbf{G}$, $T_a\mathcal{A}$ for $\mathbf{F}$, $T_a\mathcal{A} \times T_xX = T_{(a,x)}(\mathcal{A} \times X)$ for $\mathbf{F} \times \mathbf{G}$, $T_{(a,x)}\mathcal{B}$ for $\mathbf{E}$, $T_{(a,x)}\pi_1$ for p_1 and $T_{(a,x)}\pi$ for p. The conclusion becomes 19.3. ▮

19.4. LEMMA. Under the hypotheses of 19.1, $\mathcal{R}_\pi \subset \mathcal{A}_W$.

Proof. Because of hypothesis (1) in 19.1, X is finite dimensional. Since finite-dimensional subspaces always split, we have that, for $a \in \mathcal{A}$, $\rho_a \pitchfork W$ if and only if

(*) $$(T_x\rho_a)(T_xX) + T_yW = T_yY$$

for every $x \in \rho_a^{-1}(W)$, where $y = \rho_a(x)$. (The symbol $+$, as opposed to $\oplus$, indicates that the sum is not necessarily direct.)

Choose $a \in \mathcal{R}_\pi$, and $x \in X$ so that $y = \rho_a(x) \in W$. For

$$(\dot{a}, \dot{x}) \in T_a\mathcal{A} \times T_xX = T_{(a,x)}(\mathcal{A} \times X)$$

write

$$(T_{(a,x)}ev_\rho)(\dot{a}, \dot{x}) = (T_{1(a,x)}ev_\rho)\dot{a} + (T_{2(a,x)}ev_\rho)\dot{x}$$

(This, of course, is simply the formula for computing the derivatives from the partial derivatives.) Obviously,

$$(T_{2(a,x)}ev_\rho) = T_x\rho_a$$

Now choose $y \in T_yY$. Since $ev_\rho \pitchfork W$ (hypothesis (4)) there exists $\dot{w} \in T_yW$ and $(a, \dot{x}) \in T_{(a,x)}(\mathcal{A} \times X)$ such that

(**) $$\begin{aligned} \dot{y} &= \dot{w} + (T_{(a,x)}ev_\rho)(\dot{a}, \dot{x}) \\ &= \dot{w} + (T_{1(a,x)}ev_\rho)\dot{a} + (T_x\rho_a)\dot{x} \end{aligned}$$

Since $a \in \mathcal{R}_\pi$, $(T_{(a,x)}\pi)(T_{(a,x)}\mathcal{B}) = T_a\mathcal{A}$; i.e., there exists $\dot{b} \in T_{(a,x)}\mathcal{B}$ such that

$$(T_{(a,x)}\pi)\dot{b} = \dot{a}$$

i.e., $\dot{b} = (\dot{a}, \dot{x}_1) \in T_{(a,x)}\mathcal{B} \subset (T_a\mathcal{A}) \times (T_xX)$ for some $\dot{x}_1 \in T_xX$. Now by the definition of $\mathcal{B}$ and 17.2,

$$\begin{aligned} T_{(a,x)}\mathcal{B} &= T_{(a,x)}(ev_\rho^{-1}(W)) \\ &= (T_{(a,x)}ev_\rho)^{-1}T_yW \end{aligned}$$

hence $(T_{(a,x)}ev_\rho)\dot{b} \in T_yW$. But

$$(T_{(a,x)}ev_\rho)\dot{b} = (T_{1(a,x)}ev_\rho)\dot{a} + (T_x\rho_a)\dot{x}_1$$

so

$$(T_{1(a,x)}ev_\rho)\dot{a} \in T_yW + (T_x\rho_a)(T_xX)$$

Thus by (**), $\dot{y} \in T_yW + (T_x\rho_a)T_xX$. This establishes (*). Hence $\rho_a \pitchfork W$; hence $a \in \mathcal{A}_W$. Thus $\mathcal{R}_\pi \subset \mathcal{A}_W$. ∎

19.5 LEMMA. Under the hypotheses of 19.1,

$$\mathcal{A}_W \subset \mathcal{R}_\pi$$

Proof. For $a \in \mathcal{A}_W$, we will show that $(T_{(a,x)}\pi)(T_{(a,x)}\mathcal{B}) = T_a\mathcal{A}$ for every $x \in X$, such that $(a, x) \in \mathcal{B}$. Choose x so that $(a, x) \in \mathcal{B}$, and $\dot{a} \in T_a\mathcal{A}$. Since $\rho_a \pitchfork W$, there exists $\dot{w} \in T_yW$ (where $y = \rho_a(x)$) and $\dot{x} \in T_xX$ such that

$$(T_{1(a,x)}ev_\rho)\dot{a} = (T_x\rho_a)\dot{x} + \dot{w}$$

Hence

$$(T_{(a,x)}ev_\rho)(\dot{a}, -\dot{x}) = \dot{w} \in T_yW$$

so $(\dot{a}, -\dot{x}) \in (T_{(a,x)}ev_\rho)^{-1}T_yW = T_{(a,x)}\mathcal{B}$, and $\dot{a} \in (T_{(a,x)}\pi)(T_{(a,x)}\mathcal{B})$. Thus $(T_{(a,x)}\pi)(T_{(a,x)}\mathcal{B}) = T_a\mathcal{A}$, or $a \in \mathcal{R}_\pi$. This shows $\mathcal{A}_W \subset \mathcal{R}_\pi$. ∎

Proof of 19.1. By (2), $\mathcal{A} \times X$ is second countable. Hence $\mathcal{B}$ is second countable and therefore Lindelöf. Then the theorem follows immediately from 19.3, 19.4, 19.5, and Smale's Density Theorem (16.2). A Banach manifold, being locally homeomorphic to a complete metric space, is obviously a Baire space (i.e., every residual subset is dense); hence $\mathcal{A}_W$ is dense. ∎

§20. Isotopy Theorem

We now prove the most important property of transversality, the stability of transversal intersections. The prototype of this theorem is due to Thom [*1*].

Let $\mathcal{A}$, X, and Y be C^{r+1} manifolds ($r \geq 1$) with X compact, $\rho: \mathcal{A} \times X \to Y$ a C^{r+1} representation of mappings, $W \subset Y$ a closed submanifold, and $a_0 \in \mathcal{A}$ a point such that $\rho_{a_0} \pitchfork W$. For $a \in \mathcal{A}$, let $W_a \subset X$ be defined by $W_a = \rho_a^{-1}(W)$. By the Transversality Openness Theorem (18.2), $\rho_a \pitchfork W$ for $a \in \mathcal{A}$ sufficiently near a_0. Hence by 17.2, $W_a \subset X$ is a submanifold for $a \in \mathcal{A}$ near a_0. One might expect that for a near a_0, the submanifolds W_a and W_{a_0} are close. The Transversality Isotopy Theorem makes this precise. It says that W_a and W_{a_0} are isotopic, i.e., there is a C^r diffeomorphism of X onto itself which is isotopic to the identity and carries W_{a_0} onto W_a.

We will need the following form of the Implicit Map Theorem, which is actually a special case of the Isotopy Theorem, and the main step in its proof.

20.1. IMPLICIT SECTION THEOREM. Let U and V be open neighborhoods of the origin in Banach spaces E and F respectively. Let $f\colon U \times V \to F$ be of class C^r ($r \geqslant 1$) and suppose $f(0, 0) = 0$.

Then, if $D_2f(0, 0) \in L(F, F)$ is a toplinear isomorphism, there exist open balls (centered at the origin) U^*, V^* with $U^* \subset U$, $V^* \subset V$, and a C^r map $h\colon U^* \to V^*$ such that

$$f^{-1}(0) \cap (U^* \times V^*) = \{(x, h(x)) \mid x \in U^*\}$$

Proof. Define $F\colon U \times V \to U \times F$ by $F(x, y) = (x, f(x, y))$ for $x \in U, y \in V$. Then $DF(0, 0)$ is a toplinear isomorphism, and $F(0, 0) = (0, 0)$. By the Inverse Function Theorem, there are open sets U_1 and V_1 with $(0, 0) \in U_1 \times V_1 \subset U \times F$, and a C^r map $H\colon U_1 \times V_1 \to U \times V$ such that $F \circ H =$ identity on $U_1 \times V_1$, and $H \circ F =$ identity on $H(U_1 \times V_1)$, where $H(U_1 \times V_1)$ is an open neighborhood of $(0, 0)$ in $U \times V$.

For $(x, y) \in U_1 \times V_1$ let $H(x, y) = (h_1(x, y), h_2(x, y))$. Then, since for $(x, y) \in U_1 \times V_1$ we have $(x, y) = F \circ H(x, y) = F(h_1(x, y), h_2(x, y)) = (h_1(x, y), f \circ H(x, y))$, it follows that $h_1(x, y) = x$. Since $0 \in V_1$, we may define $h\colon U_1 \to V$ by $h(x) = h_2(x, 0)$, for $x \in U_1$. Then for $x \in U_1$, $H(x, 0) = (x, h(x))$. But $H(0, 0) = H \circ F(0, 0) = (0, 0)$; so $h(0) = 0 \in V$. Choose U^* and V^* so that

(1) U^* and V^* are open balls centered at 0;

(2) $U^* \times V^* \subset H(U_1 \times V_1) \cap (U_1 \times V_1)$;

(3) $h(U^*) \subset V^*$.

Suppose $(x, y) \in f^{-1}(0) \cap (U^* \times V^*)$. Then $F(x, y) = (x, 0) \in U^* \times V^* \subset H(U_1 \times V_1)$, and $(x, y) = H \circ F(x, y) = H(x, 0) = (x, h(x))$, so $(x, y) \in \{(x, h(x)) | x \in U^*\}$.

Conversely, suppose $(x, y) \in \{(x, h(x)) | x \in U^*\}$. Then $y = h(x)$ and $x \in U^*$; whence by (3) $h(x) \in V^*$, and $(x, y) \in U^* \times V^*$. Also $(x, y) \in U^* \times V^* \subset U_1 \times V_1$, or

$$(x, 0) = F \circ H(x, 0) = F(x, h(x)) = (x, f(x, h(x)))$$

Hence $(x, y) = (x, h(x)) \in f^{-1}(0) \cap U^* \times V^*$. ∎

Thus, near $(0, 0)$, $f^{-1}(0)$ is the image of a section of the "bundle" $U \times V \to U$.

20.2. TRANSVERSAL ISOTOPY THEOREM. Let $\mathscr{A}$, X, and Y be C^{r+1} manifolds ($r \geqslant 1$), $\rho\colon \mathscr{A} \times X \to Y$ a C^{r+1} representation of mappings, $W \subset Y$ a submanifold, and $a_0 \in \mathscr{A}$ a point. For $a \in \mathscr{A}$ let $W_a = \rho_a^{-1}(W)$. Assume that,

(1) W is closed in Y;

(2) X is compact (and therefore finite dimensional), and C^{r+3};

(3) $\rho_{a_0} \pitchfork W$.

Then there is an open neighborhood N of a_0 in $\mathscr{A}$ such that, for $a \in N$, W_a is C^r isotopic to W_{a_0}; i.e., for $a \in N$ there is a C^r diffeomorphism $F_a\colon X \to X$ such that $F_a(W_{a_0}) = W_a$ and F_a is C^r isotopic to the identity: there exists a C^r map $\varphi\colon X \times I \to X$, where I is an open interval in R containing $[0, 1]$, such that $\varphi_t = \varphi | X \times \{t\}$ is a diffeomorphism for all $t \in [0, 1]$, φ_0 is the identity, and $\varphi_1 = F_a$.

The proof follows from two lemmas. Take a C^{r+1} total tubular neighborhood of W_{a_0} in X (Lang [*1;* p. 73]); this means we have an open neighborhood E of W_{a_0} in X, a surjective map $\pi: E \to W_{a_0}$, and a C^{r+1} vector bundle structure on π, which makes E an open submanifold of X. Take a Riemannian metric on π and a reduction to the Hilbert group (Lang [*1;* Ch. VII]); let $\| \; \|: E \to \mathbf{R}$ be the Finsler associated with this Riemannian metric in the usual fashion (viz. $\|e\|^2 = \langle e, e \rangle$, where $\langle , \rangle$ is the Riemannian metric). Thus we have an admissible covering of π by VB charts (α, α_0, U) where U is an open subset of W_{a_0}, $\alpha: \pi^{-1}(U) \to \alpha_0(U) \times \mathbf{F}_\alpha$, and for each such chart a norm $\| \; \|_\alpha$ on $\mathbf{F}_\alpha$ such that $\|e\| = \|\alpha(e)\|_\alpha$ for $e \in \pi^{-1}(U)$. We call this covering the **reduced atlas of π.**

We now prove a global version of 20.1.

20.3. LEMMA. There is an open neighborhood N of a_0 in $\mathscr{A}$ such that, for $a \in N$, $W_a = \rho_a^{-1}(W)$ is the image of a C^{r+1} section of π; i.e., for $a \in \mathscr{A}$ there is $\xi_a \in \Gamma^{r+1}(\pi)$ such that $W_a = \xi_a(W_{a_0})$.

Proof. For each real number $t > 0$ we define

$$B_t = \{e \in E \mid \|e\| < t\}$$

and for an open subset U of W_{a_0} we define $B_t(U) \subset E$

$$B_t(U) = \{e \in \pi^{-1}(U) \mid \|e\| < t\}$$

If (α, α_0, U) is a member of the reduced atlas with $\alpha(\pi^{-1}(U)) = \alpha_0(U) \times \mathbf{F}_\alpha$, then $\alpha(B_t(U)) = U_\alpha \times B_{t\alpha}$ where $B_{t\alpha}$ is the open ball of radius t centered at the origin in $\mathbf{F}_\alpha$.

For each $x \in X$, we define an open neighborhood N_x of a_0 in $\mathscr{A}$ and an open neighborhood Z_x of x in X as follows:

(i) If $x \notin W_{a_0}$, then $\rho_{a_0}(x) \notin W$. Since $W \subset Y$ is closed and the evaluation map is continuous, we may take N_x and Z_x satisfying the condition

$$(*) \qquad Z_x \cap W_a = \varnothing \qquad \text{for } a \in N_x$$

(ii) Suppose $x \in W_{a_0}$. Then $\rho_{a_0}(x) \in W$. Choose an admissible chart (V, β) in Y at $\rho_{a_0}(x)$ having the submanifold property for W; i.e., $\beta(V) = V_1 \times V_2$ where V_1 and V_2 are open neighborhoods of the origin in Banach spaces $\mathbf{F}_1$ and $\mathbf{F}_2$ respectively, $\beta(\rho_{a_0}(x)) = (\mathbf{0}, \mathbf{0})$, and $\beta(V \cap W) = V_1 \times \{\mathbf{0}\}$. Because the evaluation map is continuous, we may choose an open neighborhood N_x of a_0 in $\mathscr{A}$, a VB chart (α, α_0, U) on π at x from the reduced atlas, and a real number $t > 0$, such that for $a \in N_x$, $\rho_a(B_t(U)) \subset V$. Let F_α be the model of the fiber of π in the chart (α, α_0, U), i.e., $\alpha(\pi^{-1}(U)) = \alpha_0(U) \times \mathbf{F}_\alpha$. Then $\alpha(B_t(U)) = \alpha_0(U) \times B_{\alpha t}$ where $B_{\alpha t}$ is the open ball in $\mathbf{F}_\alpha$ about the origin with radius t. Let

$$pr: V_1 \times V_2 \to V_2$$

be the projection on the second factor. Consider the map

$$f: N_x \times \alpha_0(U) \times B_{\alpha t} \to V_2$$

given by

$$f(a, u, v) = pr \circ \beta \circ \rho_a \circ \alpha^{-1}(u, v)$$

for $a \in N_x$, $u \in \alpha_0(U)$, $v \in B_{\alpha t}$. Assume for simplicity that $\alpha(x) = (\mathbf{0}, \mathbf{0})$ and $\beta(\rho_{a_0}(x)) = (\mathbf{0}, \mathbf{0})$.

Then we see $D_3f(a_0, \mathbf{0}, \mathbf{0})$ is a toplinear isomorphism as follows. Define $f_{a_0}: \alpha_0(U) \times B_{\alpha t} \to V_2$ by

$$f_{a_0}(u, v) = f(a_0, u, v)$$

for $(u, v) \in \alpha_0(U) \times B_\alpha$. Since $\rho_{a_0} \overline{\pitchfork} W$, $Df_{a_0}(\mathbf{0}, \mathbf{0})$ is surjective. But $D_1f_{a_0}(\mathbf{0}, \mathbf{0}) = 0$, since $f_{a_0}(u, \mathbf{0}) = \mathbf{0}$ for all $u \in \alpha_0(U)$ (this is because $\rho_{a_0}(W_{a_0}) = W$). Hence $D_2f_{a_0}(\mathbf{0}, \mathbf{0}) = D_3f(a_0, \mathbf{0}, \mathbf{0})$ is surjective. But, by 17.2, W_{a_0} and W have the same codimension, and by hypothesis this is finite. Hence $D_3f(a_0, \mathbf{0}, \mathbf{0})$ is a surjective linear map between two vector spaces of the same finite dimension; hence, it must be a toplinear isomorphism.

By the Implicit Section Theorem (20.1) (making N_x, $\alpha_0(U)$, and $B_{\alpha t}$ smaller if necessary) we have a C^{r+1} map h: $N_x = \alpha_0(U) \to B_{\alpha t}$ so that

(†) $$f^{-1}(\mathbf{0}) \cap (N_x \times \alpha_0(U) \times B_{\alpha t}) = \{(a, x, h(a, x)) \mid (a, x) \in N_x \times \alpha_0(U)\}$$

Take

(**) $$Z_x = \alpha^{-1}(\alpha_0(U) \times B_{\alpha t}) = B_t(U)$$

Note that

(‡) $$W_a \cap Z_x = \alpha^{-1}(f_a^{-1}(\mathbf{0}) \cap (\alpha_0(U) \times B_{\alpha t}))$$

for $a \in N_x$; here $f_a: \alpha_0(U) \times B_{\alpha t} \to V_2$ is given by $f_a(u, v) = f(a, u, v)$ for $(u, v) \in \alpha_0(U) \times B_{\alpha t}$. This completes the definition of Z_x and N_x in case (ii).

By the compactness of X, finitely many of the Z_x's cover X, say $X = Z_{x_1} \cup \cdots \cup Z_{x_n}$. Then define N by $N = N_{x_1} \cap \cdots \cap N_{x_n}$. We now assert that this neighborhood satisfies the conclusion of the lemma: for each fixed $a \in N$, $W_a \subset E$ and W_a intersects each fiber $E_x = \pi^{-1}(x)$, $(x \in W_{a_0})$, in exactly one point.

To prove this, fix $a \in N$. If $x_i \notin W_{a_0}$, then $Z_{x_i} \cap W_a = \varnothing$ by (*); for $x_i \in W_{a_0}$, $Z_{x_i} \subset E$ by (**). Thus $W_a \subset E$. Choose $x \in W_{a_0}$. We must show that $W_a \cap E_x$ consists of a single point. By (†) and (‡) (and since the Z_{x_i} cover x) $W_a \cap Z_{x_i} \cap E_x$ consists of exactly one point for some $i = 1, \ldots, n$; indeed, this is true for each $i = 1, \ldots, n$ such that $x \in Z_{x_i}$. Suppose that $W_a \cap E_x$ contains two points and let these two points be in Z_{x_i} and Z_{x_j} respectively. By (*) we must have $x_i, x_j \in W_{a_0}$. Then by (**)

$$Z_{x_i} = B_{t_i}(U_i) \qquad \text{and} \qquad Z_{x_j} = B_{t_j}(U_j)$$

where $x \in U_i \cap U_j$. But either $t_i \leqslant t_j$ or $t_j \leqslant t_i$; hence either $E_x \cap Z_{x_i} \subset E_x \cap Z_{x_j}$ or $E_x \cap Z_{x_j} \subset E_x \cap Z_{x_i}$. Thus, in either case $W_a \cap E_x \cap Z_{x_k}$ ($k = i$ or j) consists of two points contradicting our previous conclusion. This proves that $W_a \cap E_x$ contains exactly one point.

Hence W_a is the image of a section ξ_a of π for each $a \in N$. Furthermore, for $a \in N$ and each sufficiently small VB chart (α, α_0, U) of the reduced atlas, the map $h_a: \alpha_0(U) \to B_{\alpha t}$ given by $h_a(x) = h(a, x)$ for $x \in \alpha_0(U)$ (h being the map constructed above) is the principal part of a local representative of ξ_a. As h was C^{r+1}, ξ_a is C^{r+1}. ∎

The isotopy property is obtained as follows.

20.4. LEMMA. For $\xi \in \Gamma^{r+1}(\pi)$, $\xi(W_{a_0})$ is C^r isotopic to W_{a_0}.

Proof. Choose $\xi \in \Gamma^{r+1}(\pi)$. As W_{a_0} is closed in X and hence compact, there is a real number $T > 0$ such that $\xi(W_{a_0}) \subset B_T$. (Recall that $B_T = \{e \in E \mid \|e\| < T\}$.) Take a C^∞ function η: $\boldsymbol{R} \to \boldsymbol{R}$ so that

$$\eta(t) = 1 \qquad \text{for } t \leqslant T$$

$$\eta(t) = 0 \qquad \text{for } T+1 \leqslant t$$

We will define a C^r vector field ζ: $X \to T(X)$ (i.e., $\zeta \in \Gamma^r(\tau_X)$) as follows. If $x \in X \setminus E$, let $\zeta(x) = 0_x$. If $x \in E$, let $w = \pi(x) \in W_{a_0}$. Then $x \in E_w$, which is both a Banach space and a submanifold of X. Let ι: $E_w \to T_xX$ be the natural injection, that is, the composite $E_w \to T_xE_w \to T_xX$, and define $\zeta(x)$ by

$$\zeta(x) = \iota[\eta(\|x\|)\xi(w)]$$

Here the scalar multiplication is that of the vector bundle π: $E \to W_{a_0}$.

Clearly $\zeta \in \Gamma^r(\tau_X)$ and has compact support (see 21.3). Let φ: $X \times \boldsymbol{R} \to X$ be the C^r flow of ζ and for $t \in \boldsymbol{R}$, define φ_t: $X \to X$ by $\varphi_t(x) = \varphi(x, t)$, for $x \in X$. Then each φ_t is a C^r diffeomorphism from X to itself. Clearly φ_0 is the identity, and $\varphi_1(W_{a_0}) = \xi(W_{a_0})$. ▮

Proof of 20.2. The Transversal Isotopy Theorem now follows immediately from Lemmas 20.3 and 20.4. ▮

The proof shows in fact that W_a and W_{a_0} are **C^r flow isotopic:** i.e., there is a C^r flow φ: $X \times \boldsymbol{R} \to X$ on X, such that $\varphi_1(W_{a_0}) = W_a$.

5

FLOWS ON MANIFOLDS

The qualitative theory of ordinary differential equations and flows is a vast subject, and we shall consider here only those aspects which are related to transversality: generic properties of critical points, closed orbits, and stable manifolds. To place these topics in context, we recommend the recent surveys of Abraham-Marsden [*1;* Ch. V], Peixoto [*1*], Nemitskii [*1*], and Thom [*3*].

§21. Vectorfields

In this section we recall the basic terminology and properties of vector fields and flows on manifolds. We begin with the local situation and make use of the definitions of §6 pertaining to differentiable curves.

21.1. LOCAL EXISTENCE AND UNIQUENESS THEOREM. Let *E* be a Banach space, $U \subset E$ **an open set,** $x_0 \in U$ **a point and** $\xi\colon U \to E$ **a** C^r **map** ($r \geqslant 1$). **Then there is a** C^r **curve** $c\colon I \to U$ **where** $I \subset R$ **is an open interval about 0 such that**

$$c(0) = x_0$$

$$c'(t) = \xi(c(t)) \qquad \text{for } t \in I$$

Any two such curves are equal on the intersection of their domains. Moreover, there is an open neighborhood $U_0 \subset U$ of x_0, an open interval $I_0 \subset R$ about 0, and a C^r map $\varphi: U_0 \times I_0 \to U$ such that,

(I) For each $x \in U_0$ the curve $\varphi_x: I_0 \to U$ given by $\varphi_x(t) = \varphi(x, t)$ for $t \in I_0$ satisfies

$$\varphi_x(0) = x$$

and

$$\varphi_x'(t) = \xi(\varphi_x(t)) \qquad \text{for } t \in I_0$$

(II) For each $t \in I_0$ the map $\varphi_t: U_0 \to \varphi_t(U_0) \subset U$ given by $\varphi_t(x) = \varphi(x, t)$ for $x \in U_0$ is a diffeomorphism.

The function ξ in 21.1 can be thought of as assigning a vector to each point of U; the solution curves φ_x are tangent to these vectors. One can also think of ξ as defining the differential equation system

$$c'(t) = \xi(c(t))$$

with initial condition

$$c(0) = x$$

Then φ is the "general solution" of the system. For a proof of 21.1 see Dieudonné [*1*; p. 300].

To globalize this picture we make the following definitions. Let X be a C^{r+1} manifold ($r \geq 0$) and $\tau_X: T(X) \to X$ its tangent bundle. A **C^r vectorfield** on X (often called a **first-order differential equation** or a **dynamical system**) is a C^r section of τ_X; i.e., $\xi \in \Gamma^r(\tau_X)$. An **integral curve of ξ at a point** $x_0 \in X$ (also called an **orbit** of ξ) is a C^r curve $c: I \to X$ where $I \subset R$ is an open interval about 0 such that $c(0) = x_0$ and $c'(t) = \xi(c(t))$ for $t \in I$. Here $c': I \to T(X)$ is defined by

$$c'(t) = (T_t c)\, 1$$

for $t \in I$. A **flow box** of ξ at $x_0 \in X$ is a C^r map $\varphi: U \times I \to X$ where $U \subset X$ is an open neighborhood of x_0, $I \subset \boldsymbol{R}$ is an open interval about 0, and

(1) For $x \in U$ the curve $\varphi_x: I \to U$ given by $\varphi_x(t) = \varphi(x, t)$ for $t \in I$ is an integral curve for ξ at x;

(2) For each $t \in I$, the map $\varphi_t: U \to \varphi_t(U) \subset X$ given by $\varphi_t(x) = \varphi(x, t)$ is a diffeomorphism.

In this context, the Existence and Uniqueness Theorem (21.1) can be restated as follows.

21.2. FLOW BOX THEOREM. Let X be a C^{r+1} manifold ($r \geq 1$), $\xi \in \Gamma^r(\tau_X)$ and $x_0 \in X$. Then there is a flow box $\varphi: U \times I \to X$ of ξ at x_0. Moreover, if c is an integral curve to ξ at any point $x \in U$, then φ_x and c are equal on the intersection of their domains.

Note that the last statement implies that flow boxes agree on the intersection of their domains, which justifies the following definition. Let X be a C^{r+1} manifold ($r \geq 1$) and $\xi \in \Gamma^r(\tau_X)$. The **integral** of ξ is the map

$$\varphi: D \to X$$

where $D \subset X \times \boldsymbol{R}$ is the union of all sets $U \times I \subset X \times \boldsymbol{R}$ such that $\varphi \mid U \times I$ is a flow box and ξ is called **complete** if $D = X \times \boldsymbol{R}$. In this case the integral is called the **flow** (or **dynamical system**) of ξ. Note that 21.2 implies that D is open.

The **support** of ξ is the closed set $\operatorname{supp}(\xi) = \{x \in X \mid \xi(x) \neq 0\}^-$.

21.3. FLOW THEOREM. Let X, ξ, D, and φ be as above, and assume $\operatorname{supp}(\xi)$ **is compact. Then,**

(I) ξ **is complete;**

(II) for $t \in \mathbf{R}$ the map φ_t: $X \to X$ given by $\varphi_t(x) = \varphi(x, t)$ for $x \in X$, is a C^r diffeomorphism;

(III) the diffeomorphisms φ_t as t ranges over $\mathbf{R}$ form a one-parameter group, i.e.,

$$\varphi_0 = \text{identity of } X$$

$$\varphi_{s+t} = \varphi_s \circ \varphi_t \qquad \text{for } s, t \in \mathbf{R};$$

$$\varphi_{-s} = \varphi_s^{-1} \qquad \text{for } s \in \mathbf{R}$$

This is an easy consequence of 21.2; for a proof see Lang [*1*].

The Flow Box Theorem (21.2) remains true even if ξ depends on a parameter; for simplicity we consider only complete flows in this case.

Let $\mathscr{A}$, X be C^{r+1} manifolds and ξ: $\mathscr{A} \times X \to T(X)$ a C^r map. For each $\alpha \in \mathscr{A}$ define ξ_α: $X \to T(X)$ by setting $\xi_\alpha(x) = \xi(\alpha, x)$ for $x \in X$. We say ξ is a **parameterized** C^r **vectorfield** on X (depending on a parameter in $\mathscr{A}$) iff each $\xi_\alpha(\alpha \in \mathscr{A})$ is a vectorfield on X. Now let φ: $\mathscr{A} \times X \times \mathbf{R} \to X$ and $\varphi_\alpha(x, t) = \varphi(\alpha, x, t)$ for $(x, t) \in X \times \mathbf{R}$. Then φ is a **parameterized flow** of ξ iff each φ_α is the flow of ξ_α.

21.4. PARAMETERIZED FLOW THEOREM. Let $\mathscr{A}$ and X be C^{r+1} manifolds ($r \geq 1$) and ξ: $\mathscr{A} \times X \to T(X)$ a parameterized C^r vectorfield on X. If X is compact, there is a unique C^r parameterized flow of ξ.

Proof. By 21.3 there is for each $\alpha \in \mathscr{A}$ a flow $\varphi^{(\alpha)}$ for ξ_α; clearly then, the flow we want must be defined by $\varphi_\alpha = \varphi^{(\alpha)}$. Thus it is sufficient to show that $\varphi_\alpha(x, t) = \varphi(\alpha, x, t)$ is C^r in all three variables simultaneously, while at this point we only know that it is C^r for each fixed $\alpha \in \mathscr{A}$.

Define ζ: $\mathscr{A} \times X \to T(\mathscr{A} \times X) = T\mathscr{A} \times TX$ by $\zeta(\alpha, x) = (0_\alpha, \xi(\alpha, x))$ for $(\alpha, x) \in \mathscr{A} \times X$. (Here 0_α is the zero of the fiber $T_\alpha\mathscr{A}$.) Then ζ is a C^r vectorfield (without parameter) on $\mathscr{A} \times X$. By 21.2 there is a C^r flow box for ζ at each point of $\mathscr{A} \times X$. This flow box followed by projection on the second factor must agree with φ (on the common domain); hence φ is C^r. ∎

Now, note that if $\{\varphi_t\}_{t \in R}$ is the one-parameter group of a vectorfield ξ on a manifold X, then, by the fact that T is a functor (3.2), $\{T\varphi_t\}_{t \in \mathbf{R}}$ is a one-parameter group of diffeomorphisms on the tangent bundle $T(X)$. This group is generated by a vectorfield on $T(X)$, which is related to ξ as follows (see §3 for definitions).

21.5. PROPOSITION. Let X be a C^{r+1} manifold ($r \geq 2$), $\xi \in \Gamma^r(\tau_X)$, and $\varphi = \{\varphi_t\}_{t \in \mathbf{R}}$ be the flow of ξ. Then $\{T\varphi_t\}_{t \in \mathbf{R}}$ is the flow of the equation of first variation $\xi' = \omega \circ T\xi \in \Gamma^{r-1}(\tau_{T(X)})$.

The proof of 21.5 is a simple computation in local coordinates using the fact that the order of partial differentiation may be reversed; it is left to the reader. Note that to verify that a given one-parameter group of diffeomorphisms is the flow of a given vectorfield it suffices (by the one-parameter group properties) to verify the appropriate equation for small values of t.

We now discuss the local behavior of vectorfields.

Let X be a C^{r+1} manifold ($r \geq 0$) and let $\xi \in \Gamma^r(\tau_X)$. A point $x \in X$ is a **critical point** of ξ iff $\xi(x) = 0_x$; otherwise it is a **regular point.**

In the above definition, $0_x \in T_xX$ is the zero of the Banach space T_xX. In the sequel we shall often omit the subscript x.

The following theorem characterizes the local behavior of a vectorfield at a regular point.

21.6. STRAIGHTENING-OUT THEOREM. Let X be a C^{r+1} manifold ($r \geqslant 1$), $\xi \in \Gamma^r(\tau_X)$ and $x_0 \in X$ a regular point of ξ. Then there is an admissible chart (U, α) at x_0 such that $\alpha(U) \subset \mathbf{R} \times \mathbf{E}$ where $\mathbf{E}$ is a Banach space and such that ξ_α: $\alpha(U) \to \mathbf{R} \times \mathbf{E}$, the principal part of the local representative of ξ, is given by

$$\xi_\alpha(x) = (1, \mathbf{0})$$

for $x \in \alpha(U)$.

Proof. We sketch the argument and leave details for the reader. Choose any admissible chart (V, β) at x_0. By the Hahn-Banach Theorem we may suppose $\beta(V) \subset \mathbf{R} \times \mathbf{E}$ where $\mathbf{E}$ is a Banach space, $\beta(x_0) = (0, \mathbf{0})$, and ξ_β: $\beta(V) \to \mathbf{R} \times \mathbf{E}$ satisfies $\xi_\beta(0, \mathbf{0}) = (1, \mathbf{0})$. Now by 21.1 take a flow box for ξ_β, i.e., an open neighborhood $J_0 \times U_0$ of $(0, \mathbf{0})$ in $\beta(V)$, an open interval $I_0 \subset \mathbf{R}$ about 0, and a C^r map φ: $J_0 \times U_0 \times I_0 \to \beta(V)$ such that for $(s, x) \in J_0 \times U_0$ the curve $\varphi_{(s,x)}$: $I_0 \to \beta(V)$ satisfies

$$\varphi_{(s,x)}(0) = (0, \mathbf{0})$$

and

$$\varphi'_{(s,x)}(t) = \xi_\beta(\varphi_{(s,x)}(t)) \qquad \text{for } t \in I_0$$

Define

$$\psi: I_0 \times U_0 \to \beta(V)$$

by

$$\psi(t, x) = \varphi(0, x, t)$$

for $(t, x) \in I_0 \times U_0$. Then $D\psi(0, \mathbf{0})$ is the identity; hence by the Inverse Function Theorem (making I_0 and U_0 smaller if necessary) ψ is a C^r diffeomorphism onto its image. Define $U \subset X$ by $U = \beta^{-1} \circ \psi(I_0 \times U_0)$ and take $\alpha = \psi^{-1} \circ \beta$. Then for fixed x the curve $\alpha(t, x)$ is an integral curve for ξ_α, whence the chart (U, α) has the desired property. ▮

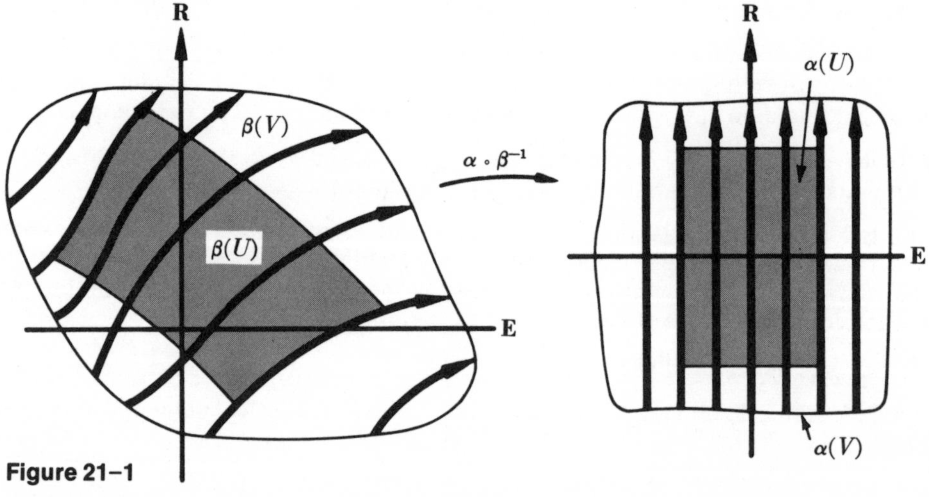

Figure 21–1

The idea of the argument is illustrated in Figure 21–1. It shows the flow for ξ in α and β coordinates. In the β coordinates, the $\mathbf{E}$ coordinate of a point x is the intersection of the integral curve through x with the $\mathbf{E}$ axis; the $\mathbf{R}$ coordinate is the time required to reach x from this intersection point. In the α coordinate system the flow is a uniform translation upwards with unit velocity.

§22. Critical Points

The characterization of the flow of a vectorfield in the neighborhood of a critical point is a classical topic of differential equations. The "linear part" or **Hessian** of the vectorfield at that point is the main ingredient of the theory, and it dominates the local flow behavior if it is **elementary.** For details of this classical theory, see Hartman [*1;* Ch. X]. In this section we give geometric interpretations of the Hessian and the elementary condition and the first application of the transversality theory. Throughout, X shall denote a finite-dimensional C^{r+1} manifold with $r \geqslant 1$, and $(TX)_0$ shall denote the zero section of the tangent bundle τ_X: $T(X) \to X$ (or perhaps more precisely, the image of the zero section). Thus

$$(TX)_0 = \{0_x \in T(X) \mid x \in X\}$$

where 0_x denotes the zero of the Banach space T_xX. Then $(TX)_0$ is a closed submanifold of $T(X)$, which is canonically diffeomorphic to X (the diffeomorphism is the zero section). Hence $T_{0_x}(TX)_0$ is toplinearly isomorphic to T_xX for $x \in X$. Elements of $T_{0_x}(TX)_0$ are called **horizontal.** For $x \in X$, T_xX is also a submanifold of $T(X)$ and since it is a Banach space, $T_{0_x}(T_xX)$ is also toplinearly isomorphic to T_xX; elements of $T_{0_x}(T_xX)$ are called **vertical.**

Now let $x \in X$ be a critical point of a vectorfield $\xi \in \Gamma^r(\tau_X)$; i.e., $\xi(x) = 0_x \in T_xX$. Then ξ: $X \to T(X)$, so

$$T_x\xi\colon T_xX \to T_{0_x}(TX) = T_{0_x}(TX)_0 \oplus T_{0_x}(T_xX)$$

Let π_V be the mapping

$$\pi_V\colon T_{0_x}(TX) \to T_xX$$

obtained by a projection on the second (vertical) summand followed by the canonical identification $T_{0_x}(T_xX) \approx T_xX$.

If x is a critical point of a vectorfield ξ, the **Hessian of ξ at** x is the linear map $\dot{\xi}(x)$: $T_xX \to T_xX$ defined by $\dot{\xi}(x) = \pi_V \circ T_x\xi$. Note that $\dot{\xi}(x)$ is defined only in case x is a critical point of ξ.

Let us compute a "local representative" of $\dot{\xi}(x)$.

Let (U, α) be an admissible chart on X at x. Let ξ_α: $\alpha(U) \to \mathbf{E}_\alpha$ be the principal part of the local representative of ξ; i.e., the local representative of ξ is the map

$$\alpha(U) \to \alpha(U) \times \mathbf{E}_\alpha$$

given by

$$y \rightsquigarrow (y, \xi_\alpha(y))$$

for $y \in \alpha(U)$. Then $T\xi$: $T(X) \to T(T(X))$ is represented by the map

$$\alpha(U) \times \mathbf{E}_\alpha \to \alpha(U) \times \mathbf{E}_\alpha \times \mathbf{E}_\alpha \times \mathbf{E}_\alpha$$

given by

$$(y,\mathbf{e}) \rightsquigarrow (y, \xi_\alpha(y), \mathbf{e}, D\xi_\alpha(y)\mathbf{e})$$

and we may consider

$$(*) \qquad D\xi_\alpha(\alpha(x)): \mathbf{E}_\alpha \to \mathbf{E}_\alpha$$

to be a local representative for the Hessian $\dot{\xi}(x)$. Now, if (V, β) is another admissible chart at x, with $z = \beta(x)$ and $y = \alpha(x)$ so $z = \beta \circ \alpha^{-1}(y)$, then by the definition of the transition maps $T(\beta \circ \alpha^{-1})$ we have

$$\begin{aligned}\xi_\beta(z) &= D(\beta \circ \alpha^{-1})(y)\, \xi_\alpha(y)\\ &= D(\beta \circ \alpha^{-1})(y)\, \xi_\alpha(\alpha \circ \beta^{-1})(z)\end{aligned}$$

whence, since $\xi_\alpha(y) = 0$ (x is a critical point), we have

$$(**) \qquad D\xi_\beta(z) = D(\beta \circ \alpha^{-1})(y) D\xi_\alpha(y) D(\alpha \circ \beta^{-1})(y)$$

by Leibnitz' Rule and the Chain Rule. This last equation has the form

$$B = PAP^{-1}$$

where P is the toplinear automorphism which changes coordinates on the fiber. Since this is the proper way for a linear map to "change coordinates," we might have used $(*)$ to define $\dot{\xi}(x)$. Note that if $\xi(x) \neq 0$, additional terms appear on the right in $(**)$ and a definition of $\dot{\xi}(x)$ (as an element of $L(T_xX, T_xX)$) is not possible.

If φ is the flow of ξ and x is a critical point, then $T_x\varphi_t: T_xX \to T_xX$ for $t \in R$. We next relate the two linear endomorphisms $T_x\phi_t$ and $\dot{\xi}(x)$. The key idea is the exponential map of the general linear group.

Let $\mathbf{E}$ be a Banach space of finite dimension n. Recall that the **exponential map**

$$\exp: L(\mathbf{E}, \mathbf{E}) \to L(\mathbf{E}, \mathbf{E})$$

is defined by the power series

$$\exp(A) = I + \frac{A}{1!} + \frac{A^2}{2!} + \frac{A^3}{3!} + \cdots$$

for $A \in L(\mathbf{E}, \mathbf{E})$, and $I \in L(\mathbf{E}, \mathbf{E})$ the identity of $\mathbf{E}$. For our purposes we need only the following two facts about the exponential map.

22.1. PROPOSITION. For $A \in L(\mathbf{E}, \mathbf{E})$, the derivative of the curve $s \rightsquigarrow \exp(sA)$ is given by

$$\frac{d}{ds} \exp(sA)|_{s=t} = \exp(tA) \circ A$$

for $t \in \mathbf{R}$, and $\exp(0A) = I$.

This can be proved by termwise differentiation.

22.2. PROPOSITION. Let $A \in L(\mathbf{E}, \mathbf{E})$ and let $\lambda_1, \ldots, \lambda_n$ be the complex eigenvalues of A (each eigenvalue appearing a number of times equal to its multiplicity). Then,

(I) $\lambda_1^k, \ldots, \lambda_n^k$ **are the complex eigenvalues of** A^k $(k = 0, \pm 1, \pm 2, \ldots)$;

(II) $\exp(\lambda_1), \ldots, \exp(\lambda_n)$ **are the complex eigenvalues of** $\exp(A)$.

The proof can be found in Chevalley [*1*; p. 5]. Now $T_x\varphi_t$ and $\dot{\xi}(x)$ are related as follows.

22.3. PROPOSITION. If x is a critical point of ξ, then

$$T_x\varphi_t = \exp(t\dot{\xi}(x))$$

for $t \in \boldsymbol{R}$.

Proof. As a function of t, $T_x\varphi_t$ is a curve in the Banach space $L(T_xX, T_xX)$. Note that

$$\frac{d}{ds} T_x\varphi_s|_{s=0} = \dot{\xi}(x)$$

In local coordinates, this amounts to the assertion that the two mixed partial derivatives in x and t are equal, i.e., that the second derivative of φ is symmetric bilinear. Hence

$$\begin{aligned}\frac{d}{ds} T_x\varphi_s|_{s=t} &= \frac{d}{ds} T_x\varphi_t \circ T_x\varphi_s|_{s=0} \\ &= T_x\varphi_t \circ \frac{d}{ds} T_x\varphi_s|_{s=0} \\ &= T_x\varphi_t \circ \dot{\xi}(x)\end{aligned}$$

But $T_x\varphi_0 = I$, the identity of T_xX. Hence by 22.1 and the uniqueness part of the Local Existence and Uniqueness Theorem (21.1), $T_x\varphi_t = \exp(t\dot{\xi}(x))$ for $t \in \boldsymbol{R}$. ∎

22.4. COROLLARY. Let x be a critical point of ξ and let $\lambda_1, \ldots, \lambda_n$ be the complex eigenvalues of $\dot{\xi}(x)$. Then for $t \in \boldsymbol{R}$, $\exp(t\lambda_1), \ldots, \exp(t\lambda_n)$ are the eigenvalues of $T_x\varphi_t$.

This is immediate from 22.2 and 22.3. This corollary explains why the eigenvalues of $\dot{\xi}(x)$ are often called the **characteristic exponents** of the critical point x, and the exponentials called the **characteristic multipliers.**

22.5. COROLLARY. Let x be a critical point of the vectorfield ξ and φ be the flow of ξ. Then:

(I) For $t \neq 0$ the following are equivalent:

(1) $\dot{\xi}(x)$ has no complex eigenvalue of the form $2k\pi i/t$ where k is an integer and $i = (-1)^{1/2}$

(2) 1 is not an eigenvalue of $T_x\varphi_t$.

(II) The following are equivalent:

(3) $\dot{\xi}(x)$ has no complex eigenvalue with real part zero;

(4) for all $t \neq 0$, $T_x\varphi_t$ has no complex eigenvalue of modulus 1;

(5) for some $t \neq 0$, $T_x\varphi_t$ has no complex eigenvalue of modulus 1.

This follows immediately from 22.2, 22.4, and the fact that $\exp(\lambda) = 1$ if and only if $\lambda = 2k\pi i$ for some integer k, and the fact that $|\exp(\lambda)| = 1$ if and only if $\mathrm{Re}(\lambda) = 0$.

Let x be a critical point of a C^r vectorfield ξ ($r \geq 1$). We say t is a **transversal period** of the critical point x iff x and t satisfy (1) and (2) in 22.5, and x is an **elementary critical point** iff it satisfies (3), (4), and (5).

The reason for the term "transversal period" will become apparent later. Note that every elementary critical point is transversal for all $t \neq 0$.

The following theorem is a trivial consequence of Taylor's Theorem (1.5). It is explicitly stated here for comparison with an analogous but more difficult theorem for closed orbits (25.1).

22.6. LOCAL REPRESENTATION OF CRITICAL POINTS. Let X be a finite-dimensional C^{r+1} manifold ($r \geq 1$), $\xi \in \Gamma^r(\tau_X)$ a vectorfield on X, and $x_0 \in X$ a critical point of ξ. Then there is a chart (U, α) on X such that,

(I) $x_0 \in U$, $\alpha(x_0) = 0$, and the principal part of ξ, ξ_α: $\alpha(U) \to R^n$, has the form

$$\xi_\alpha(x) = Ax + R(x)$$

for $x \in \alpha(U)$, with $A \in L(R^n, R^n)$, $R(0) = 0$, $DR(0) = 0$;

(II) x_0 is an elementary critical point of ξ if and only if A has no eigenvalue with real part zero.

We end this section with some more easy theorems which are included for future analogies. These comprise the *first applications of transversality to flows.*

Let X be a C^{r+1} manifold ($r \geq 1$), $\xi \in \Gamma^r(\tau_X)$ a vectorfield, and $x \in X$ a critical point of ξ. Then x is a **nondegenerate critical point** iff $\dot{\xi}(x)$: $T_xX \to T_xX$ is surjective, i.e., if $\xi \pitchfork_x (TX)_0$. Since X is finite dimensional, this is equivalent to the requirement that $\dot{\xi}(x)$ be a toplinear isomorphism. We say $\xi \in \Gamma^r(\tau_X)$ is a **0-transversal vectorfield** iff every critical point of ξ is nondegenerate, and let $\mathscr{G}_0^r(X)$ denote the set of all 0-transversal vectorfields $\xi \in \Gamma^r(\tau_X)$, i.e.,

$$\mathscr{G}_0^r(X) = \{\xi \in \Gamma^r(\tau_X) \mid \xi \pitchfork (TX)_0\}$$

where $(TX)_0$ is the image of the zero section in $T(X)$.

Note that every critical point transversal for some $t \neq 0$ is nondegenerate. Hence every elementary critical point is nondegenerate.

If $\xi \in \Gamma^r(\tau_X)$, let $\Gamma_\xi(0)$ denote the set of all critical points of ξ.

22.7. PROPOSITION. Let $\xi \in \mathscr{G}_0^r(X)$. Then $\Gamma_\xi(0)$ consists of isolated points, i.e.,

(I) the critical points of ξ are isolated;

(II) if X is compact also, then $\Gamma_\xi(0)$ is a finite set.

Proof. $\Gamma_\xi(0) = \xi^{-1}((TX)_0)$ is a submanifold of codimension zero by 17.2. ∎

22.8. PROPOSITION. Let X be compact. Then $\mathscr{G}_0^r(X)$ is open in $\Gamma^r(\tau_X)$.

Proof. This is immediate from the Transversality Openness Theorem (18.2). Let $\mathscr{A} = \Gamma^r(\tau_X)$, $W = (TX)_0$, and ρ: $\Gamma^r(\tau_X) \to \mathscr{C}^r(X, T(X))$ be the identity injection. ∎

22.9. PROPOSITION. Let X be compact, and $\xi \in \mathscr{G}_0^r(X)$. Then there is a neighborhood N of ξ in $\mathscr{G}_0^r(X)$ such that for $\zeta \in N$, ξ and ζ have the same (finite) number of critical points.

Proof. As in 22.8, consider the C^r representation

$$\rho: \Gamma^r(\tau_X) \to \mathscr{C}^r(X, T(X))$$

and let $W = (TX)_0 \subset T(X)$ be the image of the zero section. The set of critical points of $\zeta \in \Gamma^r(\tau_X)$ is $\zeta^{-1}((TX)_0)$. By the Transversal Isotopy Theorem, there is a neighborhood N of ξ in $\Gamma^r(\tau_X)$ such that $\xi^{-1}((TX)_0)$ and $\zeta^{-1}((TX)_0)$ are isotopic; hence, since $\xi^{-1}((TX)_0)$ is finite by 18.7, $\zeta^{-1}((TX)_0)$ must also be finite and have the same number of points. By 22.8 we may suppose $N \subset \mathcal{G}_0^r(X)$. ▮

§23. Closed Orbits

The behavior of a flow near a closed orbit is analogous to its behavior near a critical point. In this section we develop a transversal context for closed orbits, comparable to that of the previous section. Again, X will denote a fixed finite-dimensional C^{r+1} manifold with $r \geqslant 1$. For simplicity we shall also assume X is compact; this will ensure that every vectorfield on X has a complete flow.

If $\xi \in \Gamma^r(\tau_X)$ is a vectorfield on X, we shall let $\varphi^\xi: X \times \boldsymbol{R} \to X$ denote its flow. The map $\Gamma^r(\tau_X) \to C^r(X \times \boldsymbol{R}, X)$ given by $\xi \to \varphi^\xi$ is a C^r representation by the Parameterized Flow Theorem (21.4); here the parameter is the vectorfield itself! When no confusion can result, we shall omit the superscript ξ and thus denote the flow of ξ simply by φ. As usual we define for $t \in \boldsymbol{R}$ the map $\varphi_t: X \to X$ by $\varphi_t(x) = \varphi(x, t)$ for $x \in X$, and for $x \in X$ the map $\varphi_x: \boldsymbol{R} \to X$ by $\varphi_x(t) = \varphi(x, t)$ for $t \in \boldsymbol{R}$. Thus φ_x is the integral curve or orbit of ξ at x.

An integral curve φ_x of ξ is called a **closed orbit** of ξ iff φ_x is nonconstant (i.e., x is not a critical point) and for some $\tau \neq 0$, $\varphi_\tau(x) = x$; in this case we say that τ is a **period** of the closed orbit φ_x. The smallest positive period of a closed orbit is called the **prime period** of the closed orbit.

Note that an orbit which is a closed subset is not necessarily a closed orbit. It is well known that a regular orbit is a closed orbit iff it is a compact subset (see Abraham-Marsden [*1;* p. 23]). Here and in the sequel we shall use the term "closed orbit" to refer both to the curve $\varphi_x: \boldsymbol{R} \to X$ and the point set $\varphi_x(\boldsymbol{R})$, the meaning always being clear from the context. If $\gamma = \varphi_x(\boldsymbol{R})$ is a closed orbit of ξ, the prime period depends only on ξ and γ and not on the choice of $x \in \gamma$. This is because of the one-parameter group property, i.e., $\varphi_\tau(x) = \varphi_{-s} \circ \varphi_\tau \circ \varphi_s(x)$, so that if $y = \varphi_s(x) \in \gamma$ is another point of γ, then $\varphi_\tau(x) = x$ if and only if $\varphi_\tau(y) = y$. Also, one sees that the periods of γ are the integral multiples of the prime period.

Note that $T_x\varphi_t \in L(T_xX, T_yX)$ for $x \in X$, $t \in \boldsymbol{R}$, and $y = \varphi(x, t)$, and if x is a critical point of ξ or φ_x is a closed orbit of ξ of period τ, then $T_x\varphi_\tau \in L(T_xX, T_xX)$. We now study these linear automorphisms $T_x\varphi_\tau$.

23.1. PROPOSITION. Let φ be the flow of a vectorfield ξ. Then,

(I) $(T_x\varphi_t)\,\xi(x) = \xi(y)$ **for** $x \in X$, $t \in \boldsymbol{R}$, **and** $y = \varphi_t(x)$;

(II) If φ_x is a closed orbit of period τ, then $\xi(x)$ is a fixed point of the linear automorphism $T_x\varphi_\tau: T_xX \to T_xX$, and $T_x\varphi_\tau$ has 1 as an eigenvalue.

Proof. Conclusion (I) is immediate from the definition of the tangent of a map: φ_x is a curve through x whose tangent vector is $\xi(x)$ and $\varphi_t \circ \varphi_x = \varphi_y$ has tangent vector $\xi(y)$. Then (II) follows immediately from (I). ▮

The remaining $(n-1)$ complex eigenvalues of $T_x\varphi_\tau$, where τ is the *prime* period of the closed orbit φ_x, are called the **characteristic multipliers** of φ_x. These are sometimes defined equivalently by means of the Poincaré map on a local transversal section (see Abraham-Marsden [*1;* §25]). We now express some common restrictions on these eigenvalues in the language of transversality.

Let $\boldsymbol{R}^+ = (0, \infty)$ be the set of positive real numbers (a local manifold) and for $\xi \in \Gamma^r(\tau_X)$ define

$$\Phi_\xi\colon X \times \boldsymbol{R}^+ \to X \times \boldsymbol{R}^+ \times X$$

by

$$\Phi_\xi(x, t) = (x, t, \varphi_t^\xi(x))$$

for $x \in X$, $t \in \boldsymbol{R}^+$, where φ^ξ is the flow of ξ. Define the closed submanifold $\boldsymbol{\Delta}$ of $X \times \boldsymbol{R}^+ \times X$ by

$$\boldsymbol{\Delta} = \{(x, t, x) | x \in X, t \in \boldsymbol{R}^+\}$$

This is illustrated in Figure 23-1, which depicts X as one dimensional; the shaded plane is $\boldsymbol{\Delta}$. For fixed $x \in X$ and varying $t > 0$, $\Phi_\xi(x, t)$ sweeps out a curve in this "three-dimensional" space. If y is a critical point, this curve

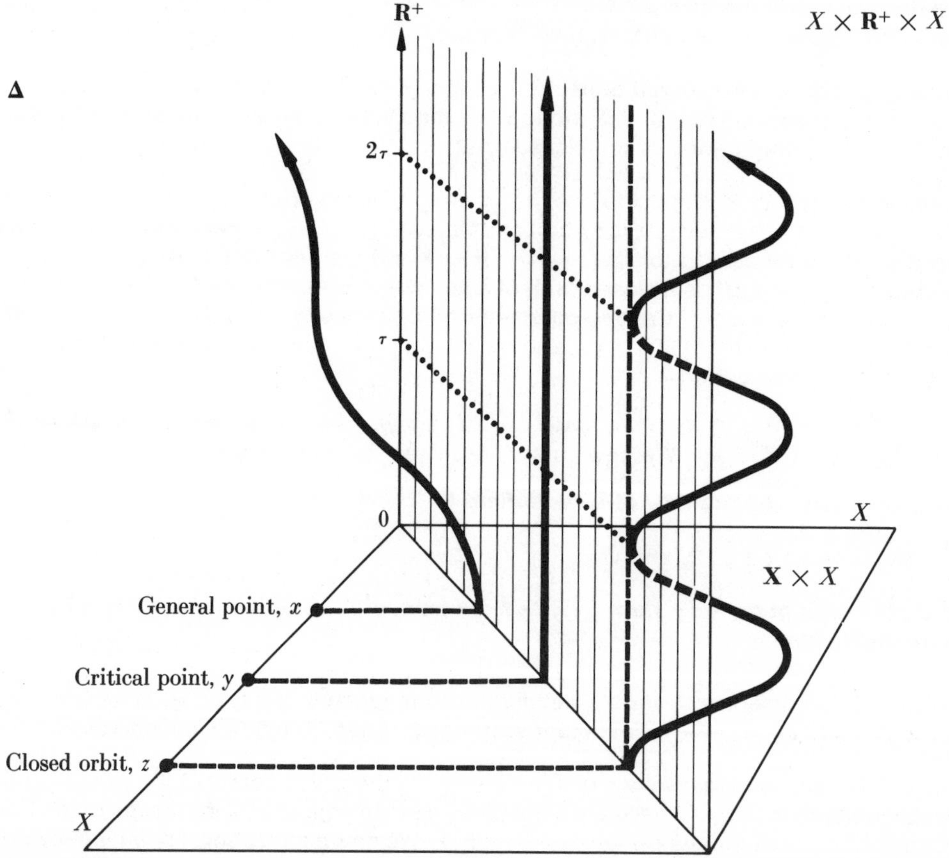

Figure 23–1

is a vertical line in Δ; if z lies on a closed orbit, the curve intersects Δ in equally spaced points all lying on the same vertical line.

In the following proposition, (I) explains why transversal critical points are so called, and (II) gives an analogous property for closed orbits.

23.2. PROPOSITION. (I) Let x be a critical point of the vectorfield $\xi \in \Gamma^r(\tau_X)$ and $\tau > 0$. Then, $\Phi \pitchfork_{(x,\tau)} \Delta$ iff τ is a transversal period for x (i.e., 1 is not an eigenvalue of $T_x\varphi_\tau$);

(II) Let φ_x be a closed orbit of the vectorfield $\xi \in \Gamma^r(\tau_X)$ and $\tau > 0$ a period of φ_x. Then $\Phi \pitchfork_{(x,\tau)} \Delta$ iff $T_x\varphi_\tau \colon T_xX \to T_xX$ has 1 as an eigenvalue with (algebraic) multiplicity 1.

Proof. We remark that the term "multiplicity" always means algebraic multiplicity, i.e., multiplicity as a root of the characteristic equation.

For $(x, \tau) \in X \times \boldsymbol{R}^+$ and $(\dot{x}, \dot{t}) \in T_{(x,\tau)}(X \times \boldsymbol{R}^+) = (T_xX) \times (T_\tau \boldsymbol{R}^+)$, we have

$$T_{(x,\tau)}\Phi(\dot{x}, \dot{t}) = (\dot{x}, \dot{t}, (T_x\varphi_\tau)\dot{x} + \dot{t}\xi(\dot{x}))$$

where we identify $\boldsymbol{R}$ and $T_\tau\boldsymbol{R}^+$. For $(x, \tau) \in X \times \boldsymbol{R}^+$,

$$T_{(x,\tau,x)}\Delta = \{(\dot{x}, \dot{t}, \dot{x}) \mid \dot{x} \in T_xX,\ \dot{t} \in T_\tau\boldsymbol{R}^+\}$$

Fix $x \in X$ and $\tau \in \boldsymbol{R}^+$ such that

$$\Phi(x, \tau) \in \Delta$$

Then the following are equivalent:

(i) $$\Phi \pitchfork_{(x,\tau)} \Delta$$

(ii) $$T_{(x,\tau)}\ \Phi(T_{(x,\tau)}(X \times \boldsymbol{R}^+)) + T_{(x,\tau)}\ \Delta = T_{(x,\tau,x)}\ (X \times \boldsymbol{R}^+ \times X)$$

(iii) For $\dot{y}_1, \dot{y}_2 \in T_xX$ and $\dot{t} \in T_\tau\boldsymbol{R}^+ \approx \boldsymbol{R}$ the equations

$$\dot{y}_1 = \dot{x}_1 + \dot{x}_2$$

$$\dot{t} = \dot{t}_1 + \dot{t}_2$$

$$\dot{y}_2 = T_x\varphi_\tau\ \dot{x}_1 + \dot{t}_1\ \xi(x) + \dot{x}_2$$

possess a solution $(\dot{x}_1, \dot{x}_2 \in T_xX;\ \dot{t}_1, \dot{t}_2 \in T_\tau\boldsymbol{R})$.

(iv) For $\dot{y} \in T_xX$ the equation

$$\dot{y} = T_x\varphi_\tau\dot{x} - \dot{x} + \dot{t}\ \xi(x)$$

possesses a solution $(\dot{x} \in T_xX,\ \dot{t} \in T_\tau\boldsymbol{R}^+ \approx \boldsymbol{R}^+)$.

Indeed (ii) is the definition of (i); (iii) is the definition of (ii), and the equivalence of (iii) to (iv) is easily seen by subtracting the first equation of (iii) from the last equation of (iii) and setting $\dot{y} = \dot{y}_2 - \dot{y}_1$, $\dot{x} = \dot{x}_1$, $\dot{t} = \dot{t}_1$.

Suppose x is a critical point, i.e., $\xi(x) = 0$. Then (iv) reduces to the assertion that the map $T_x\varphi_\tau - I$ (I being the identity of T_xX) is surjective; this is clearly equivalent to the assertion that 1 is not an eigenvalue of $T_x\varphi_\tau$. This establishes (I).

Now suppose φ_x is a closed orbit of period τ. Then $\xi(x) \neq 0$ and $\xi(x)$ is an eigenvector for $T_x\varphi_\tau$ by 23.1. Choose coordinates so that $\xi(x)$ is represented by the column vector

$$\begin{bmatrix} 1 \\ 0 \\ \vdots \\ 0 \end{bmatrix}$$

In such coordinates $T_x\varphi_\tau$ is represented by an $n \times n$ matrix

$$\begin{bmatrix} 1 & * \\ 0 & A \end{bmatrix}$$

where A is an $(n-1) \times (n-1)$ matrix. Then (iv) is equivalent to the assertion that for all values $y_1, \ldots, y_n$, the simultaneous linear equations

$$\begin{bmatrix} y_1 \\ \vdots \\ y_n \end{bmatrix} = \begin{bmatrix} 1 & * \\ 0 & A \end{bmatrix} \begin{bmatrix} x_1 \\ \vdots \\ x_n \end{bmatrix} + \begin{bmatrix} x_1 \\ \vdots \\ x_n \end{bmatrix} + \begin{bmatrix} t \\ 0 \\ \vdots \\ 0 \end{bmatrix}$$

possess a solution in $x_1, \ldots, x_n$ and t. This happens if and only if the matrix $A - I_{n-1}$ (I_{n-1} being the identity $(n-1) \times (n-1)$ matrix) is nonsingular, i.e., iff 1 is not an eigenvalue of A. This establishes (II). ∎

Propositions 22.5 and 23.2 suggest the following definition. Let φ_x be a closed orbit of a vectorfield $\xi \in \Gamma^r(\tau_X)$ and $\tau \neq 0$ a period of φ_x. Let $1, \lambda_2, \ldots, \lambda_n$ be the complex eigenvalues of $T_x\varphi_\tau$ (each counted a number of times equal to its multiplicity). Then τ is called a **transversal period** of φ_x iff $\lambda_j \neq 1$ for $j = 2, \ldots, n$, and τ is an **elementary period** of φ_x iff $|\lambda_j| \neq 1$ for $j = 2, \ldots, n$.

The above definition is independent of the choice of the point $x \in \varphi_x$, for if y is another point on the curve φ_x, say $y = \varphi_s(x)$ for some $s \in \boldsymbol{R}$, then $T_y\varphi_\tau = (T_x\varphi_s) \circ (T_x\varphi_\tau) \circ (T_x\varphi_s)^{-1}$, so that $T_y\varphi_\tau$ and $T_x\varphi_\tau$ have the same eigenvalues.

Note that an elementary period is transversal, and a closed orbit may have transversal and nontransversal periods, but not in the elementary case.

23.3. PROPOSITION. If φ_x is a closed orbit with an elementary period, then every nonzero period of φ_x is elementary and thus transversal.

Proof. Let τ_0 be the *prime* period of φ_x; then the periods of φ_x are the integral multiples of τ_0. Hence it suffices to show that for $k = \pm 1, \pm 2, \pm 3, \ldots$, τ is an elementary period if and only if $k\tau$ is an elementary period. But $T_x\varphi_{k\tau} = (T_x\varphi_\tau)^k$. Let $\lambda_1, \ldots, \lambda_n$ be the complex eigenvalues of $T_x\varphi_\tau$, each counted according to its multiplicity. By 23.2, $\lambda_1^k, \ldots, \lambda_n^k$ are the eigenvalues of $(T_x\varphi_\tau)^k = T_x\varphi_{k\tau}$. But $|\lambda| = 1$ if and only if $|\lambda^k| = |\lambda|^k = 1$. ∎

This proposition justifies the following definition. Let φ_x be a closed orbit of ξ. Then φ_x is an **elementary closed orbit** iff some (and hence every) nonzero period of φ_x is elementary.

§24. Flows Transversal to the Diagonal

In this section we put together the geometric characterizations of the last two sections and obtain an important result, the *Period Bounding Lemma.* This result, giving sufficient conditions that the set of prime periods of all closed orbits of a vectorfield be bounded above zero, is an extension of a lemma discovered by Peixoto [2] which shortens the proof of the G2-Density Theorem (§31) considerably. As before, X is a fixed finite-dimensional C^{r+1} manifold with $r \geq 1$.

Let $\xi \in \Gamma^r(\boldsymbol{\tau}_X)$ be a vectorfield on X. A **critical element** of ξ is either a critical point of ξ or a closed orbit of ξ. A **critical element of prime period 0** is simply a critical point. The set of all critical elements of ξ is denoted by Γ_ξ.

Abuse of language is very useful in talking about critical elements. For example, let γ be a critical element of ξ and $x \in X$. We write $x \in \gamma$ to mean $x = \gamma$ (in case γ is a critical point) or $\varphi_x = \gamma$ (in case γ is a closed orbit; φ is the flow of ξ). If $\gamma = \varphi_x$ is a closed orbit, we shall often use γ to denote the image of φ_x in X, and consider $\Gamma_\xi \subset X$.

Recall for $\xi \in \Gamma^r(\boldsymbol{\tau}_X)$ the map

$$\boldsymbol{\Phi}_\xi \colon X \times \boldsymbol{R}^+ \to X \times \boldsymbol{R}^+ \times X$$

defined in §23 **(**$\boldsymbol{R}^+ = (0, \infty)$ is the set of positive real numbers**)**, and the closed submanifold $\boldsymbol{\Delta} \subset X \times \boldsymbol{R}^+ \times X$ defined by

$$\boldsymbol{\Delta} = \{(x, t, x) | x \in X, t \in \boldsymbol{R}^+\}$$

For $0 < a \leq \infty$, we say $\xi \in \Gamma^r(\boldsymbol{\tau}_X)$ has an **a-transversal flow** iff $\boldsymbol{\Phi}_\xi \,\overline{\pitchfork}_{(x,t)}\, \boldsymbol{\Delta}$ for all $x \in X$ and $0 < t \leq a$, and let

$$\mathscr{G}^r_\Delta(a, X) = \mathscr{G}^r_\Delta(a)$$

denote the set of all vectorfields $\xi \in \Gamma^r(\boldsymbol{\tau}_X)$ with a-transversal flows. (See §23 for the case $a = 0$.)

Thus $\xi \in \mathscr{G}^r_\Delta(a)$ iff every critical element has nothing but transversal periods τ for $\tau \leq a$.

We now study the set Γ_ξ of critical elements, especially in the case $\xi \in \mathscr{G}^r_\Delta(a)$. Let $\Gamma_\xi(a) \subset \Gamma_\xi$ denote the set of critical elements of the vectorfield ξ having prime period $\tau \leq a$. Again, we often use $\Gamma_\xi(a)$ to denote the union of the underlying sets of its elements, and write $\Gamma_\xi(a) \subset X$.

24.1. PROPOSITION. If $\xi \in \Gamma^r(\boldsymbol{\tau}_X)$, and $0 \leq a < \infty$, then $\Gamma_\xi(a) \subset X$ is closed.

Proof. Let x_i be a sequence of points in $\Gamma_\xi(a)$ converging to a point x. It is sufficient to show that x is in $\Gamma_\xi(a)$. For each i choose $t_i \in \boldsymbol{R}$ with $a/2 \leq t_i \leq a$ and $\varphi(x_i, t_i) = x_i$. Extracting a convergent subsequence and reindexing if necessary, we know that t_i converges to a real number t with $a/2 \leq t \leq a$. By continuity of φ, $\varphi(x, t) = x$, i.e., x is either a critical point or lies on a closed orbit. ∎

The sets $\mathscr{G}^r_0(X)$ and $\mathscr{G}^r_\Delta(a)$ are comparable, and the following is analogous to 22.7.

24.2. $\Gamma(a)$ FINITENESS THEOREM. If $0 < a < \infty$ and $\xi \in \mathscr{G}^r_\Delta(a)$, then,

(I) the critical elements of $\Gamma_\xi(a)$ are isolated

(II) if X is compact, then $\Gamma_\xi(a)$ is a finite set, and

(III) there is an $\epsilon > 0$ such that ξ has no closed orbit of period τ, with $a < \tau < a + \epsilon$.

Proof. Suppose $a \in \boldsymbol{R}^+$ and $\xi \in \mathscr{G}_\Delta^r(a)$. Then $\gamma \in \Gamma_\xi(a)$ is isolated (as a subset of X) iff it has an open neighborhood U in X intersecting no other critical element $\gamma' \in \Gamma_\xi(a)$. Suppose this is not so. Then there is a sequence $\gamma, \gamma_1, \gamma_2, \gamma_3, \ldots$ of distinct elements of $\Gamma_\xi(a)$, and a sequence of points $x, x_1, x_2, x_3, \ldots$ such that $x \in \gamma$, $x_i \in \gamma_i$ $(i = 1, 2, 3, \ldots)$, and x_i converges to x. Choose a period τ_i of γ_i with $a/2 \leqslant \tau_i \leqslant a$; thus $\varphi(x_i, \tau_i) = x_i$. Choosing a subsequence if necessary, we may suppose that τ_i converges to a real number τ with $a/2 \leqslant \tau \leqslant a$. By the continuity of φ, $\varphi(x, \tau) = x$. Hence $\boldsymbol{\Phi}_\xi(x, \tau) \in \boldsymbol{\Delta}$. Since $\xi \in \mathscr{G}_\Delta^r(a)$, $\boldsymbol{\Phi}_\xi \,\overline{\pitchfork}_{(x,\tau)}\, \boldsymbol{\Delta}$. By the local representation of transversality 17.1 (see also 17.2) we may find a neighborhood V of (x, τ) in $X \times \boldsymbol{R}$ which intersects $\boldsymbol{\Phi}_\xi^{-1}(\boldsymbol{\Delta})$ in a one-dimensional submanifold S. For if X has dimension n, then $\boldsymbol{\Delta}$ has codimension n in $X \times \boldsymbol{R}^+ \times X$; $X \times \boldsymbol{R}$ has dimension $n + 1$, and codimension is preserved. With a sufficiently small open interval $I \subset \boldsymbol{R}$ about 0, the set M defined by

$$M = \{(x, \tau + s) : s \in I\} \qquad \text{if } x = \gamma \text{ is a critical point,}$$

or

$$M = \{(\varphi_s(x), \tau) : s \in I\} \qquad \text{if } \varphi_x = \gamma \text{ is a closed orbit}$$

is a connected one-dimensional submanifold of $S = V \cap \boldsymbol{\Phi}^{-1}(\boldsymbol{\Delta})$ containing the point (x, τ). Thus M must be a "subinterval" of S, and making V smaller if necessary, $M = V \cap S = V \cap \boldsymbol{\Phi}_\xi^{-1}(\boldsymbol{\Delta})$. For i sufficiently large, $(x_i, \tau_i) \in V \cap \boldsymbol{\Phi}_\xi^{-1}(\boldsymbol{\Delta})$, hence $(x_i, \tau_i) \in M$, $x_i = \varphi_s(x)$ for some $s \in I$, and $x_i \in \gamma$. This contradicts the assumption that $\gamma, \gamma_1, \gamma_2, \ldots$ are distinct, proving (I). Now (II) follows immediately from (I), and (III) is proved by following the argument above for (I), with minor modifications (left to the reader). ∎

The following is analogous to 22.8.

24.3. OPENNESS OF TRANSVERSAL FLOWS. If X is a compact C^{r+1} manifold $(r \geqslant 1)$ and $a \in R^+$, then $\mathscr{G}_\Delta^r(a)$ is an open subset of $\Gamma^r(\boldsymbol{\tau}_X)$.

Proof. By the Parameterized Flow Theorem (21.4) and 12.3, the map

$$\varphi : \Gamma^r(\boldsymbol{\tau}_X) \to \mathscr{C}^r(X \times \boldsymbol{R}, X)$$

given by

$$\varphi(\xi) = \varphi^\xi$$

for $\xi \in \Gamma^r(\boldsymbol{\tau}_X)$ is a C^r representation of mappings, i.e., the evaluation map is class C^r. Here the parameter is the vectorfield itself. From this it follows immediately that the map

$$\boldsymbol{\Phi} : \Gamma^r(\boldsymbol{\tau}_X) \to \mathscr{C}^r(X \times \boldsymbol{R}^+, X \times \boldsymbol{R}^+ \times X)$$

given by

$$\boldsymbol{\Phi}(\xi) = \boldsymbol{\Phi}_\xi$$

for $\xi \in \Gamma^r(\boldsymbol{\tau}_X)$, is a C^r representation of mappings.

Let $K = X \times [a/2, a]$. Then $\xi \in \mathscr{G}^r_{\Delta}(a)$ iff $\Phi_\xi \,\overline{\pitchfork}_{(x,t)}\, \Delta$ for $(x, t) \in K$. Indeed, if φ^ξ_x is a closed orbit with prime period $\tau < a/2$, then for a suitable integer k, $a/2 \leqslant k\tau \leqslant a$. But $T_x\varphi^\xi_{k\tau} = (T_x\varphi^\xi_\tau)^k$, and if $(T_x\varphi^\xi_\tau)^k$ has 1 as an eigenvalue of multiplicity 1, so has $T_x\varphi^\xi_\tau$ (see 22.2). As $\Delta \subset X \times \boldsymbol{R} \times X$ is closed and K is compact, the conclusion follows from the Transversal Openness Theorem (18.2). ∎

The following is analogous to 22.9.

24.4. $\Gamma(a)$ **STABILITY THEOREM. Suppose X is a compact C^{r+2} manifold ($r \geqslant 1$), $a \in \boldsymbol{R}^+$, and $\xi \in \mathscr{G}^r_{\Delta}(a)$. Let $\gamma_1, \ldots, \gamma_m$ be the elements of the critical set $\Gamma_\xi(a)$, with, say, γ_i a closed orbit of prime period τ_i ($i = 1, \ldots, l$), and $\gamma_{l+1}, \ldots, \gamma_m$ critical points. Suppose $U_i \subset X$ is an open neighborhood of $\gamma_i \subset X$ ($i = 1, \ldots, m$) such that the sets U_i are disjoint, and $\delta > 0$. Then there exists an open neighborhood N of $\xi \in \mathscr{G}^r_{\Delta}(a)$ and an $\epsilon > 0$, such that:**

(I) ξ **has no closed orbit of period τ with $a < \tau \leqslant a + 2\epsilon$;**

(II) For $\zeta \in N$ the critical set $\Gamma_\zeta(a+\epsilon)$ has exactly one element contained in each U_i, $i = 1, \ldots, m$;

(III) If γ_i' is the element of $\Gamma_\zeta(a+\epsilon)$ on U_i, $\zeta \in N$, $i = 1, \ldots, l$, then γ_i' is a closed orbit of ζ, and the prime period τ_i' of γ_i' satisfies $|\tau_i - \tau_i'| < \delta$, where τ_i is the prime period of γ_i;

(IV) If γ_i' is the element of $\Gamma_\zeta(a+\epsilon)$ in U_i, $i = l+1, \ldots, m$, then γ_i' is a critical point of ζ;

(V) The sets $\Gamma_\zeta(a+\epsilon)$, $\Gamma_\xi(a+\epsilon)$, and $\Gamma_\xi(a)$ have the same (finite) number of elements.

Proof. Although the Transversal Isotopy Theorem (20.2) does not apply directly in this situation (largely because $X \times \boldsymbol{R}^+$ is not compact) its proof can be modified so as to give a proof of 24.4. We sketch the argument and leave the details to the reader.

First note that the number of closed orbits of ξ of period $\leqslant a$ is finite by the Finiteness Theorem (24.2). By 24.2(III) we may choose $\epsilon > 0$ satisfying (I) above. Note that any N satisfying (I) can be made smaller if necessary so that $N \subset \mathscr{G}^r_{\Delta}(a)$; this is because $\mathscr{G}^r_{\Delta}(a)$ is open (24.3).

For simplicity we suppose that ξ has exactly one critical point x_0 and exactly one closed orbit γ of prime period $\tau_0 \leqslant a$. The general case offers no difficulties. Let k be the positive integer such that $k\tau_0 \leqslant a$ but $(k+1)\tau_0 > a$. Let

$$\tilde{\Phi}\colon \Gamma^r(\boldsymbol{\tau}_X) \to \mathscr{C}^r(X \times (0, a+2\epsilon), X \times (0, a+2\epsilon) \times X)$$

be the C^r representation given by

$$\tilde{\Phi}(\zeta) = \Phi_\zeta \mid X \times (0, a+2\epsilon)$$

for $\zeta \in \Gamma^r(\boldsymbol{\tau}_X)$. We also write $\tilde{\Phi}_\zeta$ instead of $\tilde{\Phi}(\zeta)$. We define

$$W = \Delta \cap (X \times (0, a+2\epsilon) \times X)$$

and for $\zeta \in \Gamma^r(\boldsymbol{\tau}_X)$, let

$$W_\zeta = \tilde{\Phi}_\zeta^{-1}(W)$$

The connected components of W_ξ are $C_0, C_1, \ldots, C_k$ where

$$C_0 = \{x_0\} \times (0, a+2\epsilon)$$

and for $j = 1, \ldots, k$

$$C_j = \gamma \times \{j\tau_0\}$$

Take nonintersecting open neighborhoods U_0 of x_0 and U of γ in X. Choose nonoverlapping open intervals $I_1, \ldots, I_k \subset R$ such that,

(i) $j\tau_0 \in I_j$ for $j = 1, \ldots, k$;

(ii) The right end point of I_k is $< a + \epsilon$;

(iii) The left end point of I_1 is $2b$, where $b > 0$, but b is so small that for $t \leqslant b$ there are at least $k+2$ integral multiples of t between b and $a + \epsilon$;

(iv) For $t \in I_1$, $kt < a + \epsilon$;

(v) The length of I_1 is $< \delta$.

Finally take C^r tubular neighborhoods (as in §20) π_i: $E_i \to C_i$ ($i = 0, 1, \ldots, k$) such that

$$E_0 \subset U_0 \times (0, a + 2\epsilon)$$

$$\pi_0^{-1}(x_0, t) \subset U_0 \times \{t\}$$

and

$$E_i \subset U \times I_i \qquad \text{for } i = 1, \ldots, k$$

The case $k = 3$ is illustrated in Figure 24–1. Here we have pictured X as two dimensional. We see that C_0 is a "vertical line" and $C_1, \ldots, C_k$ are simple closed curves stacked "on top of one another." The tubular neighborhood E_0 is a cylinder having C_0 as its axis; the tubular neighborhood $E_i (i = 1, \ldots, k)$ is a solid torus about the circle C_i. Note that the height of each circle is the associated period τ of γ.

Just as in the Transversal Isotopy Theorem (20.2), we define for each $(x, t) \in X \times (0, a+2\epsilon)$ an open neighborhood $Z_{(x,t)}$ of (x, t) in $X \times (0, a+2\epsilon)$ and an open neighborhood $N_{(x,t)}$ of ξ in $\Gamma^r(\tau_X)$, such that,

(j) If $(x, t) \notin W_\zeta$, then $Z_{(x,t)} \cap W_\zeta = \varnothing$ for $\zeta \in N_{(x,t)}$;

(jj) If $(x, t) \in C_i$ for some $i = 0, 1, 2, \ldots, k$, then for $\zeta \in N_{(x,t)}$, $Z_{(x,t)} \cap W_\zeta = h_{\zeta i}(Z_{(x,t)} \cap C_i)$ where $h_{\zeta i}$: $C_i \to E_i$ is a C^r section of π_i.

Now cover $X \times [b, a + \epsilon]$ by finitely many sets $Z_{(x,t)}$, say

$$X \times [b, a + \epsilon] \subset Z_{(x_1,t_1)} \cup \cdots \cup Z_{(x_m,t_m)}$$

and define N by

$$N = N_{(x_1,t_1)} \cap \cdots \cap N_{(x_m,t_m)}$$

Now choose $\zeta \in N$. Then

$$W_\zeta \cap X \times [b, a + \epsilon] = C_{\zeta 0} \cup C_{\zeta 1} \cup \ldots \cup C_{\zeta k}$$

where

$$C_{\zeta 0} = h_{\zeta 0}(\{x_0\} \times [b, a+\epsilon\,])$$

and

$$C_{\zeta i} = h_{\zeta i}(C_i) \qquad (i = 1, \ldots, k)$$

Since a section is a homeomorphism onto its image, $C_{\zeta 0}$ is a simple arc (with end points) and $C_{\zeta 1}, \ldots, C_{\zeta k}$ are simple closed curves.

Corresponding to each cirtical point of ζ is a component of $\mathbf{W}_\zeta$ which intersects $X \times [b, a+\epsilon]$ in a vertical line (with end points). Hence ζ has exactly one critical point. By (iii) above, if ζ had a closed orbit of period $\tau' \leqslant b$, then $W_\zeta \cap [b, a+\epsilon]$ would have $k+2$ components; hence ζ has no such closed orbit. Finally the component $C_{\zeta 1}$ of W_ζ corresponds to a closed orbit of period τ'_0 where $\tau'_0 \in I_1$. Hence by (iv) above this curve must determine k components of $W_\zeta \cap X \times [b, a+\epsilon]$. It follows that ζ has exactly one closed orbit of period $\tau'_0 < a+\epsilon$. (v) implies (iii). ▮

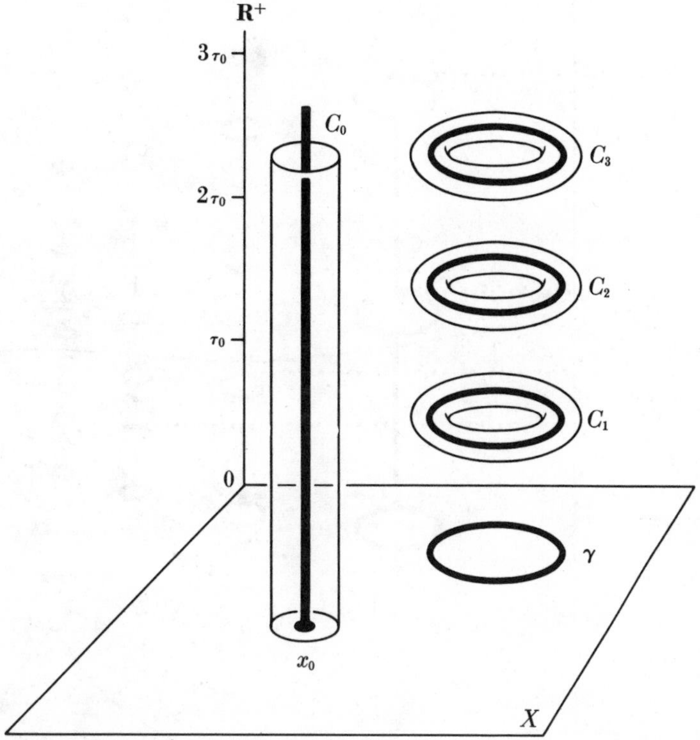

Figure 24–1

From the Finiteness Theorem (24.2) it follows that for compact X and $\xi \in \mathscr{G}^r_\Delta(a, X)$ (for any $a > 0$) there is a positive lower bound for the set of all periods of closed orbits of ξ. From the proof above, we see that this is extended as follows.

24.5. COROLLARY. Let X, a, and ξ be as in 24.3. Then there is an open neighborhood N of ξ in $\mathscr{G}^r_\Delta(a)$ and a real number $b > 0$ such that for $\zeta \in N$, every closed orbit of ζ has prime period $\geqslant b$.

This bounding of periods holds with weaker hypotheses as well.

24.6. PERIOD BOUNDING LEMMA. Let X be a compact C^{r+2} manifold ($r \geqslant 1$) and ξ a 0-transversal vectorfield, i.e., $\xi \in \mathscr{G}^r_0(X)$. Then there is an open neighborhood N of ξ in $\Gamma^r(\tau_X)$, and a real number $b > 0$, such that, for $\zeta \in N$, every closed orbit of ζ has prime period $\geqslant b$.

Proof. In view of 24.5 it suffices to find a real number $a > 0$ such that $\xi \in \mathscr{G}^r_\Delta(a)$. Hence, by 22.5 and 22.7 every critical point of ξ is transversal at time t if t is sufficiently small. Hence, it suffices to show that there is a real number $a > 0$ such that every closed orbit of ξ has prime period $\geqslant a$. Suppose on the contrary that no such real number $a > 0$ exists. Then there is a sequence γ_i of closed orbits where γ_i has period τ_i and $\tau_i \to 0$ as $i \to \infty$. For

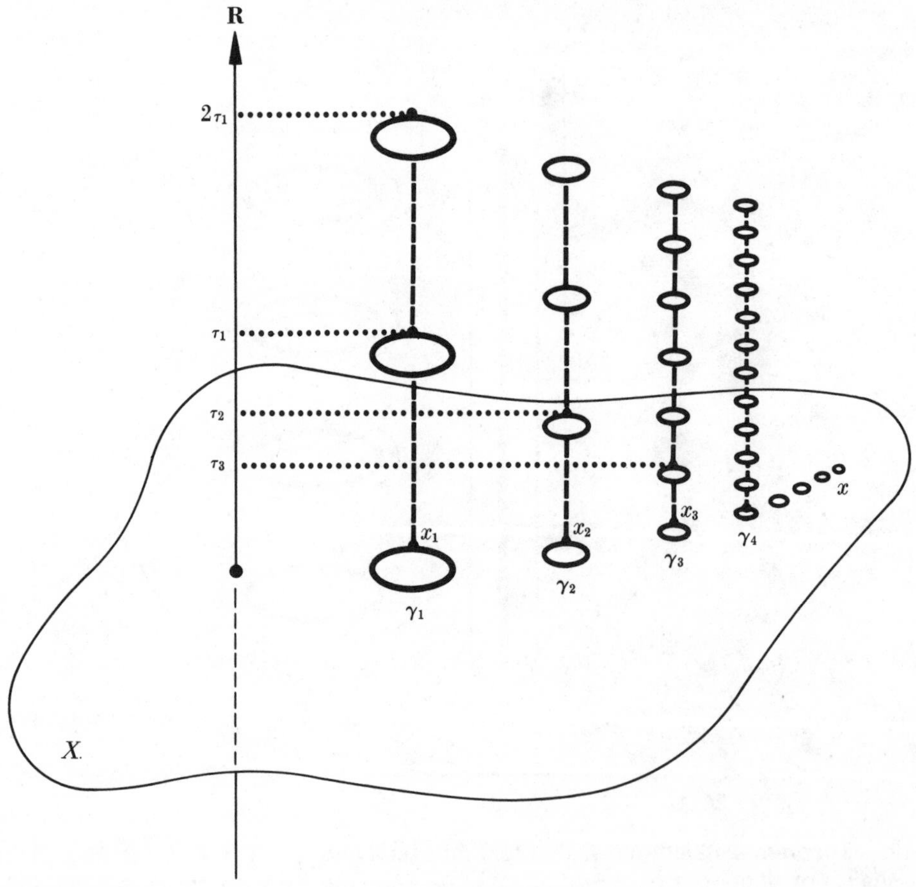

Figure 24–2

each $i = 1, 2, \ldots$ choose a point $x_i \in \gamma_i$. By the compactness of X we may suppose that the sequence x_i converges to a point $x \in X$. (See Figure 24–2.) By the argument used in 24.1, x is either a critical point or else lies on a closed orbit. Suppose the former. By 23.1, $T_{x_i}\varphi_{\tau_i}$ has 1 as an eigenvalue; hence by continuity of the flow $T\varphi$ (again using the trick of 24.1) $T_x\varphi_t$ has 1 as an eigenvalue for some small $t > 0$. But by 22.5 this contradicts the fact that t is a transversal period of the critical point x. Hence we need only show that x is a critical point.

Suppose x is not a critical point. Then by the Straightening Out Theorem (15.6) x has a neighborhood U such that no closed orbit of ξ is entirely contained in U. But by the Mean Value Theorem (and the fact that $t_i \to 0$) we have $\gamma_i \subset U$ for sufficiently large i. This contradiction completes the proof. ∎

6

STABLE MANIFOLDS

Among the most important special features of the orbit configuration of a vectorfield are the *stable, center,* and *unstable manifolds* of the critical elements. For an elementary critical element only the stable and unstable manifolds occur. If only elementary critical elements are present, the positions of all of the stable and unstable manifolds give important insight into the qualitative behavior of the entire dynamical system. This chapter, together with Appendix C by A. Kelley, establishes the existence and basic properties of these features.

In §22 a normal form for the local representative of a vectorfield in a neighborhood of an elementary critical point is given (22.6). The first two sections of this chapter are devoted to obtaining a similar normal form in a neighborhood of an elementary closed orbit. With these normal forms, the existence of a portion of the stable and unstable manifolds near the critical element is proved in Appendix C, both cases being treated simultaneously. In the remaining two sections of this chapter these local manifolds are extended to the full stable and unstable manifolds following Smale [*1*], and are parameterized in a manner which will be useful in the last chapter.

§25. Pseudocharts for Closed Orbits

Two difficulties encountered in the derivation of the normal form at a closed orbit are avoided by constructing a chart on the universal covering of a tubular neighborhood of the closed orbit, which we call a *pseudochart.* In this section we obtain a well-adapted pseudochart that puts the local representative almost in normal form. Throughout, X will denote an $n+1$ dimensional C^{r+2} manifold with $r \geqslant 1$, $\xi \in \Gamma^r(\boldsymbol{\tau}_X)$ a vectorfield on X, φ its flow, γ a closed orbit of ξ of prime period τ, and S^1 will denote the one-sphere; i.e.,

$$S^1 = \{(x, y) \in \boldsymbol{R}^2 \mid x^2 + y^2 = 1\}$$

Frequently we shall identify a half-open interval $[0, a)$ with S^1 via the bijection $[0, a) \to S^1$ given by

$$\theta \leadsto \left(\cos \frac{2\pi\theta}{a}, \sin \frac{2\pi\theta}{a}\right)$$

for $0 \leqslant \theta < a$. Thus, for example, a function periodic in a real variable θ will be thought of as being defined on S^1.

The tangent bundle of S^1 is trivial, i.e.,

$$T(S^1) = S^1 \times \mathbf{R}$$

Hence

$$\begin{aligned} T(S^1 \times \mathbf{R}^n) &= T(S^1) \times T(\mathbf{R}^n) \\ &= S^1 \times \mathbf{R}^n \times \mathbf{R}^1 \times \mathbf{R}^n \\ &= S^1 \times \mathbf{R}^n \times \mathbf{R}^{n+1} \end{aligned}$$

Now if U is an open neighborhood of γ in X and $\alpha\colon U \to S^1 \times \mathbf{R}^n$ is a diffeomorphism, then $(T\alpha)^{-1} \circ \xi \circ \alpha$ is a vectorfield on $S^1 \times \mathbf{R}^n$ and (since $T(S^1 \times \mathbf{R}^n) = S^1 \times \mathbf{R}^n \times \mathbf{R}^{n+1}$ is trivial) it has the form

$$(T\alpha)^{-1} \circ \xi \circ \alpha(y) = (y, \xi_\alpha(y))$$

for $y \in S^1 \times \mathbf{R}^n$. Note that (U, α) differs from a manifold chart only in that $\alpha(U) = S^1 \times \mathbf{R}^n$ rather than an open subset of a Banach space.

Also we shall say that γ is **twisted** (resp. **untwisted**) iff for $x \in \gamma$ the tangent of the flow

$$T_x\varphi_\tau\colon T_xX \to T_xX$$

is orientation reversing (resp. orientation preserving). Recall (§3) that a top-linear isomorphism is orientation preserving if its determinant is positive. One easily sees that the definition is independent of the choice of $x \in \gamma$, for if $y = \varphi_t(x)$ is another point on γ, then

$$T_x\varphi_\tau = (T_x\varphi_t)^{-1} \circ T_y\varphi_\tau \circ T_x\varphi_t$$

25.1. PROPOSITION. If X is orientable, γ is untwisted.

Proof. The diffeomorphism $\varphi_\tau\colon X \to X$ is isotopic to the identity. Hence by 4.1, φ_τ is orientation preserving. ∎

Our next proposition is the first step toward a normal form for closed orbits.

25.2. PROPOSITION. Let X, ξ, γ be as above, and suppose γ is untwisted. Then there is an open neighborhood U of γ and a C^r diffeomorphism $\alpha\colon U \to S^1 \times \mathbf{R}^n$ such that $\alpha(\gamma) = S^1 \times \{0\}$ and $\xi_\alpha(\theta, 0) = (1, 0)$ for $\theta \in S^1$.

The proof uses the following definitions and two lemmas.

For $x \in X$ let $\langle \xi(x) \rangle$ denote the one-dimensional subspace of T_xX spanned by $\xi(x)$, i.e.,

$$\langle \xi(x) \rangle = \{a\xi(x) \mid a \in \mathbf{R}\}$$

As γ is a simple closed curve, and hence a one-dimensional submanifold of X, we may form its tangent bundle

$T\gamma$ and identify it with a sub-bundle of $TX \mid \gamma$; in fact $T_x\gamma = \langle \xi(x) \rangle$ for $x \in \gamma$, so

$$T\gamma = \bigcup_{x \in \gamma} \langle \xi(x) \rangle$$

For $x \in \gamma$ let

$$N_x\gamma = \frac{T_xX}{T_x\gamma} = \frac{T_xX}{\langle \xi(x) \rangle}$$

be the quotient space of T_xX by $T_x\gamma$, and define

$$N\gamma = \bigcup_{x \in \gamma} N_x\gamma$$

Then the map $N\gamma \to \gamma$ given by $\dot{x} \rightsquigarrow x$ for $\dot{x} \in N_x\gamma$ may be given the structure of a C^r vector bundle as in Lang [*1;* p. 45]. It is called the **normal bundle** of γ.

Now for $x \in \gamma$ and $t \in \mathbf{R}$, the linear map

$$T_x\varphi_t \colon T_xX \to T_yX$$

where $y = \varphi_t(x)$ satisfies

$$T_x\varphi_t\xi(x) = \xi(y)$$

by 23.1. Hence we may define the quotient map

$$N_x\varphi_t \colon N_x\gamma \to N_y\gamma$$

i.e., $N_x\varphi_t$ is the unique linear map which makes the diagram

$$\begin{array}{ccc} T_xX & \xrightarrow{\quad T_x\varphi_t \quad} & T_yX \\ \downarrow & & \downarrow \\ N_x\gamma & \xrightarrow{\quad N_x\varphi_t \quad} & N_y\gamma \end{array}$$

commute. Here the maps on the sides are the natural projections into the quotient spaces.

Recall that τ is the prime period of γ. Fix $x \in \gamma$, then as γ is untwisted, $T_x\varphi_\tau \colon T_xX \to T_xX$ is orientation preserving; hence, since $T_x\varphi_\tau\xi(x) = \xi(x)$, $N_x\varphi_\tau \colon N_x\gamma \to N_x\gamma$ is orientation preserving. We use this fact to prove that the normal bundle is trivial when γ is untwisted.

25.3. LEMMA. Let E be a finite-dimensional Banach space and $P \subset L(E, E)$ the set of orientation preserving toplinear automorphisms of E. Then P is open and (C^∞) pathwise connected.

Proof. Obviously P is open because

$$P = \{A \mid \det(A) > 0\}$$

To show P is pathwise connected, choose $A \in P$ and take a basis for $\mathbf{E}$ so that the matrix $\tilde{A}$ representing A is in real canonical form (see Coddington and Levinson [*1;* p. 340]). Then construct a path $\tilde{B}_t$ for $t \in \mathbf{R}$ connecting

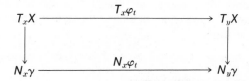

$\tilde{A}$ with the identity. For example, if $\tilde{A}$ is

$$\begin{pmatrix} -1 & 0 \\ 0 & -1 \end{pmatrix}$$

let

$$\tilde{B}_t = \begin{pmatrix} \cos \frac{\pi t}{\tau} & \sin \frac{\pi t}{\tau} \\ \sin \frac{\pi t}{\tau} & \cos \frac{\pi t}{\tau} \end{pmatrix}$$

for $t \in [0, \tau]$. Then $\tilde{B}_0$ is the identity, $\tilde{B}_\tau = \tilde{A}$ and $\det(\tilde{B}_t) > 0$ for all $t \in [0, \tau]$. ∎

25.4. LEMMA. If γ is untwisted, the normal bundle $N\gamma \to \gamma$ is trivial, i.e., there is a C^r vector bundle isomorphism between the vector bundle $N\gamma \to \gamma$ and the trivial vector bundle $S^1 \times R^n \to S^1$.

Proof. Recall that τ is the prime period of γ and fix a point $x \in \gamma$. By 25.3 we may construct a C^∞ curve A: $\mathbf{R} \to L(N_x\gamma, N_x\gamma)$ given by $t \rightsquigarrow A_t$ for $t \in \mathbf{R}$ such that,

(1) A_0 is the identity map of $N_x\gamma$;

(2) $A_\tau = (N_x\varphi_\tau)^{-1} = N_x\varphi_{-\tau}$;

(3) A_t: $N_x\gamma \to N_x\gamma$ is a toplinear automorphism for all $t \in \mathbf{R}$.

Define, for $0 \leqslant t \leqslant \tau$ and $y = \varphi_t(x)$,

$$B_t\colon N_x\gamma \to N_y\gamma$$

by

$$B_t = N_x\varphi_t \circ A_t$$

Then $B_0 = B_\tau =$ identity. We identify $[0, \tau)$ with S^1 via the map

$$\theta \rightsquigarrow \left(\cos \frac{2\pi\theta}{\tau}, \sin \frac{2\pi\theta}{\tau}\right)$$

for $0 \leqslant \theta < \tau$. We will write $[0, \tau) \equiv S^1$ to remind the reader of this identification. Then the map

$$g\colon S^1 \times N_x\gamma \to N\gamma$$

given by

$$(\theta, \dot{x}) \rightsquigarrow B_\theta \dot{x}$$

for $\theta \in S^1 \equiv [0, \tau)$ and $\dot{x} \in N_x\gamma$ is continuous and class C^{r-1} for $\theta \neq 0$. By the Weiestrass Approximation Theorem, we may change B_t slightly so that g is C^r. It follows that the bundle $N\gamma \to \gamma$ is trivial. ∎

Proof of 25.2. Let f: $N\gamma \to X$ be a C^r tubular neighborhood of γ (see §20 and Lang [*1*; p. 73]). Take $U = f(N\gamma) \subset X$. Then f: $N\gamma \to U$ is a C^{r-1} diffeomorphism, U is an open neighborhood of γ in X, and the diagram

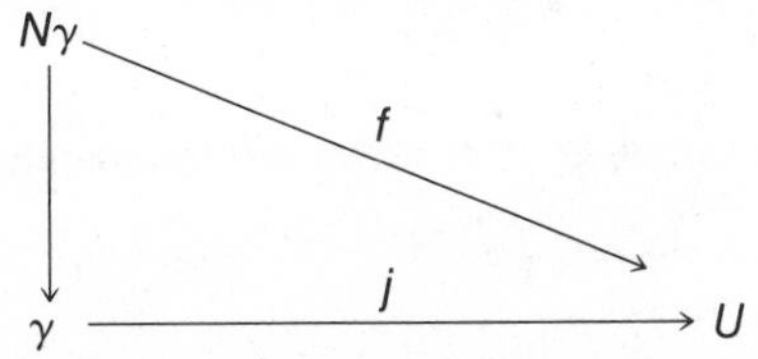

(where j is the injection) commutes. Define $\alpha: U \to S^1 \times \boldsymbol{R}^n$ by

$$\alpha = g^{-1} \circ f^{-1}$$

where $g: S^1 \times \boldsymbol{R}^n \to N\gamma$ is the C^r bundle isomorphism defined above. The reader may verify that for $\theta \in S^1 \equiv [0, \tau)$ and $t \in \boldsymbol{R}$ we have

$$\alpha \circ \varphi_t \circ \alpha^{-1}(\theta, \mathbf{0}) = (\theta + t, \mathbf{0})$$

Since the map $t \rightsquigarrow \alpha \circ \varphi_t \circ \alpha^{-1}(\theta, \mathbf{0})$ is the integral curve to the vectorfield $T\alpha \circ \xi \circ \alpha^{-1}$ through the point $(\theta, \mathbf{0})$, it follows that $\xi_\alpha(\theta, \mathbf{0}) = (1, \mathbf{0})$. ∎

In the untwisted case, our "almost normal" form is obtained as follows. By 25.2 and Taylor's Formula, we choose a diffeomorphism $\alpha: U \to S^1 \times \boldsymbol{R}^n$, U a neighborhood of γ, such that $\xi_\alpha = (\xi_{1\alpha}, \xi_{2\alpha})$, where $\xi_{1\alpha}: S^1 \times \boldsymbol{R}^n \to \boldsymbol{R}$ and $\xi_{2\alpha}$: $S^1 \times \boldsymbol{R}^n \to \boldsymbol{R}^n$ have the form

$$(*) \qquad \begin{aligned} \xi_{1\alpha}(\theta, \mathbf{x}) &= 1 + \tilde{Q}(\theta, \mathbf{x}) \\ \xi_{2\alpha}(\theta, \mathbf{x}) &= B(\theta)\mathbf{x} + R(\theta, \mathbf{x}) \end{aligned}$$

for $\theta \in S^1$, $\mathbf{x} \in \boldsymbol{R}^n$. Here $B(\theta) \in L(\boldsymbol{R}^n, \boldsymbol{R}^n)$, $Q(\theta, \mathbf{0}) = \mathbf{0}$, $R(\theta, \mathbf{0}) = \mathbf{0}$, and $D\tilde{R}(\theta, \mathbf{0}) = \mathbf{0}$ for all $\theta \in S^1$.

In the twisted case, we may obtain a similar "local representation" by going twice around the normal bundle. As $\varphi_{2\tau} = \varphi_\tau \circ \varphi_\tau$, we obtain a trivial bundle in this case, but the "chart" is actually defined on a covering of the normal bundle. This motivates the following definition, which applies to both the twisted and untwisted cases.

Let γ be a closed orbit of prime period τ of a vectorfield $\xi \in \Gamma^r(\tau_X)$. A C^k **pseudochart** for γ is a pair (σ, U) where U is an open neighborhood of γ in X and $\sigma: \boldsymbol{R}^{n+1} = \boldsymbol{R} \times \boldsymbol{R}^n \to U$ is a C^k map onto U such that

(PC1) σ is a local diffeomorphism (i.e., immersion);

(PC2) $\sigma(\boldsymbol{R} \times \{\mathbf{0}\}) = \gamma$;

We say the pseudochart (σ, U) is **demiperiodic with period** τ iff in addition

(PC3) $\sigma \circ \alpha = \sigma$, where $J \in L(\boldsymbol{R}^n, \boldsymbol{R}^n)$ is an involution, and $\alpha: \boldsymbol{R}^{n+1} \to \boldsymbol{R}^{n+1}$ is defined by $\alpha(\theta, \mathbf{x}) = (\theta + \tau, J\mathbf{x})$ for $(\theta, \mathbf{x}) \in \boldsymbol{R} \times \boldsymbol{R}^n = \boldsymbol{R}^{n+1}$.

It follows that $\sigma(\theta, \mathbf{x})$ is demiperiodic in θ with period τ, that is,

$$\sigma(\theta + \tau, \mathbf{x}) = \sigma(\theta, J\mathbf{x})$$

and thus $\sigma(\theta, \mathbf{x})$ is periodic in θ with period 2τ.

If γ is untwisted, J may be taken to be the identity, so $\sigma(\theta, \mathbf{x})$ is periodic in θ with period τ. In this case σ is a universal covering of U, and factoring mod τ yields a diffeomorph of U. If γ is twisted, J may be taken to be any orientation reversing involution. Then σ is a universal covering, and factoring mod 2τ yields an orientable double covering of U (see §4).

Let (σ, U) be a pseudochart for γ. Then for $(\theta, \mathbf{x}) \in \boldsymbol{R} \times \boldsymbol{R}^n$, the linear map

$$T_{(\theta, x)}\sigma: T_{(\theta, x)}\boldsymbol{R}^{n+1} \to T_{\sigma(\theta, x)}X$$

is a toplinear isomorphism. Hence we may define a map $\sigma_* \xi\colon \mathbf{R}^{n+1} \to T\mathbf{R}^{n+1}$ by

$$\sigma_* \xi(\theta, \mathbf{x}) = [T_{(\theta,\mathbf{x})}\sigma]^{-1} \xi(\sigma(\theta, \mathbf{x}))$$

This map is a vectorfield on $\mathbf{R}^{n+1}$. We let $\xi_\sigma\colon \mathbf{R}^{n+1} \to \mathbf{R}^{n+1}$ denote its principal part. Then ξ_σ is called the **principal part of the local representative of ξ with respect to the pseudochart** (σ, U).

By properly choosing a pseudochart for a twisted closed orbit γ, the principal part takes an "almost normal" form analogous to $(*)$ above.

25.5. PSEUDOCHART REPRESENTATION OF CLOSED ORBITS. Let X be a C^{r+2} $(n+1)$-manifold $(r \geqslant 1)$, $\xi \in \Gamma^r(\tau_X)$ a vectorfield on X, and γ a closed orbit of ξ (twisted or untwisted) of prime period τ. Then there is a C^r demiperiodic pseudochart (σ, U) for γ, where U is an open neighborhood of γ in X, such that the principal part of the local representative of ξ with respect to the pseudochart (σ, U), $\xi_\sigma = (\xi_{\sigma 1}, \xi_{\sigma 2})$ where $\xi_{\sigma 1}\colon \mathbf{R} \times \mathbf{R}^n \to \mathbf{R}$ and $\xi_{\sigma 2}\colon \mathbf{R} \times \mathbf{R}^n \to \mathbf{R}^n$, has the form

$$\xi_{\sigma 1}(\theta, \mathbf{x}) = 1 + Q(\theta, \mathbf{x})$$
$$\xi_{\sigma 2}(\theta, \mathbf{x}) = B(\theta)x + R(\theta, \mathbf{x})$$

for $(\theta, \mathbf{x}) \in \mathbf{R} \times \mathbf{R}^n$, where $B(\theta) \in L(\mathbf{R}^n, \mathbf{R}^n)$, $Q(\theta, \mathbf{0}) = 0$, $R(\theta, \mathbf{0}) = 0$, $D_2 R(\theta, \mathbf{0}) = 0$, and *A, Q, and R* are demiperiodic in θ with period τ. That is,

$$Q(\theta + \tau, \mathbf{x}) = Q(\theta, J\mathbf{x})$$
$$R(\theta + \tau, \mathbf{x}) = JR(\theta, J\mathbf{x})$$

and

$$B(\theta + \tau) = JB(\theta)J$$

where J is the linear involution of the pseudochart (σ, U).

Proof of 25.5. As in the proof of 25.2, let $\nu\colon N\gamma \to \gamma$ be the normal bundle of γ, and $f\colon N\gamma \to X$ be a total C^r tubular neighborhood of γ. Choosing a point $x_0 \in \gamma$, let $c\colon \mathbf{R} \to X$ be the complete integral curve of ξ at x_0. Then $c(\mathbf{R}) = \gamma$, and c is periodic with prime period τ. The pullback of ν by c (see Lang [*1*; p. 38]),

$$c_* \nu\colon E \to \mathbf{R}$$

is then a trivializable bundle, and the composite map

$$E \xrightarrow{\ c^*\ } N\gamma \xrightarrow{\ f\ } U$$

is almost a pseudochart, where $U = f(N\gamma)$. As in the proof of 25.2, we may choose a trivialization of $c_* \nu$,

$$\begin{array}{ccc} E & \xrightarrow{\ \ g\ \ } & \mathbf{R} \times \mathbf{R}^n \\ \downarrow{\scriptstyle c_*\nu} & & \downarrow{\scriptstyle \pi_1} \\ \mathbf{R} & \xrightarrow{\ \ g_0\ \ } & \mathbf{R} \end{array}$$

such that g_0 is the identity, and the composite map

$$\mathbf{R} \times \mathbf{R}^n \xrightarrow{\ g^{-1}\ } E \xrightarrow{\ c^*\ } N\gamma \xrightarrow{\ f\ } U$$

is a demiperiodic pseudochart. Note that by 25.3, the orientation reversing toplinear isomorphisms also comprise an open, pathwise-connected subset. If $\sigma = f \circ c^* \circ g^{-1}$, it follows immediately that ξ_σ has the "almost normal" form of 22.5. For $\sigma \mid \mathbf{R} \times \{\mathbf{0}\} = c$, so $\xi_\sigma(\theta, \mathbf{0}) = (1, \mathbf{0})$, and $\sigma \circ \alpha = \sigma$, so $\alpha_\star \sigma_\star \xi = \sigma_\star \xi$. But $\alpha: \mathbf{R} \times \mathbf{R}^n \to \mathbf{R} \times \mathbf{R}^n$ is defined by

$$\alpha(\theta, \mathbf{x}) = (\theta + \tau, J\mathbf{x})$$

where J is a linear involution, so we find for any vectorfield

$$\eta: \mathbf{R} \times \mathbf{R}^n \to T(\mathbf{R} \times \mathbf{R}^n) = (\mathbf{R} \times \mathbf{R}^n) \times (\mathbf{R} \times \mathbf{R}^n)$$

with $\eta(\theta, \mathbf{x}) = (\theta, \mathbf{x}; \eta_1(\theta, \mathbf{x}), \eta_2(\theta, \mathbf{x}))$, that $\alpha_\star \eta \equiv (T\alpha)^{-1} \circ \eta \circ \alpha = \eta$ iff

$$\eta_1(\theta + \tau, \mathbf{x}) = \eta_1(\theta, J\mathbf{x})$$

and

$$\eta_2(\theta + \tau, \mathbf{x}) = J\eta_2(\theta + \tau, J\mathbf{x})$$

Note that if γ is untwisted and we take J to be the identity, we obtain the "almost normal" form of 25.2. In either case, this form differs from the normal form desired only in that $B(\theta)$ depends on θ. ∎

§26. Floquet Normal Form

In this section we obtain the desired normal form for representation of a vectorfield near a closed orbit, by removing from the pseudochart representation (25.5) the dependence of $B(\theta)$ on θ. This is one aspect of the classical Floquet theory (see, e.g., Pontriagin [*1;* p. 146]), and the main step is the following classical theorem.

26.1. FLOQUET'S THEOREM. Let $B: \mathbf{R} \to L(\mathbf{R}^n, \mathbf{R}^n)$ be a C^r map, $J \in L(\mathbf{R}^n, \mathbf{R}^n)$ an involution, and suppose B is demiperiodic with period τ, that is,

$$B(\theta + \tau) = JB(\theta)J$$

Then there exists a C^r map $P: \mathbf{R} \to L(\mathbf{R}^n, \mathbf{R}^n)$ such that

(I) $P(\theta)$ is an isomorphism for each $\theta \in \mathbf{R}$;

(II) $P(\theta)$ is periodic with period 2τ, that is $P(\theta + 2\tau) = P(\theta)$;

(III) $P(\theta)^{-1} \circ B(\theta) \circ P(\theta) + P'(\theta) \circ P^{-1}(\theta)$ is independent of θ.

Proof. This is somewhat like the Straightening Out Theorem (21.6). Let η be the vectorfield on $\mathbf{R} \times \mathbf{R}^n$ defined by

$$\eta(\theta, \mathbf{x}) = (\theta, \mathbf{x}; 1, B(\theta)\mathbf{x})$$

for $\theta \in \mathbf{R}$ and $\mathbf{x} \in \mathbf{R}^n$. We use the flow of η to introduce new coordinates in which η has a simple local representative. It is clear that η is complete, and its flow has the form

$$\Phi(\theta, \mathbf{x}; t) = (\theta + t, \varphi_t(\theta)\mathbf{x})$$

where $\varphi_t(\theta) \in L(\mathbf{R}^n, \mathbf{R}^n)$ is an isomorphism, and the map $t \rightsquigarrow \varphi_t(\theta)$ is a one-parameter group. That is,

$$\varphi_{t+s}(\theta) = \varphi_t(\theta + s) \circ \varphi_s(\theta)$$

As B is demiperiodic with period τ, we have, as in the proof of 25.5, that η is also, or $\alpha_\star \eta = \eta$, where

$$\alpha(\theta, \mathbf{x}) = (\theta + \tau, J\mathbf{x})$$

Thus, the diffeomorphism α commutes with the flow of η, or

$$\varphi_t(\theta + \tau) = J\varphi_t(\theta)J$$

for all t and θ. For $\theta = 0$ and $t = \tau$, we have therefore

$$\varphi_{2\tau}(0) = J\varphi_\tau(0)J\varphi_\tau(0)$$

so $\varphi_{2\tau}(0)$ has a square root. Recall, however, that an isomorphism $B \in L(\mathbf{R}^n, \mathbf{R}^n)$ has a logarithm iff it has a square root. The proof is found, for example, in Pontriagin [*1*; pp. 285–291]. Thus, there exists a map $A \in L(\mathbf{R}^n, \mathbf{R}^n)$ such that

$$\exp(2\tau A) = \varphi_{2\tau}(0)$$

Now define $P\colon \mathbf{R} \to L(\mathbf{R}^n, \mathbf{R}^n)$ by

$$P(\theta) = \exp(\theta A) \circ [\varphi_\theta(0)]^{-1}$$

for $\theta \in \mathbf{R}$. Then P is C^r, and clearly satisfies (I) and (II). For (III) we consider the map $\beta\colon \mathbf{R} \times \mathbf{R}^n \to \mathbf{R} \times \mathbf{R}^n$ defined by

$$\beta(\theta, \mathbf{x}) = (\theta, P(\theta)\mathbf{x}), \qquad \text{for } \theta \in \mathbf{R}, \mathbf{x} \in \mathbf{R}^n$$

This is a C^r diffeomorphism, and by the transformation rule in the proof of 25.5, we have

$$T\beta \circ \eta \circ \beta^{-1}(\theta, \mathbf{x}) \equiv \beta^\star\eta(\theta, \mathbf{x}) = (\theta, \mathbf{x}; 1, [P(\theta)^{-1} \circ B(\theta) \circ P(\theta) + P'(\theta) \circ P^{-1}(\theta)]\mathbf{x})$$

But the integral curve of η through $(0, \mathbf{x})$ is mapped by β into the curve

$$t \rightsquigarrow (t, \exp(tA)\mathbf{x})$$

so $P(\theta) \circ B(\theta) \circ P(\theta)^{-1} + P'(\theta) \circ P^{-1}(\theta) = A$. ∎

Note: The mapping P is not demiperiodic with period τ, but is still periodic with period 2τ.

Applying Floquet's Theorem to the "almost normal" form (25.6) we obtain immediately (I) of the following.

26.2. FLOQUET NORMAL FORM. Let X be a C^{r+2} manifold ($r \geqslant 1$), $\xi \in \Gamma^r(\tau_X)$ a vectorfield on X, and γ a closed orbit of ξ (twisted or untwisted) of prime period τ. Then:

(I) There is a C^r pseudochart (σ, U) for γ, where U is an open neighborhood of γ in X, such that the principal part of the local representative of ξ with respect to the pseudochart (σ, U), $\xi_\sigma = (\xi_{\sigma1}, \xi_{\sigma2})$ where $\xi_{\sigma1}\colon \mathbf{R} \times \mathbf{R}^n \to \mathbf{R}$ and $\xi_{\sigma2}\colon \mathbf{R} \times \mathbf{R}^n \to \mathbf{R}^n$, has the form

$$\xi_{\sigma1}(\theta, \mathbf{x}) = 1 + Q(\theta, \mathbf{x})$$

$$\xi_{\sigma2}(\theta, \mathbf{x}) = Ax + R(\theta, \mathbf{x})$$

for $(\theta, \mathbf{x}) \in \mathbf{R} \times \mathbf{R}^n$, where $A \in L(\mathbf{R}^n, \mathbf{R}^n)$; $Q(\theta, \mathbf{0}) = 0$, $R(\theta, \mathbf{0}) = \mathbf{0}$ and $D_2R(\theta, \mathbf{x}) = \mathbf{0}$ for all $\theta \in \mathbf{R}$, and Q and R are periodic in θ with period 2τ:

(II) In such a pseudochart, γ is an elementary closed orbit iff A has no eigenvalue with real part zero.

Conclusion (II) follows immediately from the following.

26.3. LEMMA. Let ξ_σ be the vectorfield on R^{n+1} defined in 26.2(I), and φ its flow, with

$$\varphi(\theta, \mathbf{x}) = (\chi_t(\theta, \mathbf{x}), \psi_t(\theta, \mathbf{x}))$$

Then

$$D_2\psi_t(\theta, \mathbf{0}) = \exp(tA)$$

for $t \in R$ and $\theta \in R$.

Proof. Since ψ_0 is the identity, $D_2\psi_0(\theta, \mathbf{0})$ is the identity. Then by the uniqueness part of 21.1 and by 22.1 it suffices to show that

$$\frac{d}{ds}\{D_2\psi_s(\theta, \mathbf{0})\}_{s=t} = D_2\psi_t(\theta, \mathbf{0}) \circ A$$

for $t \in R$.

Interchanging the order of differentiation, we obtain

$$\frac{d}{ds}\{D_2\psi_s(\theta, \mathbf{0})\}_{s=0} = A$$

One can verify that

$$D_2\psi_{t+s}(\theta, \mathbf{x}) = D_2\psi_t(\psi_s(\theta, \mathbf{0})) \circ D_2\psi_s(\theta, \mathbf{0})$$

because of the one-parameter group property and the chain rule. Hence

$$\begin{aligned}\frac{d}{ds}\{D_2\psi_s(\theta, \mathbf{0})\}_{s=t} &= \frac{d}{ds}\{D_2\psi_{t+s}(\theta, \mathbf{0})\}_{s=0}\\ &= \frac{d}{ds}\{D_2\psi_t(\psi_s(\theta, \mathbf{0})) \circ D_2\psi_s(\theta, \mathbf{0})\}_{s=0}\\ &= \frac{d}{ds}\{D_2\psi_t(\psi_s(\theta, \mathbf{0}))\}_{s=0} \circ D_2\psi_0(\theta, \mathbf{0})\\ &\quad + D_2\psi_t(\theta, \mathbf{0}) \circ \frac{d}{ds}\{D_2\psi_s(\theta, \mathbf{0})\}_{s=0}\\ &= \mathbf{0} + D_2\psi_t(\theta, \mathbf{0}) \circ A\end{aligned}$$

Therefore, $D_2\psi_t(\theta, \mathbf{0}) = \exp(tA)$. ▮

Note that in the Floquet normal form, as in the representation of the previous section, the representative is defined on a universal covering of a neighborhood of the closed orbit, or by restricting to the interval $[0, 2\tau)$, a double covering (see Figure 26-1). The double covering was essential in the "almost normal" form only for untwisting a twisted closed orbit, by "going around twice." Here, however, going around twice may be neces-

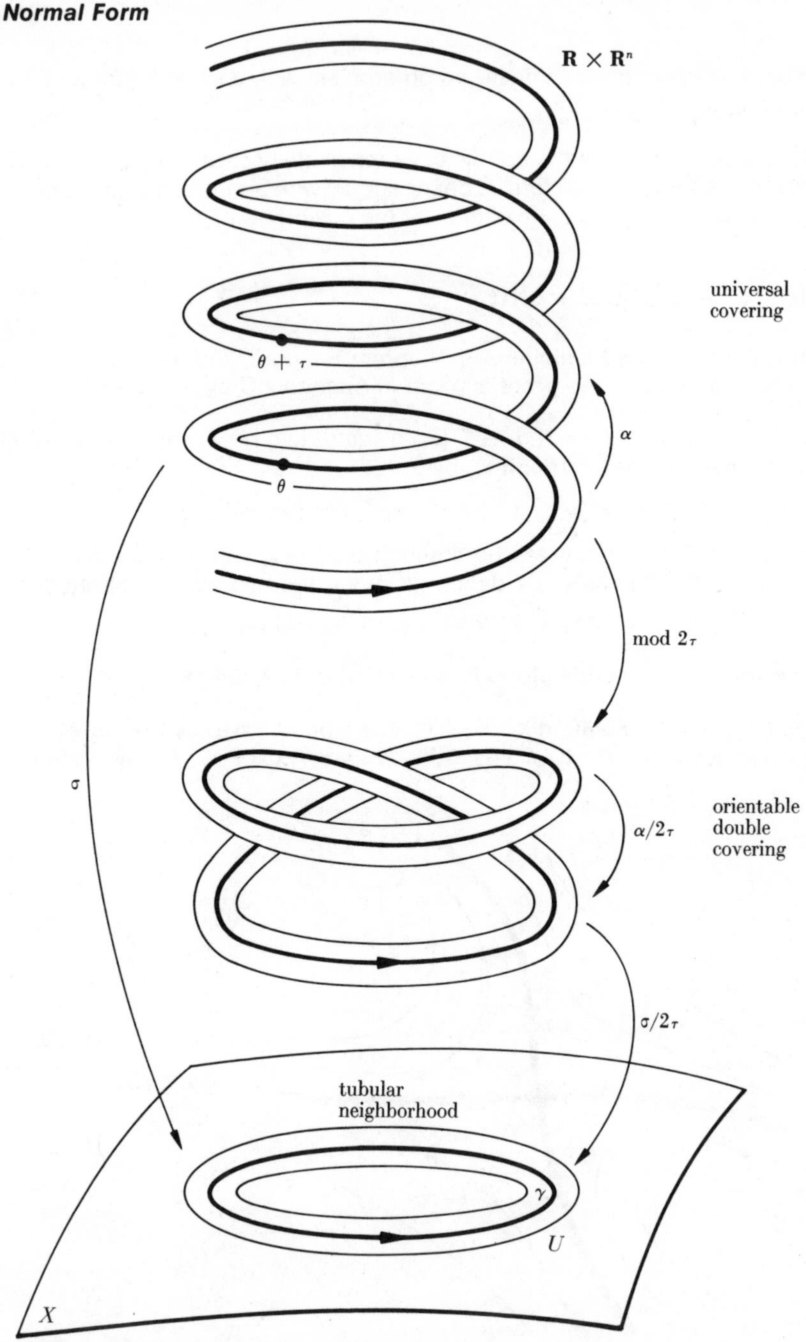

Figure 26–1. The structure of a pseudochart.

sary even in the untwisted case, in order to get a linear automorphism with a square root and thus a logarithm, which is used in the proof of Floquet's Theorem (26.1).

For these reasons it is most convenient to use the double covering in every case. Note, however, that even on a double covering of period 2τ, the Floquet normal form is demiperiodic with period τ in some sense, as the "pulled-up" vectorfield $\sigma_*\xi$ is invariant under the *natural* involution of the covering.

§27. Stable Manifolds of a Critical Point

In this section we prove the Existence and Uniqueness Theorem for the stable and unstable manifolds of an elementary critical point. The main step of the proof is given in Appendix C by A. Kelley.

Let X be a finite-dimensional C^{r+2} manifold ($r \geq 1$), $\xi \in \Gamma^r(\tau_X)$ a vectorfield on X, and $x_0 \in X$ a critical point of ξ. We define $W^+(\xi, x_0)$, the **stable manifold of** ξ **through** x_0, by

$$W^+(\xi, x_0) = \{x \in X \mid \varphi_t(x) \to x_0 \quad \text{as } t \to \infty\}$$

Here φ is the flow of ξ. In case φ is not complete, the notation $\varphi_t(x) \to x_0$ as $t \to \infty$ is understood to entail that $\varphi_t(x)$ is defined for all positive $t \in \mathbf{R}$. Similarly, we define $W^-(\xi, x_0)$, **the unstable manifold of** ξ **through** x_0, by

$$W^-(\xi, x_0) = \{x \in X \mid \varphi_t(x) \to x_0 \quad \text{as } t \to -\infty\}$$

Again, the notation $\varphi_t(x) \to x_0$ as $t \to -\infty$ is understood to entail that $\varphi_t(x)$ is defined for all negative t.

Let W_1 and W_2 be C^1 submanifolds of a C^1 manifold X, and $x \in X$ be a point. We say W_1 and W_2 are **transversal at** x, in symbols: $W_1 \pitchfork_x W_2$, iff either $x \notin W_1 \cap W_2$ or $x \in W_1 \cap W_2$ and $T_xX = T_xW_1 + T_xW_2$. We say W_1 and W_2 are

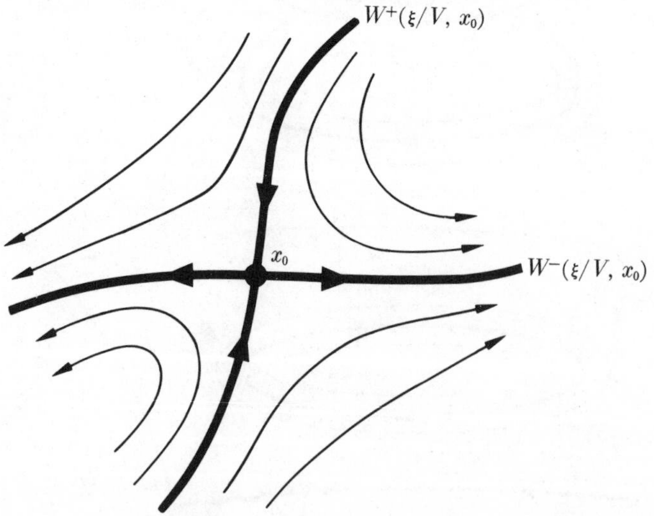

Figure 27–1. Local stable manifolds of a critical point.

transversal; in symbols: $W_1 \pitchfork W_2$, iff $W_1 \pitchfork_x W_2$ for all $x \in X$. Note this is essentially the same as the definition of $\pitchfork$ in §17, for if $i_1\colon W_1 \to X$ is the inclusion, then $W_1 \pitchfork W_2$ iff $i_1 \pitchfork W_2$.

The next theorem describes the local configuration of the stable and unstable manifolds of an elementary critical point.

27.1. LOCAL STABLE MANIFOLD THEOREM FOR CRITICAL POINTS. Let X **be a finite-dimensional** C^{r+1} **manifold** ($r \geq 1$), $\xi \subset \Gamma^r(\tau_X)$ **a vectorfield on** X, **and** $x_0 \in X$ **an elementary critical point of** ξ. **Then there is an open neighborhood** V **of** x_0 **in** X, **such that,**

(I) $W^+(\xi|V, x_0) \cap W^-(\xi|V, x_0) = \{x_0\}$;

(II) $W^+(\xi|V, x_0)$ **and** $W^-(\xi|V, x_0)$ **are** C^r **submanifolds;**

(III) $W^+(\xi|V, x_0) \pitchfork_{x_0} W^-(\xi|V, x_0)$.

This situation is illustrated in Figure 27-1. We have depicted X as two dimensional and $W^+(\xi|V, x_0)$ and $W^-(\xi|V, x_0)$ each as one dimensional. The theorem does not preclude the possibility that one or the other of W^+ or W^- may be zero dimensional, i.e., the point x_0. The reader is cautioned that $W^+(\xi|V, x_0)$ and $W^+(\xi, x_0) \cap V$ need not be the same. In fact, it is possible that $W^+(\xi, x_0) = W^-(\xi, x_0)$ as in Figure 27-2.

For the proof of 27.1 we need a technical lemma.

If $U \subset \mathbf{R}^n$ is an open subset of $\mathbf{R}^n$ and $f\colon U \to \mathbf{R}^n$ is a C^r map, we may identify f with the vectorfield on U of which f is the principal part. Accordingly, if $x_0 \in U$ is such that $f(x_0) = \mathbf{0}$, we may define $W^+(f, x_0)$ and $W^-(f, x_0)$ as above.

Recall that a square matrix is a **contraction** (resp. **expansion**) **matrix** iff all its complex eigenvalues have negative

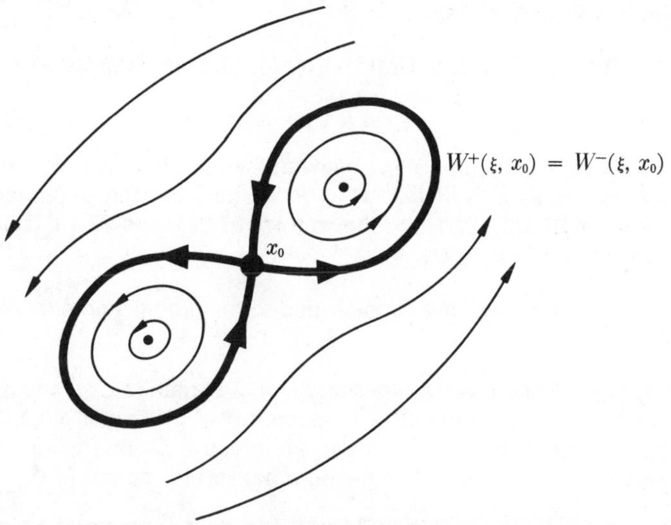

Figure 27–2. Global stable manifolds of a critical point.

(resp. positive) real part, and any (real) square matrix having no complex eigenvalue with real part zero may, by a linear change of coordinates, be put in the form

$$\begin{pmatrix} A & 0 \\ 0 & B \end{pmatrix}$$

where A (resp. B) is a square contraction (resp. expansion) matrix in **real canonical form** (see Coddington-Levinson [*1*; p. 340]).

For each integer m and real number $\delta > 0$, let $B_m(\delta)$ denote the open unit ball in R^m of radius δ centered at the origin, i.e.,

$$B_m(\delta) = \{\mathbf{e} \in \boldsymbol{R}^m \mid \|\mathbf{e}\| < \delta\}$$

27.2. LEMMA. Let $U \subset \boldsymbol{R}^n \approx \boldsymbol{R}^k \times \boldsymbol{R}^{n-k}$ be an open neighborhood of 0 and $f \in \mathscr{B}^r(U, \boldsymbol{R}^n)$ (see §6). Suppose $f = f_1 \times f_2$ where $f_1\colon U \to \boldsymbol{R}^k$ and $f_2\colon U \to \boldsymbol{R}^{n-k}$ have the form

$$f_1(\mathbf{x}, \mathbf{y}) = A\mathbf{x} + Q(\mathbf{x}, \mathbf{y})$$

$$f_2(\mathbf{x}, \mathbf{y}) = B\mathbf{x} + R(\mathbf{x}, \mathbf{y})$$

for $(\mathbf{x}, \mathbf{y}) \in U$ $(\mathbf{x} \in \boldsymbol{R}^k, \mathbf{y} \in \boldsymbol{R}^{n-k})$, with A a $k \times k$ contraction matrix in real canonical form, B an $(n-k) \times (n-k)$ expansion matrix in real canonical form, $Q(0, 0) = 0$, $R(0, 0) = 0$, $DQ(0, 0) = 0$, and $DR(0, 0) = 0$.

Then there exists $\delta > 0$, a neighborhood V of 0 in $\boldsymbol{R}^n$, and a C^r map $G^+\colon B_k(\delta) \to \boldsymbol{R}^{n-k}$, such that,

(I) $G^+(0) = 0$ and $DG^+(0) = 0$;

(II) $W^+(f|V, 0)$ is the graph of G^+, or $W^+(f|V, 0) = \{(\mathbf{x}, \mathbf{y}) \mid \mathbf{x} \in B_k(\delta), \mathbf{y} = G^+(\mathbf{x})\}$.

Also, this theorem remains true if W^+, k, $n-k$, and G^+ are replaced by W^-, $n-k$, k, and G^- respectively.

The proof is given in Appendix C by A. Kelley.

Proof of 27.1. By the Local Representation of Critical Points (22.6) we may choose a chart (U, β) at $x_0 \in X$, such that

$$\xi_\beta(\mathbf{u}) = C\mathbf{u} + R(\mathbf{u})$$

where C is a real $n \times n$ matrix having no complex eigenvalue with real part zero. By a further linear change of coordinates, we obtain a chart (U, α) with $\alpha(U) \subset \boldsymbol{R}^k \times \boldsymbol{R}^{n-k}$ such that the principal part ξ_α has the form of f in 27.1. Thus 27.1(II) follows from 27.2(II), 27.1(III) follows from 27.2(I), and 27.1(I) follows from 27.1(III), by taking a sufficiently small neighborhood V of x_0 in U. ∎

The local stable manifold $W^+(\xi|V, x_0)$ may now be extended to the global stable manifold $W^+(\xi, x_0)$ using the flow of ξ, and the unstable manifold as well.

Recall that a C^r map $(r \geq 1)$ $\psi\colon P \to X$ between finite-dimensional C^r manifolds P and X is an **immersion** iff for every $p \in P$ the tangent map $T_p\psi\colon T_pP \to T_{\psi(p)}X$ is injective. A subset W of a C^r manifold X is called a **C^r immersed submanifold** iff it is the image of some C^r manifold P under an injective C^r immersion (i.e., $\psi\colon P \to X$ and $W = \psi(P)$). Then ψ is called a **parameterization** of W and P is called a **parameter space** of ψ.

A curve which approaches itself without touching (Figure 27-2) is an example of a closed, immersed submanifold which is not a submanifold (see Lang [*1*; p. 19]).

27.3. GLOBAL STABLE MANIFOLD THEOREM FOR CRITICAL POINTS. **Let X be a compact C^{r+2} manifold ($r \geq 1$), $\xi \in \Gamma^r(\tau_X)$ a vectorfield on X, and $x_0 \in X$ an elementary critical point of ξ. Then $W^+(\xi, x_0)$ and $W^-(\xi, x_0)$ are C^r immersed submanifolds of X, parameterized by Euclidean spaces.**

Proof. Choose a chart (U, α) at x_0 so that ξ_α, the principal part of the local representative of ξ, has the form of f in 27.2. Take G^+, G^- and δ as in 27.2. Then a parameterization $\psi^+\colon \mathbf{R}^k \to W(\xi, x_0)$ is defined as follows.

As G^+ is a mapping from $B_k(\delta)$ into $\mathbf{R}^{n-k}$, the mapping $g\colon B_k(\delta) \to \mathbf{R}^n$ defined by $g(\mathbf{x}) = (\mathbf{x}, G^+(\mathbf{x}))$ is a diffeomorphism onto the graph of G^+, and $\gamma = \alpha^{-1} \circ g$ is a diffeomorphism onto $W^+(\xi|U, x_0)$. As ξ is tangent to $W^+(\xi|U, x_0)$, ξ may be pulled back to a vectorfield on $B_k(\delta)$. Let η denote the pulled-back vectorfield, or

$$\eta(\mathbf{x}) = (\mathbf{x}, [T(\gamma)(\mathbf{x})]^{-1}\xi(\gamma(\mathbf{x}))$$

Then $\eta(\mathbf{0}) = (\mathbf{0}, \mathbf{0})$, and the characteristic exponents of η at $\mathbf{0}$ are the same as those of $\xi | W^+(\xi|U, x_0)$ at x_0. As η is C^r, with $r \geq 1$, we may expand in a Taylor's formula, obtaining

$$\eta(\mathbf{x}) = (\mathbf{x}, A\mathbf{x} + R(\mathbf{x})(\mathbf{x}, \mathbf{x}))$$

where $A \in L(\mathbf{R}^k, \mathbf{R}^k)$ is a contraction, and $R(\mathbf{x}) \in L_s^2(\mathbf{R}^k, \mathbf{R}^k)$. Therefore (see Appendix C, Lemma 1), there exists a positive real number μ such that

$$\langle A\mathbf{x}, \mathbf{x}\rangle \leq -2\mu \langle \mathbf{x}, \mathbf{x}\rangle$$

where $\langle \mathbf{x}, \mathbf{y}\rangle$ is the standard scalar product on $\mathbf{R}^k$. From the Taylor expansion of η above, it follows that there exists a real number $\delta_0 \in (0, \delta)$, such that for all $\mathbf{x} \in B_k(\delta_0)$,

(*) $$\langle \eta(\mathbf{x}), \mathbf{x}\rangle \leq 0 \quad \text{and} \quad \eta(\mathbf{x}) = \mathbf{0} \quad \text{iff} \quad \mathbf{x} = \mathbf{0}$$

We now restrict $\gamma = \alpha^{-1} \circ g$ to $B_k(\delta_0)$, and continue the construction of ψ.

Let $\mathbf{R}^+ = (0, \infty)$ be the positive real numbers and $h\colon \mathbf{R}^+ \to (0, \delta_0)$ a C^∞ diffeomorphism such that $h(t) = t$ for $0 < t \leq \delta_0/2$; define $h(0) = 0$. Let $\|\ \|$ be the usual norm on Euclidean space so that the map $\mathbf{e} \rightsquigarrow \|\mathbf{e}\|$ is C^∞ for $\mathbf{e} \neq \mathbf{0}$. Define a C^∞ diffeomorphism $H_k\colon \mathbf{R}^k \to B_k(\delta_0)$ by

$$H_k(\mathbf{e}) = \frac{h(\|\mathbf{e}\|)\mathbf{e}}{\|\mathbf{e}\|} \qquad \text{for } \mathbf{e} \neq \mathbf{0}$$

$$H_k(\mathbf{e}) = \mathbf{0} \qquad \text{for } \mathbf{e} = \mathbf{0}$$

Let $q\colon \mathbf{R} \to \mathbf{R}$ be a C^∞ function such that,

(1) $q(t) = 0$ for $0 \leq t \leq \delta_0/2$;

(2) $q(t)$ is strictly increasing for $t > \delta_0/2$;

(3) $q(t) \to \infty$ as $t \to \infty$ (see Figure 27-3).

Now we define $\psi^+\colon \mathbf{R}^k \to X$ by

$$\psi^+(\mathbf{e}) = \varphi_{-q(\|\mathbf{e}\|)}(\alpha^{-1}(H_k(\mathbf{e}), G^+(H_k(\mathbf{e}))))$$

for $\mathbf{e} \in \mathbf{R}^k$. Here φ is the flow of ξ.

Thus to compute $\psi^+(\mathbf{e})$ for $\mathbf{e} \in \mathbf{R}^k$, we move $\mathbf{e}$ into $B_k(\delta_0)$ by a diffeomorphism H_k, find the point $(H_k(\mathbf{e}), G^+(H_k(\mathbf{e}))$ in the local stable manifold, move to the manifold via α^{-1}, and go backwards in time, for a length of time dependent only on the norm of $\mathbf{e}$, along an orbit of ξ.

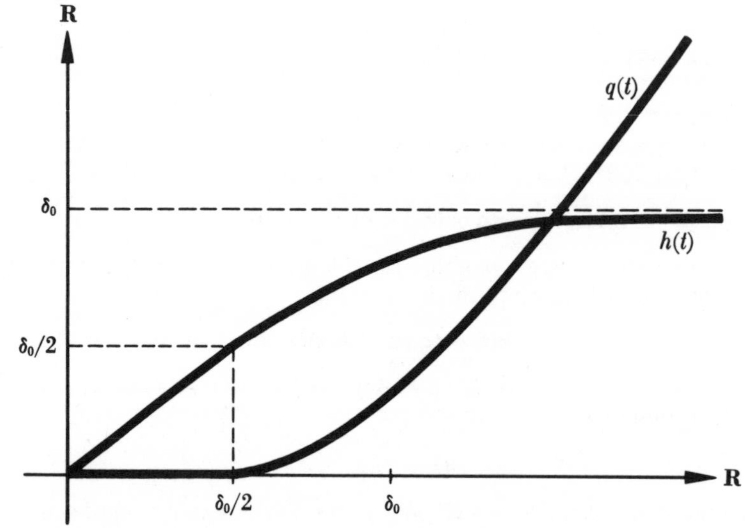

Figure 27-3

Now it is obvious that ψ^+ is a bijection onto the set $W^+(\xi, x_0)$, so it is a parameterization of the stable manifold if, in addition, $T\psi^+(\mathbf{e})$ is injective for all $\mathbf{e} \in \mathbf{R}^k$. This condition is easily proved by the following computation.

Let b: $\mathbf{R}^k \to X$ be the composite

$$\mathbf{R}^k \xrightarrow{H_k} B^k(\delta_0) \xrightarrow{\gamma} X$$

or $b = \gamma \circ H_k$ and a: $\mathbf{R}^k \to \mathbf{R}$ be defined by $a(\mathbf{e}) = -q(\|\mathbf{e}\|)$. Then if φ: $\mathbf{R} \times X \to X$ is the flow of ξ, the proposed parameterization ψ is defined by

$$\psi^+(\mathbf{e}) = \varphi(a(\mathbf{e}), b(\mathbf{e}))$$

Then the tangent of ψ^+ at $\mathbf{e} \in \mathbf{R}^k$ is given by

$$(**) \qquad T\psi^+(\mathbf{e})\mathbf{f} = [Ta(\mathbf{e})\mathbf{f}]\xi(\psi^+(\mathbf{e})) + T\varphi_{a(\mathbf{e})}(b(\mathbf{e}))Tb(\mathbf{e})\mathbf{f}$$

for $\mathbf{f} \in \mathbf{R}^k$, where $\varphi_a(x) = \varphi(a, x)$.

We now show that $T\psi^+(\mathbf{e})$ is injective. Consider first the case $\mathbf{e} = \mathbf{0}$. Then as $\psi^+ = \gamma$ in a neighborhood of $\mathbf{0}$, $T\psi^+(\mathbf{0}) = T\gamma(\mathbf{0})$, which is obviously injective. Next we consider the case $\mathbf{e} \neq \mathbf{0}$, and show that $T\psi^+(\mathbf{e})\mathbf{f} = \mathbf{0}$ and $\mathbf{f} \neq \mathbf{0}$ contradicts condition (*) on page 87.

In equation (**) above, we set the left-hand side equal to zero, and apply the isomorphism $[T\varphi_{a(\mathbf{e})}(b(\mathbf{e}))]^{-1}$. By the invariance of ξ under the diffeomorphism $\varphi_{a(\mathbf{e})}$ (23.1(I)), we find

$$[Ta(\mathbf{e})\mathbf{f}]\xi(b(\mathbf{e})) + Tb(\mathbf{e})\mathbf{f} = \mathbf{0}$$

As $b = \gamma \circ H_k$, and η is the pullback of ξ by γ, we may rewrite this equation in the form

$$T\gamma(H_k(\mathbf{e}))\{[Ta(\mathbf{e})\mathbf{f}]\eta(H_k(\mathbf{e})) + TH_k(\mathbf{e})\mathbf{f}\} = \mathbf{0}$$

As $T\gamma(H_k(\mathbf{e}))$ is injective, we have

$$[Ta_0(\mathbf{e}_0)\mathbf{f}_0]\eta(\mathbf{e}_0) + \mathbf{f}_0 = \mathbf{0}$$

where we have used the substitutions $a_0 = a \circ H_k^{-1}$, $\mathbf{e}_0 = H_k(\mathbf{e})$, and $\mathbf{f}_0 = TH_k(\mathbf{e})\mathbf{f}$, and thus $Ta(\mathbf{e})\mathbf{f} = Ta_0(\mathbf{e}_0)\mathbf{f}_0$. Thus $\mathbf{f}_0 = \lambda\eta(\mathbf{e}_0)$, where $\lambda = -Ta_0(\mathbf{e}_0)\mathbf{f}_0$, and substituting into the preceding equation, we have

$$\lambda[Ta_0(\mathbf{e}_0)\eta(\mathbf{e}_0) + 1]\eta(\mathbf{e}_0) = \mathbf{0}$$

But $\mathbf{e} \neq \mathbf{0}$ by hypothesis, so $\eta(\mathbf{e}_0) \neq \mathbf{0}$ by condition (*) on page 87, and as we have assumed $\mathbf{f} \neq \mathbf{0}$ also, $\lambda \neq 0$. Thus under our hypothesis, we must have

(***) $$Ta_0(\mathbf{e}_0)\eta(\mathbf{e}_0) + 1 = 0$$

Now, let us compute the first term of this expression by actual differentiation. As $a_0 = a \circ H_k^{-1}$ and obviously, for any $\mathbf{e}_1 \in B_k(\delta_0)$ with $\mathbf{e}_1 \neq \mathbf{0}$,

$$H_k^{-1}(\mathbf{e}_1) = \frac{h^{-1}(\|\mathbf{e}_1\|)}{\|\mathbf{e}_1\|}\mathbf{e}_1$$

we see that

$$a_0(\mathbf{e}_1) = -q \circ h^{-1}(\|\mathbf{e}_1\|)$$

Thus, for any $\mathbf{f}_1 \in \mathbf{R}^k$,

$$Ta_0(\mathbf{e}_1)\mathbf{f}_1 = -(q \circ h^{-1})'(\|\mathbf{e}_1\|)\frac{\langle \mathbf{e}_1, \mathbf{f}_1\rangle}{\|\mathbf{e}_1\|}$$

Taking $\mathbf{e}_1 = \mathbf{e}_0$ and $\mathbf{f}_1 = \eta(\mathbf{e}_0)$ and substituting in (***) above, we have

$$\langle \mathbf{e}_0, \eta(\mathbf{e}_0)\rangle = \|\mathbf{e}_0\|[(q \circ h^{-1})'(\|\mathbf{e}_0\|)]^{-1}$$

As it follows immediately from the hypotheses for q and h in the original construction that q and h^{-1} are nondecreasing, this equation contradicts condition (*) above. Therefore, we have shown that $T\psi^+(\mathbf{e})$ is injective for all $\mathbf{e} \in \mathbf{R}^k$, so ψ^+ is an immersion, and thus a parameterization of $W^+(\xi, x_0)$. The proof required choosing δ_0 sufficiently small to obtain condition (*).

The definition of the parameterization $\psi^-: \mathbf{R}^{n-k} \to X$ of $W^-(\xi, x_0)$ is analogous. Define $H_{n-k}: \mathbf{R}^{n-k} \to B_{n-k}(\delta_0)$ by

$$H_{n-k}(\mathbf{e}) = \frac{h(\|\mathbf{e}\|)\mathbf{e}}{\|\mathbf{e}\|} \qquad \text{for } \mathbf{e} \in \mathbf{R}^{n-k},\ \mathbf{e} \neq \mathbf{0}$$

$$H_{n-k}(\mathbf{e}) = \mathbf{0} \qquad \text{for } \mathbf{e} = \mathbf{0} \in \mathbf{R}^{n-k}$$

Then $\psi^-: \mathbf{R}^{n-k} \to X$ is defined by

$$\psi^-(\mathbf{e}) = \varphi_{q(\|\mathbf{e}\|)}(\alpha^{-1}(H_{n-k}(\mathbf{e}), G^+(H_{n-k}(\mathbf{e}))))$$

for $\mathbf{e} \in \mathbf{R}^{n-k}$. Note that in this case we go forward in time along the flow to find $\psi^-(\mathbf{e})$. ∎

In §32 we will need the parameterization not only for ξ, but also for vectorfields near ξ.

27.4. PARAMETERIZATION THEOREM FOR CRITICAL POINTS. Let X be a compact C^{r+2} manifold ($r \geqslant 1$), $\xi \in \Gamma^r(\tau_X)$ a vectorfield, and $x_0 \in X$ an elementary critical point of ξ. Then there exists an open neighborhood N of ξ in $\Gamma^r(\tau_X)$, a neighborhood V of x_0 in X, and for every $\zeta \in N$ there exist C^r maps $\psi_\zeta^+ : \mathbf{R}^k \to X$ and $\psi_\zeta^- : \mathbf{R}^{n-k} \to X$, such that,

(I) For $\zeta \in N$, ζ has a unique critical point $x_\zeta \in V$, and this critical point is elementary;

(II) For $\zeta \in N$, ψ_ζ^+ and ψ_ζ^- parameterize $W^+(\zeta, x_\zeta)$ and $W^-(\zeta, x_\zeta)$ respectively, i.e., ψ_ζ^+ and ψ_ζ^- are injective C^r immersions, $\psi_\zeta^+(\mathbf{R}^k) = W^+(\zeta, x_\zeta)$, and $\psi_\zeta^-(\mathbf{R}^{n-k}) = W^-(\zeta, x_\zeta)$;

(III) The maps $N \to \mathscr{C}^r(\mathbf{R}^k, X)$ and $N \to \mathscr{C}^r(\mathbf{R}^{n-k}, X)$ given respectively by $\zeta \rightsquigarrow \psi_\zeta^+$ and $\zeta \rightsquigarrow \psi_\zeta^-$ for $\zeta \in N$ are C^1 pseudorepresentations (see §18).

For the proof of 27.4 we need the following stronger version of Lemma 27.2.

27.5. LEMMA. Let f and U be as in 27.2. Then there exists:

(1) $\delta > 0$;

(2) a neighborhood N_f of f in $\mathscr{B}^r(U, \mathbf{R}^n)$;

(3) a neighborhood V of 0 in $\mathbf{R}^n$;

(4) (for every $g \in N_f$) a C^r map

$$G_g^+ : B_k(\delta) \to \mathbf{R}^{n-k}$$

such that,

(I) For each $g \in N_f$, there exists a unique $x_g \in V$ with $g(x_g) = 0$, this critical point being elementary;

(II) For $g \in N_f$, $W^+(g|V, x_g)$ is the graph of G_g^+;

(III) The map $N_f \to \mathscr{C}^r(B_k(\delta), \mathbf{R}^{n-k})$ given by $g \rightsquigarrow G_g^+$ is a C^1 pseudorepresentation.

Also this theorem remains true, reading W^-, $n-k$, k, and G^- for W^+, k, $n-k$, and G^+ respectively.

The proof is given in Appendix C by A. Kelley.

Proof of 27.4. This follows from 27.5 in exactly the same way as the proof of 27.3 follows from 27.2. Let (α, U) be the chart of 27.3. Take $f = \xi_\alpha$ in 27.3 and let $N \subset \Gamma^r(\tau_X)$ be defined by

$$N = \{\zeta \in \Gamma^r(\tau_X) \mid \zeta_\alpha \in N_f\}$$

The definition of ψ_ζ^+ is exactly the same as the definition of ψ except we replace φ (the flow of ξ) by φ^ζ, the flow of ζ, and G^+ by $G_{\zeta\alpha}^+$, i.e.,

$$\psi_\zeta^+(\mathbf{e}) = \varphi^\zeta_{-q(\|\mathbf{e}\|)}(\alpha^{-1}(H_k(\mathbf{e}), G_{\zeta\alpha}^+(H_k(\mathbf{e}))))$$

for $\mathbf{e} \in \mathbf{R}^k$; ψ_ζ^- is similarly defined. Since $\zeta \rightsquigarrow \varphi^\zeta$ is a C^r representation (by 22.4) and $\zeta \rightsquigarrow \zeta_\alpha$ is continuous linear (at least if (α, U) is pseudocompact; see §7), it follows from 27.4(III) that $\psi_\zeta^+(\mathbf{e})$ is continuous in ζ and $\mathbf{e}$. Similarly $T\psi_\zeta^+(\mathbf{e})$ is continuous in ζ and $\mathbf{e}$. Hence $\zeta \rightsquigarrow \psi_\zeta^+$ is a C^1 pseudorepresentation. This establishes (III) for ψ^+; the argument for ψ^- is the same, while (I) and (II) in 27.4 follow from (I) and (II) in 27.5 just as before. ∎

§28. Stable Manifolds of a Closed Orbit

In this section we prove the existence of stable and unstable manifolds for elementary closed orbits. This method is analogous to the preceding section, and, again, the main step is proved in Appendix C, by A. Kelley.

Let X be a C^{r+2} manifold of dimension $n+1$, $\xi \in \Gamma^r(\tau_X)$ a vectorfield, φ the flow of ξ, $x \in X$, and γ a closed orbit of ξ. We say $\varphi_t(x) \to \gamma$ as $t \to \infty$ (resp. $t \to -\infty$) iff $\varphi_t(x)$ is defined for all positive (resp. negative) t and for every open neighborhood U of γ in X there exists a real number $t_0 > 0$ (resp. $t_0 < 0$) such that $\varphi_t(x) \in U$ for $t > t_0$ (resp. $t < t_0$). We define $W^+(\xi, \gamma)$, the **stable manifold** of γ by

$$W^+(\xi, \gamma) = \{x \in X \mid \varphi_t(x) \to \gamma \text{ as } t \to \infty\}$$

Similarly, we define $W^-(\xi, \gamma)$, the **unstable manifold** of γ by

$$W^-(\xi, \gamma) = \{x \in X \mid \varphi_t(x) \to \gamma \text{ as } t \to -\infty\}$$

The following theorem is analogous to §27.1.

28.1. LOCAL STABLE MANIFOLD THEOREM FOR A CLOSED ORBIT. Let X be a finite-dimensional C^{r+2} manifold ($r \geqslant 1$), $\xi \in \Gamma^r(\tau_X)$ a vectorfield on X, and γ an elementary closed orbit of ξ. Then there exists a neighborhood V of γ in X such that

(I) $W^+(\xi|V, \gamma) \cap W^-(\xi|V, \gamma) = \gamma$;

(II) $W^+(\xi|V, \gamma)$ **and** $W^-(\xi|V, \gamma)$ **are C^r submanifolds of X;**

(III) $W^+(\xi|V, \gamma) \pitchfork_x W^-(\xi|V, \gamma)$ **for** $x \in \gamma$.

The proof requires the next two lemmas. Recall that the tangent bundle $T(S^1 \times \boldsymbol{R}^n) = S^1 \times \boldsymbol{R}^n \times \boldsymbol{R}^{n+1}$ so that if $f\colon S^1 \times \boldsymbol{R}^n \to \boldsymbol{R}^{n+1}$ is a C^r map, it may be identified with the C^r vectorfield on $S^1 \times \boldsymbol{R}^n$ of which it is the principal part. If γ is a closed orbit of this vectorfield, define $W^+(f, \gamma)$ and $W^-(f, \gamma)$ as above.

28.2. LEMMA. Let U be an open neighborhood of $S^1 \times \{0\}$ in $S^1 \times \boldsymbol{R}^n$ and $f \in \mathscr{B}^r(U, \boldsymbol{R}^{n+1})$ have the form $f = f_1 \times f_2 \times f_3$ where $f_1\colon U \to \boldsymbol{R}$, $f_2\colon U \to \boldsymbol{R}^k$, and $f_3\colon U \to \boldsymbol{R}^{n-k}$ have the form

$$f_1(\theta, \mathbf{x}, \mathbf{y}) = 1 + Q(\theta, \mathbf{x}, \mathbf{y})$$

$$f_2(\theta, \mathbf{x}, \mathbf{y}) = A\mathbf{x} + R(\theta, \mathbf{x}, \mathbf{y})$$

$$f_3(\theta, \mathbf{x}, \mathbf{y}) = B\mathbf{y} + S(\theta, \mathbf{x}, \mathbf{y})$$

for $\theta \in S^1$, $\mathbf{x} \in \boldsymbol{R}^k$, $\mathbf{y} \in \boldsymbol{R}^{n-k}$, where A is a $k \times k$ contraction matrix in real canonical form, B an $(n-k) \times (n-k)$ expansion matrix in real canonical form, $Q(\theta, \mathbf{0}, \mathbf{0}) = 0$, $R(\theta, \mathbf{0}, \mathbf{0}) = \mathbf{0}$, $S(\theta, \mathbf{0}, \mathbf{0}) = \mathbf{0}$, $D_2R(\theta, \mathbf{0}, \mathbf{0}) = 0$, $D_3R(\theta, \mathbf{0}, \mathbf{0}) = 0$, $D_2S(\theta, \mathbf{0}, \mathbf{0}) = 0$, and $D_3S(\theta, \mathbf{0}, \mathbf{0}) = 0$ for all $\theta \in S^1$.

Then there exists $\delta > 0$, an open neighborhood V of $S^1 \times \{\mathbf{0}\}$ in $S^1 \times \boldsymbol{R}^n$, and a C^r map $G^+\colon S^1 \times B_k(\delta) \to \boldsymbol{R}^{n-k}$, such that,

(I) $G^+(\theta, \mathbf{0}) = \mathbf{0}$ **and** $DG^+(\theta, \mathbf{0}) = 0$ **for all** $\theta \in S^1$;

(II) $W^+(f|U, S^1 \times \{\mathbf{0}\})$ **is the graph of** G^+.

These remain true, reading W^-, $n-k$, k, and G^- for W^+, k, $n-k$, and G^+, respectively.

The proof is given in Appendix C by A. Kelley.

Now recall that a pseudochart (σ, U) for a closed orbit γ of a vectorfield ξ on X is a map $\sigma: \mathbf{R}^{n+1} \to U$, where U is a neighborhood of $\gamma \subset X$, which is a local diffeomorphism onto U satisfying $\sigma(\theta + 2\tau, z) = \sigma(\theta, z)$ and $\sigma(\mathbf{R} \times \{\mathbf{0}\}) = \gamma$, where $(\theta, z) \in \mathbf{R} \times \mathbf{R}^n$. Let S^1 denote $\mathbf{R}$ mod 2τ, and $\pi: \mathbf{R}^{n+1} = \mathbf{R} \times \mathbf{R}^n \to S^1 \times \mathbf{R}^n$ be the natural projection onto the quotient. Then σ factors through $S^1 \times \mathbf{R}^n$ because it has period 2τ in θ, so we have a map $\sigma_2: S^1 \times \mathbf{R}^n \to U$ such that $\sigma = \sigma_2 \circ \pi$, and σ_2 is a double covering of U. Thus, there is a unique map $\beta_2: S^1 \times \mathbf{R}^n \to S^1 \times \mathbf{R}^n$, such that $z \in \sigma_2^{-1}(x)$ implies $\sigma_2^{-1}(x) = \{z, \beta_2(z)\}$.

The map β_2 is an involutive diffeomorphism, and covers the identity of U, or $\sigma_2 \circ \beta_2 = \sigma_2$.

Let β denote the induced diffeomorphism of $\mathbf{R}^{n+1}$, or

$$\beta(\theta, z) = (\theta + \tau, \beta_\theta(z))$$

where $\beta_\theta(z)$ is the second component of $\beta_2([\theta], z)$. Then we have a commutative diagram

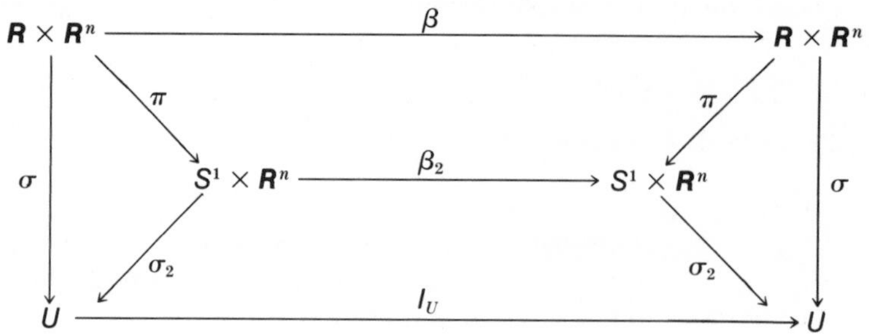

Furthermore, $\sigma(\mathbf{R} \times \{\mathbf{0}\}) = \sigma_2(S^1 \times \{\mathbf{0}\}) = \gamma$. As σ_2 is a local diffeomorphism, there is a unique vectorfield ξ_2 on $S^1 \times \mathbf{R}^n$ such that locally $(T_{(\theta,z)}\sigma_2)\xi_2(\theta, z) = \xi(\sigma_2(\theta, z))$, or $\sigma_2^*\xi_2 = \xi$. As $\sigma_2 \circ \beta_2 = \sigma_2$, we have also that $(\sigma_2 \circ \beta_2)_*\xi = (\sigma_2)_*\xi$, or $\beta_{2*}\xi_2 = \xi_2$, so the pulled-up vectorfield ξ_2 is invariant under the natural involution β_2 of the double covering. Obviously $\gamma_2 = S^1 \times \{0\}$ is a closed orbit of ξ_2, and the following lemma is immediate.

28.3. LEMMA. Let (σ, U) be a pseudochart for γ, a closed orbit of $\xi \in \Gamma^r(\tau_X)$ of prime period τ. Then $y \in \gamma$ has a neighborhood Z such that there exist open sets Z_1 and Z_2 in $S^1 \times \mathbf{R}^n$ satisfying,

(1) $\sigma_2^{-1}(Z) = Z_1 \cup Z_2$;

(2) $\sigma_2|Z_i$ **maps** Z_i **diffeomorphically onto** Z, **for** $i = 1, 2$;

(3) $\sigma_2(W^+(\xi_2, \gamma_2) \cap Z_i) = W^+(\xi, \gamma) \cap Z$, **for** $i = 1, 2$.

We now prove 28.1 using these two lemmas. The idea is to take a pseudochart (σ, U) for γ in which ξ_α has the Floquet Normal Form (§26), obtain a local stable manifold by Lemma 28.2, and project it down into U to obtain a local stable manifold of γ according to Lemma 28.3.

Proof of 28.1. Let (ρ, U) be a pseudochart for γ such that the local representative ξ_ρ is in Floquet Normal Form (26.1(I)),

$$\xi_{\rho 1}(\theta, z) = 1 + Q(\theta, z)$$

$$\xi_{\rho 2}(\theta, z) = Cz + T(\theta, z)$$

where Q and R are periodic in θ with period 2τ.

As γ is elementary by hypothesis, C has no eigenvalue with real part zero (26.1(II)), so by a further change of coordinates

$$(\theta, z) \rightsquigarrow (\theta, Pz)$$

where P is a suitable linear isomorphism, we obtain a pseudochart (σ, U) with ξ_σ in the form

$$\xi_{\sigma 1}(\theta, x, y) = 1 + Q(\theta, x, y)$$

$$\xi_{\sigma 2}(\theta, x, y) = Ax + R(\theta, x, y)$$

$$\xi_{\sigma 3}(\theta, x, y) = By + S(\theta, x, y)$$

for $z = (x, y) \in \boldsymbol{R}^k \times \boldsymbol{R}^{n-k}$, where A is a contraction and B an expansion, and Q, R, S satisfy the conditions in 28.2. Further, Q, R, and S are periodic in θ with period 2τ, so passing to the double covering $\sigma_2\colon S^1 \times \boldsymbol{R}^n \to U$, the pulled-up vectorfield ξ_2 (using the notations preceding 28.3) has local representative of the form f in 28.2. Thus, there is a neighborhood V_2 of $S^1 \times \{\boldsymbol{0}\} = \gamma_2$ in $S^1 \times \boldsymbol{R}^n$ such that $W^+(\xi_2|V_2, \gamma_2)$ is a submanifold. If V is a neighborhood of $\gamma \subset X$ such that $V \subset U$ and $\sigma_2^{-1}(V) \subset V_2$, then by 28.3, $W^+(\xi|V, \gamma)$ is a submanifold as well. For if φ is the flow of ξ and ψ the flow of ξ_2, then $\psi_t(\theta, z) \to \gamma_2$ as $t \to +\infty$, if and only if $\varphi_t(\sigma_2(\theta, z)) \to \gamma$ as $t \to +\infty$. Thus

$$\sigma(W^+(\xi_2|V_2, \gamma_2) = W^+(\xi|\sigma V_2, \gamma)$$

The argument for $W^-(\xi|V, \gamma)$ is the same, so 28.2(II) is proved, and conclusions (I) and (III) follow immediately from 28.2(II) and 28.3 in a similar fashion. ∎

For the analogue of the Global Stable Manifold Theorem (27.3) we must admit more complicated parameter spaces. Suppose γ is an elementary closed orbit of $\xi \in \Gamma^r(\tau_X)$, with prime period τ, flow φ, and stable manifold $W^+ = W^+(\xi, \gamma)$. Then locally, W^+ is a submanifold, so T_xW^+ is well defined for $x \in W^+$. If $x \in \gamma$, then T_xW^+ is the eigenspace of $T_x\varphi_\tau$ corresponding to the eigenvalue 1 and those with real part negative. Let $N_\gamma W^+ = \bigcup_{x \in \gamma} T_xW^+/\langle\xi(x)\rangle$, with the obvious projection onto γ, $N_\gamma W^+ \to \gamma$ is a vector bundle over γ, which may be identified with S^1. If $W^- = W^-(\xi, \gamma)$ is the unstable manifold, we may similarly define a vector bundle $N_\gamma W^- \to \gamma \approx S^1$, of eigenspaces of positive real part. Intuitively, these bundles are linear approximations to the local stable and unstable submanifolds of γ.

If $N_\gamma W^+$ and $N_\gamma W^-$ are trivial, they could be replaced by the isomorphic trivial bundles $S^1 \times \boldsymbol{R}^k \to S^1$ and $S^1 \times \boldsymbol{R}^{n-k}$ (recall that X is $n+1$ dimensional, and here k is the number of eigenvalues of $T_x\varphi_\tau$ having negative real part). In this case these trivial bundles could be used as parameter spaces for W^+ and W^-, analogous to the parameter spaces $\boldsymbol{R}^k$ and $\boldsymbol{R}^{n-k}$ in the case of an elementary critical point. However, even if γ is untwisted, it may happen that $N_\gamma W^+$ or $N_\gamma W^-$ is not trivial. Thus we use these bundles themselves as parameter spaces. For example, if $N_\gamma W^+$ is not trivial, it is a higher-dimensional Möbius band. That is, it is VB isomorphic to the vector bundle

$S^1 \dot{\times} \boldsymbol{R}^k \to S^1$, where $S^1 \dot{\times} \boldsymbol{R}^k$ is the quotient space of $\boldsymbol{R} \times \boldsymbol{R}^k$ under the equivalence relation

$$(\theta; x_1, \ldots, x_k) \equiv (\theta + k\tau; (-1)^k x_1, x_2, \ldots, x_k)$$

where k is an integer.

28.4. GLOBAL STABLE MANIFOLD THEOREM FOR CLOSED ORBITS. Let X be a compact C^{r+2} manifold, $\xi \in \Gamma^r(\tau_X)$ a vectorfield, and γ an elementary closed orbit of ξ. Then $W^+(\xi, \gamma)$ and $W^-(\xi, \gamma)$ are C^r immersed submanifolds of X.

This is proved very easily from the Local Stable Manifold Theorem 28.1, following the example of 27.3. The details are left to the reader. The manifold $W^+(\xi, \gamma)$ is parameterized by $N_\gamma W^+(\xi, \gamma)$, etc.

To simplify notations in the following parameterization theorem, which is analogous to 27.4, we write $P^+(\xi, \gamma)$ instead of $N_\gamma W^+(\xi, \gamma)$ and $P^-(\xi, \gamma)$ instead of $N_\gamma W^-(\xi, \gamma)$.

28.5. PARAMETERIZATION THEOREM FOR CLOSED ORBITS. Let X, ξ, and γ be as in 28.1. Then there exists an open neighborhood N of ξ in $\Gamma^r(\tau_X)$, an open neighborhood V of γ in X, and (for every $\zeta \in N$) C^r maps ψ_ζ^+: $P^+(\xi, \gamma) \to X$ and ψ_ζ^-: $P^-(\xi, \gamma) \to X$, such that,

(I) For $\zeta \in N$, ζ has a unique closed orbit $\gamma_\zeta \subset V$, and this closed orbit is elementary;

(II) For $\zeta \in N$, ψ_ζ^+ and ψ_ζ^- parameterize $W^+(\zeta, \gamma_\zeta)$ and $W^-(\zeta, \gamma_\zeta)$ respectively, i.e., ψ_ζ^+ and ψ_ζ^- are C^{r-1} injective immersions,

$$\psi_\zeta^+(P^+(\xi, \gamma)) = W^+(\zeta, \gamma_\zeta)$$

$$\psi_\zeta^-(P^-(\xi, \gamma)) = W^-(\zeta, \gamma_\zeta)$$

(III) The maps $N \to \mathscr{C}^r(P^+(\xi, \gamma), X)$ and $N \to \mathscr{C}^r(P^-(\xi, \gamma), X)$ given respectively by $\zeta \rightsquigarrow \psi_\zeta^+$ and $\zeta \rightsquigarrow \psi_\zeta^-$, for $\zeta \in N$, are C^1 pseudorepresentations.

The proof, as in the case of a critical point (27.4), follows easily from Lemma 28.3 and the following local lemma.

28.6. LEMMA. Let f and U be as in 28.4. Then there exists $\delta > 0$, a neighborhood N_f of f in $\mathscr{B}^r(U, \boldsymbol{R}^n)$, a neighborhood V of $S^1 \times \{0\}$ in $S^1 \times \boldsymbol{R}^n$, and, for every $g \in N_f$, a C^r map G_g^+: $S^1 \times \boldsymbol{R}^n \to \boldsymbol{R}^{n-k}$, such that,

(I) For $g \in N_f$, g has a unique closed orbit $\gamma_g \subset V$, and this closed orbit is elementary;

(II) For $g \in N_f W^+(g|V, \gamma_g)$ is the graph of G_g^+;

(III) The map $N_f \to \mathscr{C}^r(S^1 \times B_k(\delta), \boldsymbol{R}^{n-k})$ given by $g \rightsquigarrow G_g^+$ for $g \in N_f$ is a C^1 pseudorepresentation.

Also this theorem remains true reading W^-, $n-k$, k, and G^- for W^+, k, $n-k$, and G^+, respectively.

The proof is given in Appendix C by A. Kelley.

7

GENERIC PROPERTIES OF FLOWS

In this chapter the theorems of Kupka and Smale on generic properties of flows are proved by combining the transversality theory and qualitative theory of flows of the preceding chapters. Although conceptually simple, the ideas of the proofs are disguised by rather complicated notations and topological details. As a guide, we begin with an outline. Throughout, X is a C^∞ manifold.

§29. Outline

We prove the G3 Density Theorem of Kupka [1] and Smale [1] in a sequence of steps, each of the following form. If $G(\xi)$ is a property of vectorfields $\xi \in \Gamma^r(\boldsymbol{\tau}_X)$, let $\mathscr{G}^r(X)$ denote the set of vectorfields having this property, or

$$\mathscr{G}^r(X) = \{\xi \in \Gamma^r(\boldsymbol{\tau}_X) \mid G(\xi)\}$$

When X is fixed, we write $\mathscr{G}^r$ rather than $\mathscr{G}^r(X)$. Then $G(\xi)$ is a C^r generic property iff $\mathscr{G}^r \subset \Gamma^r(\boldsymbol{\tau}_X)$ contains a residual set. Recall that residual means a countable intersection of open dense sets, and residual implies dense in our context. Thus, if $G(\xi)$ is a C^r generic property and $\xi \in \Gamma^r(\boldsymbol{\tau}_X)$, then arbitrarily close to ξ, is a vectorfield $\zeta \in \Gamma^r(\boldsymbol{\tau}_X)$ such that $G(\zeta)$ is true.

In this chapter we consider a sequence of properties $G\alpha$ and show they are generic. In fact, in each case we show that the associated subset $\mathscr{G}^r_\alpha \subset \Gamma^r(\tau_X)$ is residual, or open and dense. The properties are the following.

29.1. DEFINITION. Suppose $\xi \in \Gamma^r(\tau_X)$ and $0 \leqslant a \leqslant \infty$. Then

(0) **G0**(ξ) iff ξ is transversal to $(TX)_0$;

(1) **G1**(ξ) iff all critical points of ξ are elementary;

(Δ) **GΔ**(a, ξ) iff all periods τ of closed orbits of ξ, with $\tau \leqslant a$, are transversal periods;

($\frac{3}{2}$) **G$\frac{3}{2}$**(a, ξ) iff $G1(\xi)$ and $G\Delta(a, \xi)$;

(2) **G2**(a, ξ) iff $G1(\xi)$ and all periods τ of closed orbits of ξ, with $\tau \leqslant a$, are elementary periods.

If ψ_i: $P_i \to X$ is a C^1 map ($i = 1, 2$), then ψ_1 and ψ_2 are **transversal,** or $\psi_1 \pitchfork \psi_2$, iff $\psi_1 \times \psi_2 \pitchfork \Delta$, where $\Delta \subset X \times X$ is the diagonal.

If W_1, $W_2 \subset X$ are immersed submanifolds, then W_1 and W_2 are **transversal,** or $W_1 \pitchfork W_2$, iff there exists a parameterization ψ_i of W_i ($i = 1, 2$) with $\psi_1 \pitchfork \psi_2$. If γ_1 and γ_2 are elementary critical elements of ξ, we say γ_1 and γ_2 are ***W*-transversal** iff

$$W^+(\gamma_1, \xi) \pitchfork W^-(\gamma_2, \xi) \qquad \text{and} \qquad W^+(\gamma_2, \xi) \pitchfork W^-(\gamma_1, \xi)$$

(3) **G3**(a, ξ) iff $G2(a, \xi)$ and for critical elements γ_1 and γ_2 of ξ having prime period $\tau \leqslant a$, γ_1 and γ_2 are W-transversal.

The associated subsets of $\Gamma^r(\tau_X)$ are denoted by $\mathscr{G}^r_0(X)$, $\mathscr{G}^r_1(X)$, $\mathscr{G}^r_\Delta(a, X)$, $\mathscr{G}^r_{3/2}(a, X)$, $\mathscr{G}^r_2(a, X)$, and $\mathscr{G}^r_3(a, X)$. When X is fixed we write $\mathscr{G}^r_0$ instead of $\mathscr{G}^r_0(X)$, etc. Also, we sometimes write $\mathscr{G}^r_2(X)$ for $\mathscr{G}^r_2(\infty, X)$, etc.

Note that $\mathscr{G}^r_0$ has been defined in §22, and $\mathscr{G}^r_\Delta$ in §23. These subsets are obviously related as follows.

29.2. PROPOSITION. If $\xi \in \Gamma^r(\tau_X)$ and $0 \leqslant a \leqslant \infty$, then,

(I) $\mathscr{G}^r_{3/2}(a) = \mathscr{G}^r_1 \cap \mathscr{G}^r_\Delta(a)$;

(II) $\mathscr{G}^r_\alpha(\infty) = \cap \{\mathscr{G}^r_\alpha(a) \mid a$ **is a positive integer**$\}$; **for** $\alpha = \Delta, \frac{3}{2}$, **or** 3;

(III) $\mathscr{G}^r_3(a) \subset \mathscr{G}^r_2(a) \subset \mathscr{G}^r_{3/2}(a) \subset \mathscr{G}^r_1 \subset \mathscr{G}^r_0$;

(IV) $\mathscr{G}^r_\alpha(b) \subset \mathscr{G}^r_\alpha(a)$, **for** $b > a$, **and** $\alpha = \Delta, \frac{3}{2}$, 2, **or** 3.

The Kupka-Smale G3 Density Theorem says that $\mathscr{G}^r_3(\infty) \subset \Gamma^r(\tau_X)$ is residual, if X is compact. In the following sections this is proved as follows. In §30, we prove that $G1$ is generic. This is an easy application of transversality theory and illustrates several typical arguments. The basic facts of semialgebraic sets (Appendix B) are used. In §31, we prove that $G2$ is generic. This is a typical difficult application of transversality and is accomplished according to the following program.

Step 1. $\mathscr{G}^r_2(a)$ is open (31.3).

This is proved by the Transversal Openness Theorem (18.2), and the Period Bounding Lemma (24.7).

Step 2. $\mathscr{G}^r_{3/2}(a)$ is open (31.4).

This is a trivial consequence of the openness of $\mathscr{G}^r_1$ and $\mathscr{G}^r_\Delta(a)$ (24.4).

Step 3. For $\xi \in \mathscr{G}^r_1(X)$ there is an open neighborhood N of ξ and an $a_0 > 0$ such that $\mathscr{G}^r_2(a_0) \cap N = N$ (31.5).

This is one aspect of the Period Bounding Lemma (24.7).

Step 4. $\mathscr{G}^r_2(a) \cap N$ dense in N implies $\mathscr{G}^r_{3/2}\left(\frac{3}{2}a\right) \cap N$ dense in N (31.6).

This is the difficult step. The Transversal Density Theorem (19.1) is used. The verification of its hypothesis requires the perturbation theory of §32.

Step 5. $\mathscr{G}^r_{3/2}(a) \cap N$ dense in N implies $\mathscr{G}^r_2(a) \cap N$ dense in N (31.9).

The proof of this step is a long but straightforward application of the perturbation theory of §32.

Step 6. $\mathscr{G}^r_2(a) \cap N$ dense in N implies $\mathscr{G}^r_2\left(\frac{3}{2}a\right) \cap N$ dense in N (31.14).

This is immediate from Steps 4 and 5.

Step 7. $\mathscr{G}^r_2(a) \cap N$ is dense in N (31.15).

This follows from Steps 3 and 6 by induction on k, in $a_k = \left(\frac{3}{2}\right)^k a_0$. The basic idea of this induction is due to Peixoto. It is essential to this proof at Step 4, because a direct application of the Transversal Density Theorem without this induction fails, in that the hypothesis of transversality of the evaluation map is not satisfied.

In §32 we prove some lemmas on the perturbation of the flow φ^ξ caused by a change in the vectorfield ξ. These are used in both §31 and §33. In §33 we prove that $G3$ is generic, another easy application of the transversality theory.

All of these steps are proved under the assumption that X is compact. The $G3$ Density Theorem has been extended to the noncompact case by Peixoto [2].

§30. G1 Density

In this section we prove that $G1$ is a generic property on compact manifolds. Throughout, we let X denote a fixed C^∞ manifold of finite dimension n, a Finsler on $J^r(\tau_X)$ is fixed once and for all, and $\Gamma^r(\tau_X)$ denotes the Banach space determined by this Finsler (Chapter II). The subset $\mathscr{G}^r_1(X)$ is defined in the outline (29.1).

30.1. G1 DENSITY THEOREM. Let X be a compact C^∞ manifold and $r \geq 1$. Then $\mathscr{G}^r_1(X)$ is an open-dense subset of $\Gamma^r(\tau_X)$.

The proof requires the next two lemmas. We consider the 1-jet bundle $\pi^1: J^1(\tau_X) \to X$ (§8). For $\xi \in \Gamma^r(\tau_X)$ define $\rho_\xi: X \to J^1(\tau_X)$ by

$$\rho_\xi(x) = j^1\xi(x)$$

for $x \in X$. Then by 12.4(I) the map

$$\rho: \Gamma^r(\tau_X) \to \Gamma^{r-1}(J^1(\tau_X))$$

given by $\xi \rightsquigarrow \rho_\xi$ for $\xi \in \Gamma^r(\tau_X)$ is a C^{r-1} representation of mappings. Also, by 12.4(II), the evaluation map ev_ρ: $\Gamma^r(\tau_X) \times X \to J^1(\tau_X)$ is transversal to points and hence, *a fortiori*, $ev_\rho \pitchfork W$ for every submanifold W in $J^1(\tau_X)$.

If (α, α_0, U) is a natural VB chart on π^1, then

$$\alpha((\pi^1)^{-1}(U)) = \alpha_0(U) \times \mathbf{E}_\alpha \times L(\mathbf{E}_\alpha, \mathbf{E}_\alpha)$$

where $\mathbf{E}_\alpha$ is the ambient space of $\alpha_0(U)$. Define the subset $\mathbf{W} \subset J^1(\tau_X)$ by stipulating that $p \in \mathbf{W}$, if and only if in some (and hence every) natural VB chart (α, α_0, U) with $\pi^1(p) \in U$ we have

$$\alpha(p) = (x, \mathbf{0}, A) \in \alpha_0(U) \times \mathbf{E}_\alpha \times L(\mathbf{E}_\alpha, \mathbf{E}_\alpha)$$

where $A \in L(\mathbf{E}_\alpha, \mathbf{E}_\alpha)$ has at least one eigenvalue with real part zero.

30.2. *W*-STRUCTURE LEMMA. $\mathbf{W} \subset J^1(\tau_X)$ is closed. Furthermore, $\mathbf{W} = W_1 \cup \cdots \cup W_k$ where $W_1, \ldots, W_k$ are submanifolds of $J^1(\tau_X)$ of codimension $\geq n + 1$, where n is the dimension of X.

We postpone the proof of 30.2 briefly.

30.3. $\pitchfork$ CHARACTERIZATION LEMMA. For $\xi \in \Gamma^r(\tau_X)$ the following are equivalent:

(1) $\xi \in \mathscr{G}_1^r(\tau_X)$;

(2) $\rho_\xi(X) \cap \mathbf{W} = \varnothing$;

(3) $\rho_\xi \pitchfork W_i$, **for** $i = 1, \ldots, k$.

Proof. The equivalence of (1) and (2) is immediate from the definitions, and (2) implies (3) is trivial. Since, by 30.2, the codimension of W_i is greater than the dimension of X, ρ_ξ could not intersect W_i and be transversal to it. Hence (3) implies (2). ∎

Proof of 30.1. In view of Lemma 30.3, $\mathscr{G}_1^r(X) = \bigcap_{i=1}^{k} \Gamma_{W_i}^r(\tau_X)$, where $\Gamma_{W_i}^r(\tau_X)$ is the subspace of vectorfields ξ such that $\rho_\xi \pitchfork W_i$. It suffices to show that $\Gamma_{W_i}^r(\tau_X)$ is dense and that $\mathscr{G}_1^r(X)$ is open. The latter is immediate, for $r \geq 1$, from the Openness of Nonintersection (18.1), as W is a closed subset (30.2) and X is compact. To prove $\Gamma_{W_i}^r(\tau_X)$ dense, we suppose first that $r \geq 2$. Then ρ satisfies the hypotheses of the Transversal Density Theorem (19.1), so $\Gamma_{W_i}^r(\tau_X)$ is residual, and hence dense. For $r = 1$, we use a "2ϵ argument" typical of applications of the Density Theorem, which we call the **indifference of** r, to show that $\mathscr{G}_1^2 \subset \Gamma^2(\tau_X)$ dense implies $\mathscr{G}_1^1 \subset \Gamma^1(\tau_X)$ dense.

Choose $\xi \in \Gamma^1(\tau_X)$ and an open neighborhood $N \subset \Gamma^1(\tau_X)$ of ξ. Then, since $\Gamma^2(\tau_X) \subset \Gamma^1(\tau_X)$ is dense in the C^1 topology, there is a $\xi_1 \in N \cap \Gamma^2(\tau_X)$. But the C^1 topology is weaker than the C^2 topology, so $N \cap \Gamma^2(\tau_X)$ is open in

$\Gamma^2(\tau_X)$. Hence by the special case $r \geq 2$, there is $\xi_2 \in N \cap \mathcal{G}_1^2(\tau_X)$, or $N \cap \mathcal{G}_1^1 \neq \emptyset$. This shows that $\mathcal{G}_1^1(X)$ is dense in $\Gamma^1(\tau_X)$. ∎

We now return to the ***W***-Structure Lemma (30.2). Recall that n is the dimension of X. Let $\mathbf{M}$ be the set of real linear maps in $L(\mathbf{R}^n, \mathbf{R}^n)$ having some eigenvalue with real part zero. Choosing natural VB charts on $\boldsymbol{\pi}^1$ (see the definition of $\mathbf{W}$) we see that it suffices to prove the following.

30.4. *M*-STRUCTURE LEMMA. The subset $M \subset L(\mathbf{R}^n, \mathbf{R}^n)$ is closed. Furthermore, M is a finite union of submanifolds of codimension ≥ 1.

The rest of the section (four propositions) is devoted to the proof of this lemma; for the idea behind this we are indebted to Robert Gunning. Let $\mathbf{C}$ denote the field of complex numbers. Define the **Newton map** $\boldsymbol{\nu}: \mathbf{C}^n \to \mathbf{C}^n$ by

$$\boldsymbol{\nu}(c_1, \ldots, c_n) = (\sigma_1(c_1, \ldots, c_n), \ldots, \sigma_n(c_1, \ldots, c_n))$$

where $\sigma_1, \ldots, \sigma_n$ are the elementary symmetric polynomials. Then if $a_i = \sigma_i(c_1, \ldots, c_n)$, for $i = 1, \ldots, n$, $a_1 + a_2 z + \cdots + a_n z^{n-1} + z^n$ is the unique monic polynomial whose roots are $c_1, \ldots, c_n$.

30.5. LEMMA. The Newton map $\boldsymbol{\nu}: \mathbf{C}^n \to \mathbf{C}^n$ is closed, i.e., maps closed subsets to closed subsets.

Proof. Suppose we have a sequence $\mathbf{c}^{(k)} = (c_1^{(k)}, \ldots, c_n^{(k)})$ of points in $\mathbf{C}^n$ such that $\boldsymbol{\nu}(\mathbf{c}^{(k)}) \to \mathbf{a} = (a_1, \ldots, a_n) \in \mathbf{C}^n$. It suffices to show that there is a convergent subsequence of $\mathbf{c}^{(k)}$, which converges to a point $\mathbf{c} \in \mathbf{C}^n$ such that $\boldsymbol{\nu}(\mathbf{c}) = \mathbf{a}$.

Let g_k be the monic polynomial whose roots are $c_1^{(k)}, \ldots, c_n^{(k)}$; let g_∞ be the monic polynomial with coefficients $a, \ldots, a_n$, i.e.,

$$g_\infty(z) = a_1 + a_2 z + \cdots + a_n z^{n-1} + z^n$$

Then $g_k \to g_\infty$ uniformly on compact subsets. But $g_k(z) - z^n$, for $k = 1, 2, \ldots, \infty$, is a polynomial of degree $\leq n-1$. Hence if γ is a sufficiently large circle in $\mathbf{C}$ centered at the origin,

$$|g_k(z) - z^n| < |z^n|$$

for $z \in \gamma$ and $k = 1, 2, \ldots, \infty$. Then by Rouché's Theorem (Ahlfors [*1*; p. 124]), all the roots of the polynomials $g_1, g_2, \ldots, g_\infty$ are contained within the interior of γ. Hence we may choose a convergent subsequence of $\mathbf{c}^{(r)}$ with limit $\mathbf{c}$. By the continuity of $\boldsymbol{\nu}$, $\boldsymbol{\nu}(\mathbf{c}) = \mathbf{a}$. ∎

Now let $\mathbf{k}: L(\mathbf{R}^n, \mathbf{R}^n) \to \mathbf{R}^n$ be the map which assigns to a linear map A the coefficients of the characteristic polynomial of A, i.e., $\mathbf{k}(A) = (a_1, \ldots, a_n)$ where $\det(Ix - A) = a_1 + a_2 x + \cdots + a_n x^{n-1} + x^n$. Let $\mathbf{V} \subset \mathbf{R}^{2n} \approx \mathbf{C}^n$ be defined by

$$\mathbf{V} = \{(x_1 + iy_1, \ldots, x_n + iy_n) \mid x_1 = 0 \text{ or} \ldots \text{or } x_n = 0\}$$

Obviously $\mathbf{M}$ and $\mathbf{V}$ are related as follows.

30.6. LEMMA. $\mathbf{M} = \mathbf{k}^{-1}(\boldsymbol{\nu}(\mathbf{V}))$.

The structure of ***V***, ***M***, and thus ***W*** is obtained from the theory of semialgebraic sets. A map $\mathbf{f}: \mathbf{R}^p \to \mathbf{R}^q$ is **algebraic** iff $\mathbf{f}$ has the form

$$\mathbf{f}(x_1, \ldots, x_p) = (f_1(x_1, \ldots, x_p), \ldots, f_q(x_1, \ldots, x_p))$$

for $(x_1, \ldots, x_p) \in \boldsymbol{R}^p$, where $f_1, \ldots, f_q$ are polynomials in $x_1, \ldots, x_p$. A subset of $\boldsymbol{R}^p$ is **semialgebraic** if it is the finite union of sets defined by finitely many polynomial equalities and inequalities; i.e., iff it is the finite union of sets S where $\mathbf{x} \in S$, if

$$P_1(\mathbf{x}) = \ldots = P_j(\mathbf{x}) = 0 \quad \text{and} \quad Q_1(\mathbf{x}), \ldots, Q_m(\mathbf{x}) > 0$$

the P's and Q's being polynomials in $\mathbf{x} = (x_1, \ldots, x_p)$.

30.7. TARSKI-SEIDENBERG THEOREM. The algebraic image of a semialgebraic set is semialgebraic.

30.8. WHITNEY THEOREM. Every semialgebraic set in $\boldsymbol{R}^p$ is a finite union of submanifolds.

The proofs of 30.7 and 30.8 are given in Appendix B.

Proof of 30.4. Clearly the inverse image of a semialgebraic set under an algebraic map is a semialgebraic set. Also $\boldsymbol{V}$ is a semialgebraic set and the maps $\boldsymbol{k}$ and $\boldsymbol{\nu}$ are algebraic. Hence by 30.6 and 30.7, $\boldsymbol{M}$ is a semialgebraic set, and thus, by 30.8, $\boldsymbol{M}$ is a finite union of submanifolds. By 30.5, $\boldsymbol{\nu}(\boldsymbol{V})$ is closed. By 28.6, $\boldsymbol{M} = \boldsymbol{k}^{-1}(\boldsymbol{\nu}(\boldsymbol{V}))$ is also closed. Finally $\boldsymbol{M}$ must have codimension $\geqslant 1$ (i.e., null interior) since by an arbitrarily small perturbation, any linear map can be changed into one having eigenvalues with nonzero real parts. ∎

This completes the proof of the $\boldsymbol{M}$-Structure Lemma, so also the $\boldsymbol{W}$-Structure Lemma, and establishes the $G1$ Density Theorem.

§31. *G2* Density

In this section we prove that $G2$ is a generic property. The outline of the proof is given in §29. The main theorem is the following, originally due to Kupka [*1*] and Smale [*1*].

31.1. THEOREM. If X is compact, $r \geqslant 1$, and $0 \leqslant a < \infty$, then $\mathscr{G}_2^r(a) \subset \Gamma^r(\tau_X)$ is open and dense.

Then from §29.2(II) we get the main consequence, an easy corollary.

31.2. *G2* DENSITY THEOREM. If X is compact and $r \geqslant 1$, $\mathscr{G}_2^r \subset \Gamma^r(\tau_X)$ is residual, i.e., $G2$ is a C^r generic property.

The rest of the section is devoted to the proof of 31.1, in the seven steps outlined in §29. We assume throughout this section that X is a compact C^∞ manifold and $r \geqslant 1$.

31.3. STEP 1. For $a > 0$, $\mathscr{G}_2^r(a)$ is open in $\Gamma^r(\tau_X)$.

Proof. For $\xi \in \Gamma^r(\tau_X)$ let $\varphi^\xi \colon X \times \boldsymbol{R} \to X$ be the flow of ξ. The map

$$\varphi \colon \Gamma^r(\tau_X) \to \mathscr{C}^r(X \times \boldsymbol{R}, X)$$

given by

$$\varphi(\xi) = \varphi^\xi$$

for $\xi \in \Gamma^r(\tau_X)$ is a C^r representation, by 12.3 and the Parameterized Flow Theorem (21.4); here the parameter is the vectorfield itself.

Recall from §9 the linear map bundle

$$L(\tau_X, \tau_X): L(T(X), T(X)) \to X \times X$$

For this bundle the fiber over a point $(x, y) \in X \times X$ is $L(T_xX, T_yX)$. This suggests the map

$$\Phi': \Gamma^r(\tau_X) \to \mathscr{C}^{r-1}(X \times \boldsymbol{R}^+, L(T(X), T(X)))$$

given by

$$\Phi'(\xi) = \Phi'_\xi$$

for $\xi \in \Gamma^r(\tau_X)$, where

$$\Phi'_\xi(x, t) = T_x\varphi_t^\xi$$

for $(x, t) \in X \times \boldsymbol{R}^+$. (Here $\boldsymbol{R}^+$ is the set of positive real numbers.) Since Φ' is obtained from φ by taking the "partial tangent" in the variable x, Φ' is a C^{r-1} representation.

Let $\boldsymbol{W}' \subset L(T(X), T(X))$ be the set of $A \in L(T(X), T(X))$ such that,

(1) $L(\tau_X, \tau_X)A = (x, x)$ for some $x \in X$, i.e., $A \in L(T_xX, T_xX)$;

(2) A has two or more complex eigenvalues of modulus 1.

Then $\xi \in \mathscr{G}_2^r(a)$ if and only if $\Phi'_\xi(x, t) = T_x\varphi_t \notin \boldsymbol{W}'$ for $(x, t) \in X \times (0, a]$.

Now choose $\xi_0 \in \mathscr{G}_2^r(a)$. By the Period Bounding Lemma (24.7), take an open neighborhood N of ξ_0 and a real number $a > b > 0$, such that for $\xi \in N$ every closed orbit of ξ has period $\geqslant b$. Take $K = [b, a]$. Then for $\xi \in N$ we have $\xi \in \mathscr{G}_2^r(a)$ iff $\Phi'_\xi(K) \cap \boldsymbol{W}' = \varnothing$. But K is compact and, by an argument similar to 30.2, $\boldsymbol{W}'$ is closed. Hence by the Openness Theorem (18.2), $\mathscr{G}_2^r(a) \cap N$ is open. This proves $\mathscr{G}_2^r(a)$ is open in $\Gamma^r(\tau_X)$. ∎

It would be nice to prove that $\mathscr{G}_2^r(a)$ is dense by using the Transversal Density Theorem for the C^{r-1} representation Φ'. (It can be shown that $\boldsymbol{W}'$ is a finite union of submanifolds, as in 30.2.) Unfortunately, the Transversal Density Theorem (19.1) requires as a hypothesis that the evaluation map be transversal to $\boldsymbol{W}'$, and this is false in this case. We use instead Peixoto's induction idea.

31.4. STEP 2. For $0 < a < \infty$, $\mathscr{G}_{3/2}^r(a)$ is an open subset of $\Gamma^r(\tau_X)$.

Proof. As $\mathscr{G}_{3/2}^r(a) = \mathscr{G}_\Delta^r(a) \cap \mathscr{G}_1^r(X)$, it is open by the Openness of Transversal Flows (24.4) and G1 (30.1). ∎

31.5. STEP 3. If $\xi \in \mathscr{G}_1^r(X)$, there exists a neighborhood $N \subset \mathscr{G}_1^r(X)$ of ξ and an $a_0 > 0$ such that $\mathscr{G}_2^r(a_0) \cap N = N$.

Proof. As $\mathscr{G}_1^r \subset \mathscr{G}_0^r$ (29.2), $\xi \in \mathscr{G}_0^r$, and by the Period Bounding Lemma (24.7), there is an open neighborhood N_1 of ξ in $\Gamma^r(\tau_X)$ and a real number $a_1 > 0$, such that, for $\zeta \in N_1$, every closed orbit of ζ has prime period $\geqslant a_1$. Let $N = N_1 \cap \mathscr{G}_1^r$ and $a_0 = a_1/2$. ∎

31.6. STEP 4. If $N \subset \mathscr{G}_1^r$ is an open set, $0 < a < \infty$, and $\mathscr{G}_2^r(a) \cap N \subset N$ is dense, then $\mathscr{G}_{3/2}^r\left(\frac{3}{2}a\right) \cap N \subset N$ is dense.

The proof of Step 4 requires two lemmas.

31.7. PERTURBATION LEMMA. **If $\xi^0 \in \Gamma^r(\tau_X)$, φ^0 is the flow of ξ^0, γ is a closed orbit of ξ^0 of prime period τ, $x \in \gamma$, $\dot{x} \in T_xX$, there exists an $\eta \in \Gamma^r(\tau_X)$ such that**

$$\frac{d}{ds}\left[\varphi^s_\tau(x)\right]_{s=0} = \dot{x}$$

where φ^s is the flow of $\xi^s = \xi^0 + s\eta$.

Here the hypothesis that τ is the *prime* period is essential. The proof is given in §32. Now as we wish to apply the Transversal Density Theorem to prove Step 4, we need an appropriate representation. Recall the flowgraph representation of §24,

$$\boldsymbol{\Phi}: \Gamma^r(\tau_X) \to \mathscr{C}^r(X \times \boldsymbol{R}^+, X \times \boldsymbol{R}^+ \times X)$$

with evaluation map

$$ev: \Gamma^r(\tau_X) \times X \times \boldsymbol{R}^+ \to X \times \boldsymbol{R}^+ \times X$$

and the diagonal $\boldsymbol{\Delta} \subset X \times \boldsymbol{R}^+ \times X$.

31.8. EVALUATION TRANSVERSALITY LEMMA. **If $\xi \in \mathscr{G}^r_2(a)$, $x \in X$, $t \in \left(0, \frac{3}{2}a\right]$, then**

$$ev \,\overline{\pitchfork}_{(\xi,x,t)}\, \boldsymbol{\Delta}$$

Proof. Choose $\xi \in \mathscr{G}^r_2(a) \cap N$, $x \in X$, and $t \in (0, a]$. Since $\Gamma^r(\tau_X)$ is a Banach space, we identify $T_\xi\Gamma^r(\tau_X)$ and $\Gamma^r(\tau_X)$. Then for $\eta \in T_\xi\Gamma^r(\tau_X) = \Gamma^r(\tau_X)$, $\dot{x} \in T_xX$, and $\dot{t} \in T_t\boldsymbol{R} = \boldsymbol{R}$ we have, by the partial derivative rule, that

$$(\ddagger) \qquad T_{(\xi,x,t)}ev(\eta, \dot{x}, \dot{t}) = T_{(x,t)}\varphi^\xi(\dot{x}, \dot{t}) + \frac{d}{ds}\{ev(\xi + s\eta, x, t)\}_{s=0}$$

The last term on the right should be interpreted as a point in $T_{ev(\xi,x,t)}(X \times \boldsymbol{R}^+ \times X)$. We show that if $ev(\xi, x, \tau) \in \boldsymbol{\Delta}$ (i.e., $ev(\xi, x, \tau) = (x, \tau, x)$), then the image of the linear map $T_{(\xi,x,\tau)}ev$ contains a linear complement to $T_{(x,\tau,x)}\,\boldsymbol{\Delta}$ in $T_{(x,\tau,x)}(X \times \boldsymbol{R}^+ \times X)$, by considering two cases.

Case 1. $\boldsymbol{\Phi}_\xi \,\overline{\pitchfork}_{(x,\tau)}\, \boldsymbol{\Delta}$. This says that the first term in (‡) spans a complement to $T_{(x,\tau,x)}\,\boldsymbol{\Delta}$ (as $\dot{x}$ and $\dot{t}$ vary); this case is trivial.

Case 2. $\boldsymbol{\Phi}_\xi$ is not transversal to $\boldsymbol{\Delta}$ at (x, τ). In this case the first term in (‡) does not span a complement to $T_{(x,\tau,x)}\,\boldsymbol{\Delta}$; we must use a contribution from the second term. Since $\xi \in \mathscr{G}^r_2(a) \subset G^r_\Delta(a)$, Case 2 can only occur when $a < \tau \leqslant \frac{3}{2}a$. Let φ be the flow of ξ; then $\varphi_\tau(x) = x$. Since $\xi \in \mathscr{G}^r_2(a) \subset \mathscr{G}^r_0(X)$, x is not a critical point. So by 23.2, τ is a nontransversal period of the nonelementary closed orbit φ_x, i.e., $T_x\varphi_\tau$ has 1 as an eigenvalue with multiplicity $\geqslant 2$. But τ must be the prime period of φ_x; otherwise $\tau = k\tau_0$ where k is an integer and τ_0 is a period of φ_x such that $0 < \tau_0 \leqslant a$. In this case, as $T_x\varphi_\tau = (T_x\varphi_{\tau_0})^k$, $T_x\varphi_{\tau_0}$ must have two eigenvalues which are complex kth roots of 1. Since such eigenvalues would have modulus 1, this contradicts the assumption that $\xi \in \mathscr{G}^r_2(a)$. Therefore τ is the prime period of φ_x, and the Perturbation Lemma applies. For $s \in \boldsymbol{R}$, let $\xi^s \in \Gamma^r(\tau_X)$ be defined by $\xi^s = \xi + s\eta$, and let φ^s be the flow of ξ^s. In this notation, the second term on the right in (‡) may be rewritten

$$\frac{d}{ds}\{ev(\xi + s\eta, x, t)\}_{s=0} = \left(0_x, 0, \frac{d}{ds}\{\varphi^s_t(x)\}_{s=0}\right)$$

Since $\{0_x\} \times \{0\} \times T_xX$ is obviously a complement to $T_{(x,\tau,x)}\boldsymbol{\Delta}$, the conclusion follows at once from the Perturbation Lemma (31.7). ∎

With the aid of the Perturbation Lemma, we return to Step 4 (31.6).

Proof of Step 4. Transversality is an "open condition", i.e., if a map is transversal to a closed submanifold at a point, it is transversal to the submanifold in some neighborhood of that point (see the Local Representation of Transversality, 17.1). Lemma 31.8 tells us that ev is transversal to $\mathbf{\Delta}$ on the set $(\mathcal{G}_2^r(a) \cap N) \times X \times \left(0, \frac{3}{2}a\right]$. Hence ev is transversal to $\mathbf{\Delta}$ on some open neighborhood of this set, and since X is compact, there is an $\epsilon > 0$ such that ev is transversal to $\mathbf{\Delta}$ on $(\mathcal{G}_2^r(a) \cap N) \times X \times \left(0, \frac{3}{2}a + \epsilon\right)$. Define the C^r representation

$$\widetilde{\mathbf{\Phi}}: \mathcal{G}_2^r(a) \cap N \to \mathscr{C}^r\left(X \times \left(0, \frac{3}{2}a + \epsilon\right), X \times \mathbf{R}^+ \times X\right)$$

by

$$\widetilde{\mathbf{\Phi}}(\xi) = \mathbf{\Phi}_\xi \mid X \times \left(0, \frac{3}{2}a + \epsilon\right)$$

for $\xi \in \mathcal{G}_2^r(a) \cap N$. Note that $\mathcal{G}_2^r(a) \cap N$ is an open subset of $\Gamma^r(\boldsymbol{\tau}_X)$ by Step 1 (31.3) and is hence a manifold. If $\mathbf{\Phi}(\xi) \pitchfork \mathbf{\Delta}$ for some $\xi \in \mathcal{G}_2^r(a) \cap N$, then, *a fortiori*, $\xi \in \mathcal{G}_{3/2}^r\left(\frac{3}{2}a\right)$. But by the Transversal Density Theorem (19.1) the set

$$\{\xi \in \mathcal{G}_2^r(a) \cap N \mid \widetilde{\mathbf{\Phi}}(\xi) \pitchfork \mathbf{\Delta}\}$$

is dense in $\mathcal{G}_2^r(a) \cap N$. Therefore $\mathcal{G}_2^r(a) \cap N \cap \mathcal{G}_{3/2}^r\left(\frac{3}{2}a\right)$ is dense in $\mathcal{G}_2^r(a) \cap N$. Since $\mathcal{G}_2^r(a) \cap N$ is open dense in N (by hypothesis and 31.3), it follows that $\mathcal{G}_{3/2}^r\left(\frac{3}{2}a\right)$ is dense in N. ∎

31.9. STEP 5. If $N \subset \mathcal{G}_1^r$ is an open set, $0 < a < \infty$, and $\mathcal{G}_{3/2}^r(a) \cap N \subset N$ is dense, then $\mathcal{G}_2^r(a) \cap N \subset N$ is dense.

The proof of Step 5 consists of a brute force perturbation, based on the theory of §32. We need four lemmas, the first on linear algebra.

Let $\boldsymbol{E}$ be a finite-dimensional Banach space, $L \in \boldsymbol{L(E, E)}$, and $\boldsymbol{v} \in \boldsymbol{E}(\boldsymbol{v} \neq 0)$. Then L is **transversal for *v*** iff $L\boldsymbol{v} = \boldsymbol{v}$ and the eigenvalue 1 of L has multiplicity 1; L is **elementary for *v*** iff L is transversal for $\boldsymbol{v}$ and L has no complex eigenvalue of modulus 1, except 1.

31.10. *M'*-STRUCTURE LEMMA. Let *E* be a finite-dimensional Banach space, $L \in L(E, E)$, and $v \in E$ with $v \neq 0$. Suppose L is transversal (but not elementary) for *v*. Then there exists $A \in L(E, E)$ such that,

(I) $Av = 0$;

(II) For every curve $I \to L(E, E)$ (where I is an open interval in $\boldsymbol{R}$ about zero) given by $s \rightsquigarrow L_s$ for $s \in \boldsymbol{R}$ and satisfying the three conditions:

(i) $L_0 = L$;

(ii) $(d/ds)\, L_s|_{s=0} = A$;

(iii) For each $s \in I$, L_s **is transversal for** $\boldsymbol{v}$**;**
there exists $\epsilon > 0$ **such that for** $0 < s < \epsilon$, L_s **is elementary for** $\boldsymbol{v}$**.**

Proof. Let $\boldsymbol{P} = \{B \in L(\boldsymbol{E}, \boldsymbol{E}) \mid B\boldsymbol{v} = \boldsymbol{v}\}$ and let $\boldsymbol{M}'$ be the set of all $B \in \boldsymbol{P}$ which are transversal for $\boldsymbol{v}$ but not elementary for $\boldsymbol{v}$, i.e., if $B \in M$, then B has $\boldsymbol{v}$ as an eigenvector with complex eigenvalue λ with $\lambda \neq 1$ but $|\lambda| = 1$. Then $\boldsymbol{P}$ is a hyperplane in $L(\boldsymbol{E}, \boldsymbol{E})$ and is therefore clearly a manifold. But $\boldsymbol{M}'$ is a subset of $\boldsymbol{P}$ and is also a semialgebraic set (we identify $\boldsymbol{E}$ with $\boldsymbol{R}^n$). By the same argument used to establish the ***M***-Structure Lemma (30.4), we see that $\boldsymbol{M}'$ is a finite union of submanifolds of $\boldsymbol{P}$, each of codimension ≥ 1 in $\boldsymbol{P}$. Let $M_1, \ldots, M_k$ be the "manifold components" of $\boldsymbol{M}'$; i.e., each M_i $(i = 1, \ldots, k)$ is a submanifold of $\boldsymbol{P}$ and $\boldsymbol{M} = M_1 \cup \cdots \cup M_k$. Then there is an $A \in T_L\boldsymbol{P}$ with $A \notin T_L M_i$ $(i = 1, \ldots, k)$. As $T_L\boldsymbol{P}$ is a subspace of $T_L L(\boldsymbol{E}, \boldsymbol{E})$ which may be identified with $L(\boldsymbol{E}, \boldsymbol{E})$, we consider A as a point of $L(\boldsymbol{E}, \boldsymbol{E})$. Since $A \in T_L\boldsymbol{P}$, $A\boldsymbol{v} = \boldsymbol{0}$.

Now suppose the curve $I \to L(\boldsymbol{E}, \boldsymbol{E})$ given by $s \rightsquigarrow L_s$ satisfies (i), (ii), and (iii) in 31.10(II). For each $i = 1, \ldots, k$,

$$\frac{d}{ds} L_s\Big|_{s=0} \notin T_L M_i$$

Hence, for each $i = 1, \ldots, k$, there is a real number $\epsilon_i > 0$ such that $L_s \notin M_i$ for $0 < s < \epsilon_i$. Let ϵ be the smallest of $\epsilon_1, \ldots, \epsilon_k$; it follows that $L_s \notin \boldsymbol{M}'$ for $0 < s < \epsilon$. ∎

31.11. TANGENT PERTURBATION LEMMA. Let $\xi^0 \in \Gamma^r(\tau_X)$ $(r \geq 1)$, γ **be a closed orbit of** ξ^0 **of prime period** τ, U **a neighborhood of** γ **in** X, $x \in \gamma$, **and** $A \in L(T_xX, T_xX)$. **Then, if** $A\xi^0(x) = 0_x$, **there exists** $\eta \in \Gamma^r(\tau_X)$ **such that,**

(I) $\eta \mid \gamma \equiv 0$;

(II) $\eta \mid X \setminus U \equiv 0$;

(III) If for $s \in \boldsymbol{R}$, φ^s **is the flow of** $\xi^s = \xi^0 + s\eta$, **then**

$$\frac{d}{ds}\{T_x\varphi^s_\tau\}_{s=0} = A$$

This Lemma is proved in §32. Note that the notation

$$\frac{d}{ds}\{T_x\varphi^s_\tau\}_{s=0}$$

is interpreted as the limit of a difference quotient; this is possible since the map $s \rightsquigarrow T_x\varphi^s_t$ is a curve in the Banach space $L(T_xX, T_xX)$.

31.12. SINGLE FORCE LEMMA. Let γ **be a closed orbit of** $\xi \in \mathscr{G}^r_{3/2}(a)$ **of period** $\leq a$ **and** U **be an open neighborhood of** γ **in** X. **Then there is a vectorfield** $\eta \in \Gamma^r(\tau_X)$ **such that,**

(I) $\eta \mid \gamma \equiv 0$;

(II) $\eta \mid X \setminus U \equiv 0$;

(III) For sufficiently small $s \in \boldsymbol{R}^+$, γ **is an elementary closed orbit of the vectorfield** $\xi + s\eta$.

Proof. Take ξ, γ, and U as above. Choose any point $x \in \gamma$ and let $\tau \leq a$ be the prime period of γ. Let φ be the flow of ξ. In 31.10 read T_xX for **E**, $T_x\varphi_\tau$ for L, and $\xi(x)$ for **v**; then there exists an A satisfying (I) and (II) in 31.10. For this A, choose η according to 31.11. For $s \in \mathbf{R}$, set $L_s = T_x\varphi_\tau^s$. Since $\mathscr{G}^r_{3/2}(a)$ is open, and $\xi \in \mathscr{G}^r_{3/2}(a)$; $\xi + s\eta \in \mathscr{G}^r_{3/2}(a)$ for sufficiently small s. Thus L_s satisfies (i), (ii), and (iii) in 31.10(II); so $T_x\varphi_\tau^s$ is elementary for $\xi(x)$ for sufficiently small s. As φ^s is the flow of $\xi + s\eta$, and γ is clearly a closed orbit of $\xi + s\eta$ of period τ, this says that γ is an elementary closed orbit of $\xi + s\eta$ (for sufficiently small s). ∎

31.13. BRUTE FORCE LEMMA. For every $\xi \in \mathscr{G}^r_{3/2}(a)$ ($a \in \mathbf{R}^+$) there exists $\eta \in \Gamma^r(\tau_X)$, such that for sufficiently small $s \in \mathbf{R}^+$:

(I) The critical elements of $\xi + s\eta$ of period $\leqslant a$ are precisely the same as the critical elements of ξ of period $\leqslant a$;

(II) If γ is a critical element of ξ of period $\leqslant a$, γ is an elementary critical element of $\xi + s\eta$;

(III) $\xi + s\eta \in \mathscr{G}^r_2(a)$.

Proof. Choose $\xi \in \mathscr{G}^r_{3/2}(a)$. By 24.2, ξ has finitely many critical elements of period $\leqslant a$. Let $\gamma_1, \ldots, \gamma_k$ be the closed orbits of ξ of period $\leqslant a$ which are *not* elementary. Since $\xi \in \mathscr{G}^r_{3/2}(a)$, the prime period of each γ_i ($i = 1, \ldots, k$) is transversal. For each $i = 1, \ldots, k$ let U_i be an open neighborhood of γ_i in X, so small that it intersects no critical element of ξ of period $\leqslant a$ besides γ_i. By 31.12, we can find vectorfields $\eta_1, \ldots, \eta_k \in \Gamma^r(\tau_X)$ such that for $i = 1, \ldots, k$:

(1) $\eta_i \mid \gamma_i \equiv 0$;

(2) $\eta_i \mid X \setminus U_i \equiv 0$;

(3) For sufficiently small $s \in \mathbf{R}^+$, γ_i is an elementary closed orbit of $\xi + s\eta_i$. Let $\eta = \eta_1 + \cdots + \eta_k$. Then (I) is immediate.

By (1) and (2) all the critical elements of ξ of prime period $\leqslant a$ are critical elements of η (for any $s \in \mathbf{R}^+$); hence, by 24.5, for sufficiently small $s \in \mathbf{R}^+$, the critical elements of ξ of prime period $\leqslant a$ are the same as the critical elements of η of prime period $\leqslant a$. Then (II) follows from (3), and (III) is immediate from (II). ∎

In fact, the proof of the Brute Force Lemma looks remarkably like a transversality argument and could be obtained from the Transversal Density Theorem. However, the brute force method is shorter. With these four lemmas, we return to Step 5 (31.9).

Proof of Step 5. Suppose $U \subset N$ is an open set. We construct $\zeta \in \mathscr{G}^r_2(a) \cap U$ as follows. As $\mathscr{G}^r_{3/2}(a) \cap N \subset N$ is dense by hypothesis, we may choose $\xi \in \mathscr{G}^r_{3/2}(a) \cap U$. Then choosing η according to Lemma 31.13, we have $\xi + s\eta \in \mathscr{G}^r_2(a)$ for sufficiently small s. As U is open, there is an $s_0 > 0$ such that $\zeta = \xi + s_0\eta \in \mathscr{G}^r_2(a) \cap U$. ∎

31.14. STEP 6. If $N \subset \mathscr{G}^r_1$ is an open set, $0 < a < \infty$, and $\mathscr{G}^r_2(a) \cap N \subset N$ is dense, then $\mathscr{G}^r_{3/2}\left(\frac{3}{2}a\right) \cap N \subset N$ is dense.

Proof. The proof of Step 6 follows at once from Steps 4 and 5. In the latter, read $\frac{3}{2}a$ instead of a. ∎

31.15. STEP 7. If $\xi \in \mathscr{G}^r_1$, $0 < a < \infty$, there exists an open neighborhood N of ξ in $\mathscr{G}^r_1$ such that $\mathscr{G}^r_2(a) \cap N \subset N$ is dense.

Proof. At this point we use Peixoto's induction, based on Steps 3 and 6. From Step 3, we choose N and a_0 such that $\mathscr{G}_2^r(a_0) \cap N = N$. If k is an integer such that $b = \left(\frac{3}{2}\right)^k a_0 > a$ (as surely exists), then k iterations of Step 6 yield $\mathscr{G}_2^r(b) \cap N \subset N$ dense, while $\mathscr{G}_2^r(b) \subset \mathscr{G}_2^r(a)$. ∎

Now the main Theorem 31.1, and thus also the *G*2 Density Theorem, follow immediately from Step 2 (openness) and Step 7 (local density).

§32. Perturbation Theory

In this section we complete the proof of the *G*2 Density Theorem (31.1) by proving the two perturbation lemmas (31.7) and (31.11).

Throughout this section we shall use the notation

$$\frac{d}{dt}\{c(t)\}_{t=t_0}$$

for the tangent vector to the curve c at time t_0; more precisely, if $c\colon \mathbf{R} \to Y$ is a C^{r+1} map (where Y is a C^{r+1} manifold), then

$$\frac{d}{dt}\{c(t)\}_{t=t_0} = (T_{t_0}c)1$$

If Y happens to be a Banach space, we shall also use the notation

$$\frac{\partial}{\partial t}\{c(t)\}_{t=t_0}$$

for the limit of the difference quotient, i.e.,

$$\frac{\partial}{\partial t}\{c(t)\}_{t=t_0} = \lim_{s\to 0} \frac{1}{s}\{c(t_0+s) - c(t_0)\}$$

It will sometimes be necessary to use both notations with the same c. For example suppose $c\colon \mathbf{R} \to T_xX$ where X is a C^{r+1} manifold ($r \geqslant 1$) and $x \in X$. Then

$$\frac{d}{dt}\{c(t)\}_{t=t_0} \in T^2(X)$$

while

$$\frac{\partial}{\partial t}\{c(t)\}_{t=t_0} \in T_xX$$

Now let X be a C^{r+1} manifold, $\psi\colon X \to X$ a C^{r+1} diffeomorphism from X onto itself, and $\eta \in \Gamma^r(\boldsymbol{\tau}_X)$. Then ψ and η determine a new vectorfield $\psi_*\eta = (T\psi^{-1}) \circ \eta \circ \psi \in \Gamma^r(\boldsymbol{\tau}_X)$. To compute the value of this vectorfield at a point $x \in X$, one goes to the point $y = \psi(x)$, computes the vector $\eta(\psi(x)) \in T_yX$, and pulls this vector back to the tangent space T_xX, using the linear map $T_y\psi^{-1}\colon T_yX \to T_xX$. For this reason, $\psi_*\eta$ is called the **pullback of** η **by** ψ. The reader will note that, if $\varphi\colon X \times \mathbf{R} \to X$ is the flow of a vectorfield $\xi \in \Gamma^r(\boldsymbol{\tau}_X)$, then

$$\frac{\partial}{\partial t}\{\varphi_{t*}\eta(x)\}_{t=0} = \mathbf{L}_\xi\eta(x)$$

where $L_\xi \eta$ is the **Lie derivative** of η with respect to ξ. Also in case $\varphi = \varphi_t$, where $\{\varphi_t\}_{t \in \mathbf{R}}$ is a one-parameter group, we may write the pullback of η by φ_t as

$$\varphi_{t*}\eta = T\varphi_{-t} \circ \eta \circ \varphi_t$$

since

$$T\varphi_t^{-1} = T\varphi_{-t}$$

Our main use for this notion is the following.

32.1. PERTURBATION THEOREM. Let X be a compact C^{r+1} manifold, $r \geq 2$, $\xi^0, \eta \in \Gamma^r(\tau_X)$, φ^0 be the flow of ξ^0, and φ^λ (for $\lambda \in \mathbf{R}$) be the flow of the vectorfield $\xi^\lambda = \xi^0 + \lambda\eta$. Then for $x \in X$ and $t \in \mathbf{R}$,

(I) $$\frac{d}{d\lambda}\{\varphi_t^\lambda(x)\}_{\lambda=0} = \int_0^t T\varphi_s^0 \circ \eta \circ \varphi_{-s+t}^0(x)\, ds$$

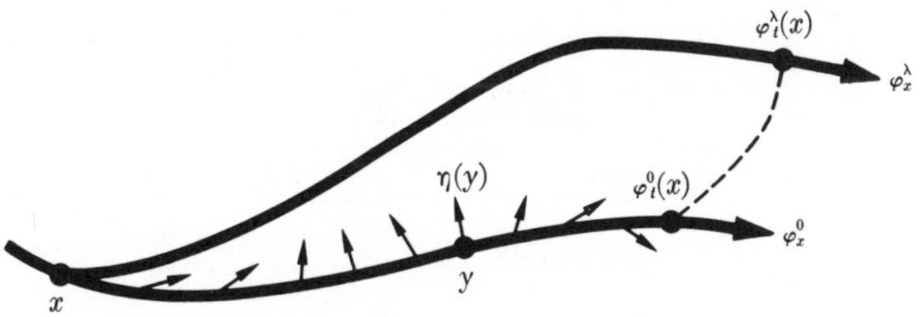

Figure 32-1. The perturbation of the flow.

Before proving the theorem we give its geometrical interpretation in Figure 32-1. For fixed t and x the curve $\mathbf{R} \to X$ given by $\lambda \rightsquigarrow \varphi_t^\lambda(x)$ passes through the point $\varphi_t^0(x)$ at $\lambda = 0$; this curve is represented in the picture by a dotted line. The upper and lower curves in the picture are the orbits φ_x^λ of ξ^λ and φ_x^0 of ξ^0 respectively; the upward pointing arrows on the lower curve represent the perturbing vectorfield η. The left side of (I) is the tangent vector to the dotted curve at $\varphi_t^0(x)$; it may be thought of as the (infinitesimal) displacement of the orbit φ_x^0 due to η after time t. For $y = \varphi_s^0(x)$ $(0 \leq s \leq t)$ one should think of $\eta(y)$ as being the instantaneous displacement of the point y; thus the integrand of the right-hand side of (I) is this instantaneous displacement transported to the tangent space at $\varphi_t(x)$, and (I) says that the (infinitesimal) displacement of the orbit φ_x^0 after time t is the sum of the instantaneous displacements of the points along the curve $\varphi_s^0(x)$ $(0 \leq s \leq t)$.

Proof of 32.1. For convenience, define for $y \in X$ and $t \in \mathbf{R}$ a vector $\zeta_t(y) \in T_yX$ by

$$\zeta_t(y) = \frac{d}{d\lambda}\{\varphi_t^\lambda(\varphi_{-t}^0(y))\}_{\lambda=0}$$

Then

(II) $\zeta_{t+s}(y) = \zeta_t(y) + (\varphi_{-t}^0)_*\zeta_s(y)$

Indeed,

$$\begin{aligned}\zeta_{t+s}(y) &= \frac{d}{d\lambda}\{\varphi^{\lambda}_{t+s}(\varphi^{0}_{-t-s}(y))\}_{\lambda=0}\\ &= \frac{d}{d\lambda}\{\varphi^{\lambda}_{t}(\varphi^{\lambda}_{s}(\varphi^{0}_{-t-s}(y)))\}_{\lambda=0}\\ &= \frac{d}{d\lambda}\{\varphi^{\lambda}_{t}(\varphi^{0}_{-t}(y))\}_{\lambda=0} + T\varphi^{0}_{t}\left(\frac{d}{d\lambda}\{\varphi^{\lambda}_{s}(\varphi^{0}_{-s-t}(y))\}_{\lambda=0}\right)\\ &= \zeta_t(y) + (T\varphi^0_t)\circ\zeta_s\circ\varphi^0_{-t}(y)\end{aligned}$$

Clearly $\zeta(y)\colon t \rightsquigarrow \zeta_t(y)$ is a differentiable curve in T_yX. Let $\zeta'_t(y) = \dfrac{\partial}{\partial s}\{\zeta_s(y)\}_{s=t}$ denote its derivative at the point t. Then we shall show that

(III) $$\zeta'_t(y) = (\varphi^0_{-t})_*\eta(y)$$

Indeed,

$$\zeta'_t(y) = \frac{\partial}{\partial s}\{\zeta_s(y)\}_{s=t} = \frac{\partial}{\partial s}\{\zeta_{s+t}(y)\}_{s=0}$$

so from (II),

$$\begin{aligned}\zeta'_t(y) &= \frac{\partial}{\partial s}\{\zeta_t(y) + (\varphi^0_{-t})_*\zeta_s(y)\}_{s=0}\\ &= \frac{\partial}{\partial s}\{T\varphi^0_t\circ\zeta_s\circ\varphi^0_{-t}(y)\}_{s=0}\\ &= (T\varphi^0_t)\frac{\partial}{\partial s}\{\zeta_s\circ\varphi^0_{-t}(y)\}_{s=0}\end{aligned}$$

and substituting for ζ_s from the definition above, we have

(IV) $$\zeta'_t(y) = (T\varphi^0_t)\,\frac{\partial}{\partial s}\left\{\frac{d}{d\lambda}[\varphi^{\lambda}_s\circ\varphi^0_{-s-t}(y)]_{\lambda=0}\right\}_{s=0}$$

Let $f\colon \boldsymbol{R}^2 \to X$ denote the map $(s, \lambda) \rightsquigarrow \varphi^{\lambda}_s\circ\varphi^0_{-s-t}(y)$ for fixed t and y. Then f is C^2 by the Parameterized Flow Theorem (21.4), as we have assumed $r \geqslant 2$. It then follows from the symmetry of D^2f that we may interchange the order of differentiation in (IV), that is,

(V) $$\frac{\partial}{\partial s}\left\{\frac{d}{d\lambda}\,[f]_{\lambda=0}\right\}_{s=0} = \frac{\partial}{\partial\lambda}\left\{\frac{d}{ds}[f]_{s=0}\right\}_{\lambda=0}$$

To prove (V), it is sufficient to consider the case in which $X=U\subset\boldsymbol{E}$, an open set in a Banach space. Then we have

$$f\colon \boldsymbol{R}^2 \to \boldsymbol{E}\colon (s, \lambda) \rightsquigarrow f(s, \lambda)$$

$$\frac{d}{ds}f\colon \boldsymbol{R}^2 \to \boldsymbol{E}\times\boldsymbol{E}\colon (s, \lambda) \rightsquigarrow (f(s, \lambda), Df(s, \lambda)(1, 0))$$

$$\frac{d}{ds}[f]_{s=0}: \boldsymbol{R} \to \boldsymbol{E}: \lambda \rightsquigarrow (x, Df(0, \lambda)(1, 0))$$

because $f(0, \lambda) = \varphi^0_{-t}(y) = x$ for all λ. Thus

$$\frac{\partial}{\partial \lambda}\left\{\frac{d}{ds}[f]_{s=0}\right\}_{\lambda=0} = (x, D^2f(0, 0)((1, 0), (0, 1)))$$

Similarly, as $f(s, 0) = x$ for all s, we obtain

$$\frac{\partial}{\partial s}\left\{\frac{d}{d\lambda}[f]_{\lambda=0}\right\}_{s=0} = (x, D^2f(0, 0)((0, 1), (1, 0)))$$

from which (V) follows by the symmetry of D^2f.

Now substituting (V) in (IV), we obtain

$$\begin{aligned}
\zeta_t'(y) &= (T\varphi_t^0)\frac{\partial}{\partial \lambda}\left\{\frac{d}{ds}[\varphi_s^\lambda \circ \varphi^0_{-s-t}(y)]_{s=0}\right\}_{\lambda=0} \\
&= (T\varphi_t^0)\frac{\partial}{\partial \lambda}\{\xi^\lambda(\varphi^0_{-t}(y)) + (T\varphi_0^\lambda)\xi^0(\varphi^0_{-t}(y))\}_{\lambda=0} \\
&= (T\varphi_t^0)\frac{\partial}{\partial \lambda}\{\xi^\lambda(\varphi^0_{-t}(y)) + \xi^0(\varphi^0_{-t}(y))\}_{\lambda=0} \\
&= (T\varphi_t^0)\eta(\varphi^0_{-t}(y))
\end{aligned}$$

which proves (III). Now to obtain (I), we have a differentiable curve $\zeta(y): s \rightsquigarrow \zeta_s(y)$ in T_yX, with $\zeta_0(y) = 0_y$, so

$$\zeta_t(y) = \int_0^t \zeta_s'(y)\, ds$$

hence by (III) and the definition of $\zeta_t(y)$,

$$\frac{d}{d\lambda}\{\varphi_t^\lambda \circ \varphi^0_{-t}(y)\}_{\lambda=0} = \int_0^t T\varphi_s^0 \circ \eta \circ \varphi^0_{-s}(y)\, ds$$

and substituting $x = \varphi^0_{-t}(y)$, (I) is obtained. ∎

We can now prove the Perturbation Lemma (31.7) used in the G2 Density Theorem.

32.2. PERTURBATION LEMMA. Let X be a compact C^{r+1} manifold, $\xi^0 \in \Gamma^r(\tau_X)$, γ a closed orbit of ξ^0 of prime period τ, $x \in \gamma$, and $\dot{x} \in T_xX$. Then there exists an $\eta \in \Gamma^r(\tau_X)$ such that if φ^λ is the flow of $\xi^\lambda = \xi^0 + \lambda\eta$ ($\lambda \in \boldsymbol{R}$), then

$$\frac{d}{d\lambda}\{\varphi_\tau^\lambda(x)\}_{\lambda=0} = \dot{x}$$

Proof. Let $g: \boldsymbol{R} \to \boldsymbol{R}$ be a C^∞ function such that $D^ig(0) = D^ig(\tau) = 0$ for $i = 0, 1, 2, \ldots, r$, and

$$\int_0^\tau g(s)\, ds = 1$$

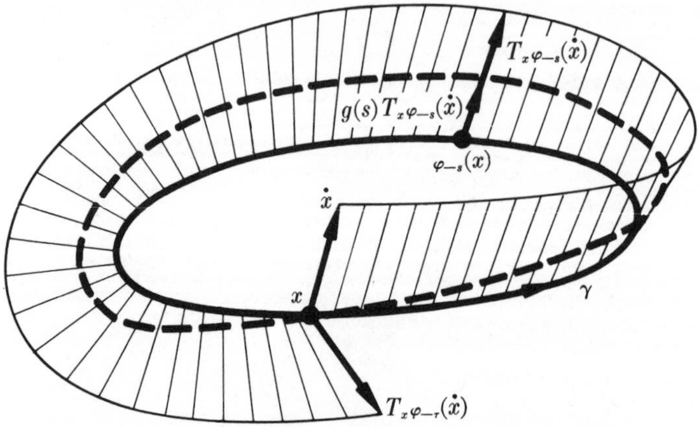

Figure 32-2. Construction of the perturbing vectorfield.

Define $\eta(y)$ for $y \in \gamma$ by (see Figure 32-2)

$$\eta(y) = g(s)(T_x\varphi^0_{-s})\dot{x}$$

where $y = \varphi_s(x)$ $(0 \leqslant s \leqslant \tau)$. Because of the conditions on the derivatives of g, η is a C^r function on γ. Thus η extends to a C^r vectorfield defined on all of X. Indeed, η may be extended to a neighborhood U of each point $y \in \gamma$ by choosing local charts such that $\gamma \cap U$ is a straight line, by the Straightening-Out Theorem (21.5). In such charts, an extension to U is trivial. Then η may be extended to all of X via partitions of unity. Since

$$\int_0^\tau T\varphi^0_s \circ \eta \circ \varphi^0_{-s}(x)\, ds = \int_0^\tau g(s)\dot{x}\, ds = \dot{x}$$

the result follows from 32.1. ∎

For the other perturbation lemma of §31, we will need an analogous theory for the perturbation of the tangent of a flow.

32.3. LEMMA. Let X, ξ^0, η, and φ^λ $(\lambda \in \boldsymbol{R})$ be as in 32.1, and $x \in X$. Then for $\dot{x} \in T_xX$ and $t \in \boldsymbol{R}$,

$$\frac{d}{d\lambda}\{T\varphi^\lambda_t(x)\}_{\lambda=0} = \int_0^t (T^2\varphi^0_s) \circ \omega \circ (T\eta) \circ T\varphi^0_{-s+t}(\dot{x})\, ds$$

Here $\omega\colon T^2(X) \to T^2(X)$ is the canonical involution (§7).

Proof. This is a special case of 32.1. Recall that $\xi^\lambda \in \Gamma^r(\tau_X)$ is defined by $\xi^\lambda = \xi^0 + \lambda\eta$ $(\lambda \in \boldsymbol{R})$, and φ^λ is the flow of ξ^λ. By 21.4, $\{T\varphi^\lambda_t\}_t$ is the flow of $\dot{\xi}^\lambda = \omega \circ T\xi^\lambda$. By 7.4, $\dot{\xi}^\lambda = \dot{\xi}^0 + \lambda\dot{\eta}$, so 32.3 follows from 32.1 by reading $T(X)$ for X, $\dot{x}$ for x, $\dot{\xi}^0$ for ξ^0, and $\dot{\eta}$ for η. ∎

We can now prove the Perturbation Lemma (31.11) used in the G2 Density Theorem.

32.4. TANGENT PERTURBATION LEMMA. Let X be a C^{r+1} manifold $r \geqslant 3$, $\xi^0 \in \Gamma^r(\tau_X)$, γ a closed orbit of ξ of

prime period τ, U an open neighborhood of γ in X, $x \in \gamma$, and $A \in L(T_xX, T_xX)$. Suppose $A\xi^0(x) = 0$. Then there exists $\eta \in \Gamma^r(\tau_X)$ such that:

(I) $\eta \mid \gamma \equiv 0$;

(II) $\eta \mid X \setminus U \equiv 0$;

(III) if, for $\lambda \in R$, φ^λ denotes the flow of $\xi^\lambda = \xi^0 + \lambda\eta$, then

$$\frac{\partial}{\partial\lambda}\{T_x\varphi_\tau^\lambda\}_{\lambda=0} = A$$

Proof. The argument is analogous to the proof of 32.2. The reader is cautioned to bear in mind two points: first, the distinction between the notations $d/d\lambda$ and $\partial/\partial\lambda$ made at the beginning of this section; second, the fact that the linear operations of the vector bundle $T\tau_X$: $T^2(X) \to T(X)$ are different from those of the vector bundle $\tau_{T(X)}$: $T^2(X) \to T(X)$.

Define a map H: $T_xX \to T^2(X)$ satisfying the following properties:

(H1) For $\dot{x} \in T_xX$ and $a \in R$,

$$\tau_{T(X)}(aHx) = T_x\varphi_\tau\dot{x}$$

(the scalar multiplication $aH\dot{x}$ is that of the bundle $\tau_{T(X)}$).

(H2) For $\dot{x} \in T_xX$ and $a \in R$,

$$T\tau_X(aH\dot{x}) = 0_x$$

where 0_x is the zero of the fiber T_xX. Hence, H: $T_xX \to (T\tau_X)^{-1}(0_x)$. Furthermore, H is linear. (The linear operations at the target being those of the fiber $(T\tau_X)^{-1}(0_x)$ of the bundle $T\tau_X$.)

(H3) $H\xi(x) = 0$ where $0 = 0_{\xi(x)}$ is the zero of the fiber $T_{\xi(x)}T(X)$ of $\tau_{T(X)}$.

(H4) If c: $R \to L(T_xX, T_xX)$ is a C^r curve such that

$$\frac{d}{d\lambda}\{c(\lambda)x\}_{\lambda=0} = H\dot{x}$$

for every $\dot{x} \in T_xX$, then

$$\frac{\partial}{\partial\lambda}\{c(\lambda)\}_{\lambda=0} = A$$

To construct a map H, satisfying the properties described above, take a natural natural VB chart on $\tau_{T(X)}$ as in §7. In such a chart let D_α, $A_\alpha \in L(\mathbf{E}, \mathbf{E})$ "represent" $T_x\varphi_\tau$ and A respectively. Then in the given coordinates, H is represented by H_α where

$$H_\alpha(x, \mathbf{e}) = (x, D_\alpha\mathbf{e}, \mathbf{0}, A_\alpha\mathbf{e})$$

and where $(x, \mathbf{e})$ are the coordinates of a point $\dot{x} \in T_xX$.

Now take a C^∞ function g: $R \to R$ as in 32.2, i.e., $D^ig(0) = D^ig(\tau) = 0$ for $i = 0, 1, 2, \ldots, r$, and

$$\int_0^\tau g(s)\, ds = 1$$

Define for $y \in \gamma$ a map $B(y)$: $T_yX \to T^2(X)$ as follows. Let $y = \varphi_s(x)$ where $0 \leqslant s < \tau$; then

$$B(y)\dot{y} = \omega((T^2\varphi_{-s})((g(s)H(T\varphi_{s-\tau}(\dot{y})))))$$

for $\dot{y} \in T_yX$. Here the scalar multiplication $g(s)H(T\varphi_{s-\tau}(\dot{y}))$ is that of the bundle $\boldsymbol{\tau}_{T(X)}$.

Then $B(y)$ has the following properties:

(B1) for $y \in \gamma$ and $\dot{y} \in T_yX$

$$T\boldsymbol{\tau}_X(B(y)\dot{y}) = \dot{y}$$

(B2) For $y \in \gamma$ and $\dot{y} \in T_yX$

$$\boldsymbol{\tau}_{T(X)}(B(y)\dot{y}) = 0_y$$

where 0_y is the zero of the Banach space T_yX. Hence $B(y)$: $T_yX \to T_{0_y}(T(X))$. Furthermore, this map $B(y)$ is linear (linear operations at the target being those of the fiber $T_{0_y}T(X)$ of the bundle $\boldsymbol{\tau}_{T(X)}$).

(B3) For $y \in \gamma$, $B(y)\xi(y) = 0$, where the zero is that of the fiber $(T\boldsymbol{\tau}_X)^{-1}(\xi(y))$ of the bundle $T\boldsymbol{\tau}_X$.

The properties (Bα) follow directly from (Hα), $\alpha = 1, 2, 3$. For (B3), use 7.2 also. We prove (B1) and leave the rest for the reader. For this, we compute directly,

$$\begin{aligned} T\boldsymbol{\tau}_X(B(y)\dot{y}) &= (T\boldsymbol{\tau}_X)(\omega(T^2\varphi_{-s}(g(s)H(T\varphi_{s-\tau}(\dot{y}))))) \\ &= \boldsymbol{\tau}_{T(X)}(T^2\varphi_{-s}(g(s)H(T\varphi_{s-\tau}(\dot{y})))) && (7.2) \\ &= (T\varphi_{-s})(\boldsymbol{\tau}_{T(X)}(g(s)H(T\varphi_{s-\tau}(\dot{y})))) && (6.2) \\ &= T\varphi_{-s} \circ T_x\varphi_\tau \circ T\varphi_{s-\tau}(\dot{y}) && (H1) \\ &= \dot{y} \end{aligned}$$

which is (B1).

Now $B(y)\dot{y}$ ($y \in \gamma$, $\dot{y} \in T_yX$) is C^r in y and $\dot{y}$. (In case $y = x$ this is because of the fact that $D^ig(0) = D^ig(\tau) = 0$ for $i = 0, 1, 2, \ldots, r$.) By (B1), (B2), (B3), and the same sort of argument used in 32.2, we may construct $\eta \in \Gamma^r(\boldsymbol{\tau}_X)$ such that,

(i) $\eta \mid \gamma \equiv 0$;

(ii) $\eta \mid X \setminus U \equiv 0$;

(iii) $T_y\eta = B(y)$ for $y \in \gamma$.

We sketch the constructions. Via a partition of unity argument, it suffices to define η in a neighborhood of each $y \in \gamma$. At $y \in \gamma$ choose a local chart as in the Straightening-Out Theorem (21.6). Then the definition of η in this chart is made according to the following.

SUBLEMMA. Let D: $\boldsymbol{R} \to L(\boldsymbol{R}^n, \boldsymbol{R}^n)$ be a C^r map such that $\mathbf{D}(s)\mathbf{e}_1 = 0$ for $s \in \boldsymbol{R}$. (Here $\mathbf{e}_1 = (1, 0, \ldots, 0) \in \boldsymbol{R}^n$.) Then there is a C^r map f: $\boldsymbol{R}^n \to \boldsymbol{R}^n$ such that for each $s \in \boldsymbol{R}$

(j) $f(s, 0, \ldots, 0) = 0$, **and**

(jj) $Df(s, 0, \ldots, 0) = \mathbf{D}(s)$.

(To prove the sublemma, take $f(s, \mathbf{x}) = \mathbf{D}(s)(0, \mathbf{x})$.)

After having defined η satisfying (i), (ii), and (iii), note that by (iii) and the definition of B, we have

$$(T^2\varphi_s^0) \circ \omega \circ (T\eta) \circ T\varphi_{-s+\tau}^0(\dot{x}) = g(s)H\dot{x}$$

for $0 \leqslant s \leqslant \tau$ and $\dot{x} \in T_xX$. Then, where φ^λ is the flow of $\xi^0 + \lambda\eta$ ($\lambda \in \mathbf{R}$), we have by 32.3,

$$\frac{d}{d\lambda}\{T\varphi_\tau^\lambda \dot{x}\}_{\lambda=0} = \int_0^t g(s)H\dot{x}\, ds = H\dot{x}$$

for $\dot{x} \in T_xX$. Hence by (H4) on page 111,

$$\frac{\partial}{\partial\lambda}\{T\varphi_\tau^\lambda\}_{\lambda=0} = A$$

This completes the proof of 32.4. ∎

§33. G3 Density

We now prove that G3 is a generic property. Although seriously obscured by superficial point set topological details, the proof is a straightforward application of the main results of each of the preceding chapters. The main goal is the following.

33.1. G3 DENSITY THEOREM. Let X be a compact C^∞ manifold, and $r \geqslant 1$. Then $\mathcal{G}_3^r(X)$ is residual in $\Gamma^r(\tau_X)$.

Following the pattern of the G2 Density Theorem, we consider $\mathcal{G}_3^r(a) \subset \mathcal{G}_2^r(a)$, but in this case we do not expect to find $\mathcal{G}_3^r(a)$ open and dense, as the property G3(a, ξ) involves transversality of noncompact manifolds. We must, therefore, do some extra work to exhibit $\mathcal{G}_3^r(a)$ as a countable intersection of open dense sets $\mathcal{G}_3^r(a, b)$. Although the definition of these sets is somewhat involved, the underlying idea is simple enough.

Step A. For $\xi \in \mathcal{G}_2^r(a)$, we find an open neighborhood N such that, if $\zeta \in N$, the critical elements of ζ of prime period $\leqslant a$ are close to those of ξ, and we can give uniform parameterizations to the stable and unstable manifolds of each. This is a combination of previous theorems.

Step B. We choose a countable *locally finite* covering $(N_c)_{c\in \mathbf{Z}^+}$ of $\mathcal{G}_2^r(a)$ by open sets having the properties of Step A ($\mathbf{Z}^+$ denotes the positive integers). Using this covering, we define sets $\mathcal{G}_3^r(a, b, c; i, j)$, of vectorfields in N_c having the stable manifold of the ith critical element transversal to the unstable manifold of the jth critical element of prime period $\leqslant a$, up to a radius b around the critical elements. Then, if

$$\mathcal{G}_3^r(a, b) = \bigcup_{c\in\mathbf{Z}^+} \bigcap_{i,j} \mathcal{G}_3^r(a, b, c; i, j)$$

for $i, j = 1, \ldots, k_c$, we show

$$\bigcap_{b\in\mathbf{Z}^+} \mathcal{G}_3^r(a, b) = \mathcal{G}_3^r(a)$$

This is all an elementary application of Step A, and point set topology.

Step C. We show $\mathcal{G}_3^r(a, b, c; i, j)$ is open by the Openness of Transversal Intersection, and therefore $\mathcal{G}_3^r(a, b)$ is open.

Step D. We show $\mathscr{G}_3^r(a, \infty, c; i, j)$ is dense. This is the main step, and uses the Transversal Density Theorem. The only difficulty is the verification of the hypothesis $ev \pitchfork W$, which requires a careful application of the perturbation theory of the previous section.

33.2. STEP A. Let X be a compact C^∞ manifold and $\xi \in \mathscr{G}_2^r(a)$, $r \geq 1$. Then there exists:

(0) $\epsilon > 0$;

(1) A neighborhood N of ξ in $\Gamma^r(\tau_X)$;

(2) Open subsets $V_1, \ldots, V_k$ of X with disjoint closures;

(3) Manifolds $P_1^\sigma, \ldots, P_k^\sigma$, $\sigma = +$ or $-$, of the form $\boldsymbol{R}^m$, $S^1 \times \boldsymbol{R}^m$, or $S^1 \times \boldsymbol{R}^m$, for some m (see §28);

(4) C^1 pseudorepresentations $N \to C^r(P_i^\sigma, X)$ ($i = 1, \ldots, k$; $\sigma = +$ or $-$) given by $\zeta \rightsquigarrow \psi_\zeta^{i\sigma}$, such that,

(I) $N \subset \mathscr{G}_2^r(a + \epsilon)$;

(II) For $\zeta \in N$, ζ has exactly k critical elements, $\gamma_\zeta^1, \ldots, \gamma_\zeta^k$ of period $\leq a + \epsilon$ (necessarily elementary);

(III) $\gamma_\zeta^i \subset V_i$ **for** $i = 1, \ldots, k$, $\zeta \in N$;

(IV) ψ_ζ^{i+} (resp. ψ_ζ^{i-}) is a parameterization of the stable (resp. unstable) manifold of ζ through γ_ζ^i ($i = 1, \ldots, k$; $\zeta \in N$);

(V) If $x \in X$ and $\zeta \in N$, there exists $t \in \boldsymbol{R}$ such that $\varphi_t^\zeta(x) \notin \bigcup_i \bar{V}_i$.

This is simply a combination of 24.5, 27.4, and 28.5. We proceed now toward Step B. Fix $a \in \boldsymbol{R}^+$. Recall that by 31.3, $\mathscr{G}_2^r(a)$ is open in $\Gamma^r(\tau_X)$, a separable Banach space. Thus there is a countable covering of $\mathscr{G}_2^r(a)$ by open sets N_c satisfying 33.2, say

$$\mathscr{G}_2^r(a) = \bigcup_{c \in \boldsymbol{Z}^+} N_c$$

where $\boldsymbol{Z}^+$ denotes the positive integers. Since $\mathscr{G}_2^r(a)$ is a subset of the metric space $\Gamma^r(\tau_X)$, it is itself a metric space. Thus it is paracompact, and so we may suppose that the cover $\{N_c\}_{c \in \boldsymbol{Z}^+}$ is **locally finite,** i.e., each $\xi \in \mathscr{G}_2^r(a)$ has a neighborhood (open in $\mathscr{G}_2^r(a)$ and hence in $\Gamma^r(\tau_X)$) intersecting at most finitely many of the open sets N_c (see J. Kelley [*1;* p. 160]).

Now for each $c \in \boldsymbol{Z}^+$, we have defined:

(0) a positive real number ϵ_c;

(1) an open subset $N_c \subset \mathscr{G}_2^r(a + \epsilon_c) \subset \mathscr{G}_2^r(a)$;

(2) open subsets $V_c^1, \ldots, V_c^{k_c}$ of X;

(3) critical elements $\gamma_\zeta^1, \ldots, \gamma_\zeta^{k_c}$ of each $\zeta \in N_c$;

(4) C^1 pseudorepresentations $N_c \to C^r(P_{c,\zeta}^{i\sigma}, X)$ given by

$$\zeta \rightsquigarrow \psi_{c,\zeta}^{i\sigma}$$

for $i = 1, \ldots, k_c$, $\zeta \in N_c$, and $\sigma = +$ or $-$.

All these objects satisfy the various conditions of 33.2. In particular each $P_{c,\zeta}^{i\sigma}$ has one of the forms $\boldsymbol{R}^m$, $S^1 \times \boldsymbol{R}^m$, or $S^1 \dot{\times} \boldsymbol{R}^m$. In addition, $\mathscr{G}_2^r(a) \subset \bigcup_{c \in \boldsymbol{Z}^+} N_c$. For $b \in \boldsymbol{R}^+$, and P one of the spaces $\boldsymbol{R}^m$, $S^1 \times \boldsymbol{R}^m$, or $S^1 \dot{\times} \boldsymbol{R}^m$, define the set $K(P, b)$ by

$$
\begin{aligned}
K(P, b) &= \{\mathbf{e} \in \boldsymbol{R}^m \mid \|\mathbf{e}\| \leqslant b\} && \text{if } P = \boldsymbol{R}^m \\
&= \{(\theta, \mathbf{e}) \in S^1 \times \boldsymbol{R}^m \mid \|\mathbf{e}\| \leqslant b\} && \text{if } P = S^1 \times \boldsymbol{R}^m \\
&= \{[(\theta, \mathbf{e})] \in S^1 \dot{\times} \boldsymbol{R}^m \mid \|\mathbf{e}\| \leqslant b\} && \text{if } P = S^1 \dot{\times} \boldsymbol{R}^m
\end{aligned}
$$

Then $K(P, b)$ is compact and

$$P = \bigcup_{b=1}^{\infty} K(P, b)$$

Now for $c \in \boldsymbol{Z}^+$ and $i, j = 1, \ldots, k_c$, let $\mathscr{G}_3^r(a, b, c; i, j)$ be the set of all $\zeta \in N_c$, such that for all

$$p^+ \in K(P_{c,\zeta}^{i+}, b), \; p^- \in K(P_{c,\zeta}^{j-}, b)$$

we have:

$$\psi_{c,\zeta}^{i+} \pitchfork_{(p^+, p^-)} \psi_{c,\zeta}^{j-}$$

that is,

$$\psi_{c,\zeta}^{i+} \times \psi_{c,\zeta}^{j-} \pitchfork_{(p^+, p^-)} \Delta$$

where

$$\psi_{c,\zeta}^{i+} \times \psi_{c,\zeta}^{j-} : P_{c,\zeta}^{i+} \times P_{c,\zeta}^{j-} \to X \times X$$

is the product map, and $\Delta \subset X \times X$ is the diagonal. Finally, let

$$\mathscr{G}_3^r(a, b) = \bigcup_{c \in \boldsymbol{Z}^+} \bigcap_{i,j=1}^{k_c} \mathscr{G}_3^r(a, b, c; i, j)$$

33.3. STEP B. $\mathscr{G}_3^r(a) = \bigcap_{b \in \boldsymbol{Z}^+} \mathscr{G}_3^r(a, b)$

Proof. A vectorfield ξ is in the set on the right-hand side iff for every $b \in \boldsymbol{Z}^+$, there exists a $c \in \boldsymbol{Z}^+$, such that $\xi \in N_c$, and $\xi \in \bigcap_{i,j} \mathscr{G}_3^r(a, b, c; i, j)$. As by assumption $(N_c)_c$ is a locally-finite cover, $\xi \in N_c$ for a finite number of values of c. Thus there must be one of these values, say c_0, such that for all $b \in \boldsymbol{Z}^+$, $\xi \in \bigcap_{i,j} \mathscr{G}_3^r(a, b, c_0; i, j)$, or

$$\xi \in \bigcap \{\mathscr{G}_3^r(a, b, c_0; i, j) \mid b \in Z^+, i, j = 1, \ldots, k_{c_0}\}$$

This condition means that for every $i, j = 1, \ldots, k_{c_0}$, we have

$$\psi_{c,\xi}^{i+} \times \psi_{c,\xi}^{j-} \pitchfork \Delta$$

throughout its domain. But as $\psi_{c,\zeta}^{i+}$ and $\psi_{c,\zeta}^{j-}$ are immersions, this is equivalent to $W^+(\gamma_\xi^i, \xi) \pitchfork W^-(\gamma_\xi^j, \xi)$, for all $i, j = 1, \ldots, k_c$, and thus for all pairs of critical elements $(\gamma_\xi^i, \gamma_\xi^j)$ of prime period $\leqslant a + \epsilon_{c_0}$, which is equivalent to $\xi \in \mathscr{G}_3^r(a)$. The inclusion $\mathscr{G}_3^r(a) \subset \bigcap_b \mathscr{G}_3^r(a, b)$ is obvious. ∎

33.4. STEP C. For all $a, b, c; i, j = 1, \ldots, k_c$, **and** $r \geqslant 1$, $\mathscr{G}_3^r(a, b, c; i, j)$ **is open in** $\mathscr{G}_2^r(a)$.

Proof. This follows immediately from the Openness of Transversal Intersection, as $\Delta \subset X \times X$ is closed (X is Hausdorff) and $K(P^+, b) \times K(P^-, b)$ is compact. ∎

To prepare for Step D (density) we fix c, i, and j and use the following simpler notations:

$$N = N_c$$

$$P^+ = P^{i+}_{c,\zeta} \qquad P^- = P^{j-}_{c,\zeta}$$

$$\gamma_\zeta = \gamma^i_\zeta \qquad \delta_\zeta = \gamma^j_\zeta$$

$$V_\gamma = V^i_c \qquad V_\delta = V^j_c$$

$$\psi^+_\zeta = \psi^{i+}_{c,\zeta} \qquad \psi^-_\zeta = \psi^{j-}_{c,\zeta}$$

$$\mathscr{G}^r_3(\gamma, \delta) = \bigcap_{b \in Z^+} \mathscr{G}^r_3(a, b, c; i, j) = \mathscr{G}^r_3(a, \infty, c; i, j)$$

Thus $\mathscr{G}^r_3(\gamma, \delta)$ is the set of all vectorfields $\zeta \in N$ such that $\psi^+_\zeta \times \psi^-_\zeta \pitchfork \Delta$.

The final step is to show $\mathscr{G}^r_3(\gamma, \delta)$ is dense by transversality theory, so we need an appropriate representation. We recall the definitions of ψ^+_ζ and ψ^-_ζ for $\zeta \in N$ (see the proof of 27.3). In fact, ψ^+_ζ has the form

(‡) $$\psi^+_\zeta(p) = \varphi^\zeta_{-q(\|p\|)}(F^\zeta_\gamma(p))$$

for $p \in P^+$, where $F^\zeta_\gamma\colon P^+ \to V_\gamma$ is an injective C^r immersion. Here φ^ζ is the flow of ζ, and q is a certain C^∞ function; ψ^-_ζ has a similar form:

(‡‡) $$\psi^-_\zeta(p) = \varphi^\zeta_{q(\|p\|)}(F^\zeta_\delta(p))$$

for $p \in P^-$. The important thing to note is that F^ζ_γ and F^ζ_δ depend only on $\zeta \mid V_\gamma$ and $\zeta \mid V_\delta$ respectively, i.e., if $\zeta \mid V_\gamma = \xi \mid V_\gamma$, then $F^\zeta_\gamma = F^\xi_\gamma$ (although ψ^+_ζ is not necessarily the same as ψ^+_ξ).

Now fix $\xi \in N$. Define $\mathscr{A} \subset N$ to be the set of all $\zeta \in N$ such that $\zeta \mid V_\gamma \cup V_\delta = \xi \mid V_\gamma \cup V_\delta$. Then $\mathscr{A}$ is the intersection of a closed hyperplane of $\Gamma^r(\boldsymbol{\tau}_X)$ with N and is hence a C^∞ Banach manifold. By virtue of the remark in the preceding paragraph, F^ζ_γ and F^ζ_δ are independent of the choice of $\zeta \in \mathscr{A}$. The flow $\varphi^\zeta_t(x)$ is C^r in all three of its arguments (by the Parameterized Flow Theorem, 21.4); by inspecting (‡) and (‡‡) above we see that the map

$$\mathscr{A} \to C^r(P^+ \times P^-, X \times X)$$

given by

$$\zeta \rightsquigarrow \psi^+_\zeta \times \psi^-_\zeta$$

is a C^r representation. (We have *not* shown that its extension to N is a C^r representation.)

Now for Step D, it will suffice to show that $\mathscr{A} \cap \mathscr{G}^r_3(\gamma, \delta)$ is dense in $\mathscr{A}$. This we accomplish via the Transversal Density Theorem. The main step is the verification of the hypothesis $ev \pitchfork \Delta$, which we now do.

33.5. MAIN LEMMA. The evaluation map $ev\colon \mathscr{A} \times P^+ \times P^- \to X \times X$ **given by**

$$ev(\zeta, p_1, p_2) = (\psi^+_\zeta(p_1), \psi^-_\zeta(p_2))$$

for $p_1 \in P^+$, $p_2 \in P^-$, **and** $\zeta \in A$, **is transversal to** Δ, **i.e.,** $ev \pitchfork \Delta$.

Proof. For $\zeta \in \mathscr{A}$ we may identify $T_\zeta\mathscr{A}$ with the closed subspace $\mathbf{F}$ of $\Gamma^r(\boldsymbol{\tau}_X)$ defined by

$$\mathbf{F} = \{\eta \in \Gamma^r(\boldsymbol{\tau}_X) \mid \eta \mid V_\gamma \cup V_\delta \equiv 0\}$$

With this identification we see that

$$(*)\qquad (T_{(\zeta,p_1,p_2)}ev)(\eta,\dot{p}_1,\dot{p}_2) = \frac{d}{d\lambda}\{ev(\zeta+\lambda\eta, p_1, p_2)\}_{\lambda=0} + (T_{2(\zeta,p_1,p_2)}ev)\dot{p}_1 + (T_{3(\zeta,p_1,p_2)}ev)\dot{p}_2$$

for $(\zeta, p_1, p_2) \in \mathscr{A} \times P^+ \times P^-$ and

$$(\eta, \dot{p}_1, \dot{p}_2) \in \mathbf{F} \times T_{p_1}P^+ \times T_{p_2}P^-$$

Now suppose $ev(\zeta, p_1, p_2) \in \Delta$, say $\psi_\zeta^+(p_1) = \psi_\zeta^-(p_2) = x \in X$. We must show

$$(T_xX) \times (T_xX) = T_{(x,x)}\Delta + (T_{(\zeta,p_1,p_2)}ev)(T_\zeta\mathscr{A} \times T_{p_1}P^+ \times T_{p_2}P^-)$$

In fact, we show more, viz.,

$$(T_xX) \times (T_xX) = T_{(x,x)}\Delta + (T_{(\zeta,p_1,p_2)}ev)(T_\zeta\mathscr{A} \times \{0\} \times \{0\})$$

We consider first the case $\gamma \neq \delta$, and show that if $x \notin \bar{V}_\gamma$ ($\bar{V}_\gamma =$ closure of V_γ), then the first term of (*) (as η varies over $\mathbf{F}$) spans $T_xX \times \{0\}$, while if $x \notin \bar{V}_\delta$, then this term spans $\{0\} \times T_xX$. Since both $T_xX \times \{0\}$ and $\{0\} \times T_xX$ are linear complements of $T_{(x,x)}\Delta$ in $T_{(x,x)}(X \times X) = T_xX + T_xX$, and since $\bar{V}_\gamma \cap \bar{V}_\delta = \varnothing$, it suffices to prove:

(I) If $x \notin \bar{V}_\gamma$, then for every $\dot{x} \in T_xX$ there exists $\eta \in \mathbf{F}$ such that

$$\frac{d}{d\lambda}\{\psi^+_{\zeta+\lambda\eta}(p_1)\}_{\lambda=0} = \dot{x}$$

(II) If $x \notin \bar{V}_\delta$, then for every $\dot{x} \in T_xX$ there exists $\eta \in \mathbf{F}$ such that

$$\frac{d}{d\lambda}\{\psi^-_{\zeta+\lambda\eta}(p_2)\}_{\lambda=0} = \dot{x}$$

We prove (II); (I) is analogous. Suppose $x \notin \bar{V}_\delta$. The situation is illustrated in Figure 33-1.

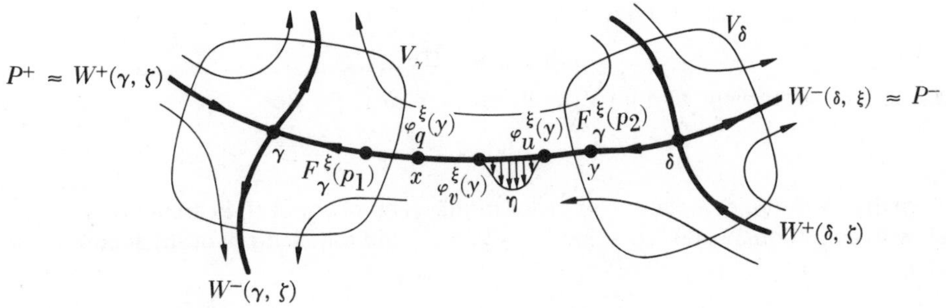

(a)

Figure 33-1(a). Perturbation of nontransversal stable manifolds.

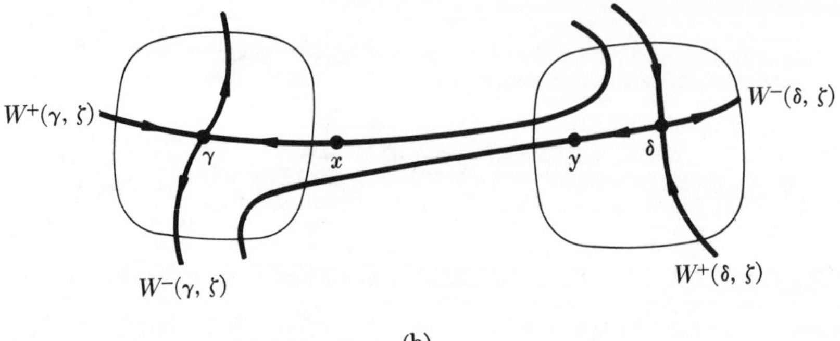

Figure 33-1 (b). Stable manifolds after perturbation.

By (‡) on page 116 we see that

(i) $$\psi_\zeta^-(p_2) = \varphi_q^\zeta(y)$$

where $q = q\|p_2\| > 0$ and $y = F_\gamma^\zeta(p_2)$ (y is independent of $\zeta \in \mathscr{A}$). Since $x \notin \bar{V}_\delta$, and since we have assumed $\bar{V}_\gamma \cap \bar{V}_\delta = \varnothing$, we may find real numbers u and v with $u < v < q$ such that

$$\varphi_s^\zeta(y) \notin \bar{V}_\gamma \cup \bar{V}_\delta$$

for all $u \leqslant s \leqslant v$. Now by (i) above and the Perturbation Lemma (32.1) we have for $\eta \in \boldsymbol{F}$ that

(ii) $$\frac{d}{d\lambda}\{\psi_{\zeta+\lambda\eta}^-(p_2)\}_{\lambda=0} = \frac{d}{d\lambda}\{\varphi_q^{\zeta+\lambda\eta}(y)\}_{\lambda=0} = \int_0^q T\varphi_s^\zeta \circ \eta \circ \varphi_{-s+q}^\zeta(y)\, ds$$

Now let $g\colon \boldsymbol{R} \to \boldsymbol{R}$ be a C^∞ function such that,

(1) $g(s) = 0$ for $s < u$ or $v < s$;

(2) $\int_0^q g(s)\, ds = 1$.

Choose $\dot{x} \in T_xX$. Define $\eta(\varphi_{-s+q}^\zeta(y))$ for $0 \leqslant s \leqslant q$ by

$$\eta(\varphi_{-s+q}^\zeta(y)) = (T\varphi_{-s}^\zeta)\dot{x}$$

We may extend η to a C^r vectorfield with $\eta \mid V_\alpha \cup V_\beta \equiv 0$, i.e., $\eta \in \boldsymbol{F}$. But

$$\int_0^q T\varphi_s^\zeta \circ \eta \circ \varphi_{-s+q}^\zeta(y)\, ds = \int_0^q g(s)\dot{x}\, ds = \dot{x}$$

This equation, together with (ii), completes the proof of (II). The proof of (I) is analogous. If $\gamma = \delta$, the proof is almost identical, with condition 33.2(5) replacing $\bar{V}_\gamma \cap \bar{V}_\delta = \varnothing$, and following (I) or (II) according as t is positive or negative in 33.2(5). ∎

33.6. STEP D. With $a \in \boldsymbol{R}^+$, $c \in \boldsymbol{Z}^+$, $i, j = 1, \ldots,$ or k_c,

$$\mathscr{G}_3^r(a, \infty, c; i, j) \equiv \bigcap_{b \in \boldsymbol{Z}^+} \mathscr{G}_3^r(a, b, c; i, j)$$

is dense in N_c.

Proof. If $\xi \in N_c$ and U is an open neighborhood of ξ in N_c, let $\mathscr{A}_\xi$ be the hyperplane in $\Gamma^r(\tau_X)$ through ξ defined in Step C. Then if $r \geqslant \dim X + 1$, $\mathscr{A}_\xi \cap \mathscr{G}_3^r(a, \infty, c; i, j)$ is dense in $\mathscr{A}_\xi \cap N_c$ by the Transversal Density Theorem (19.1). For $\operatorname{codim}(\Delta \subset X \times X) = \dim X$, $\dim(p^+ \times p^-) \leqslant 2 \dim X$, and $ev \pitchfork \Delta$ by the main lemma (33.6). Thus

$$U \cap \mathscr{G}_3^r(a, \infty, c; i, j) \neq \varnothing$$

Now if $1 \leqslant r \leqslant \dim X$, we use "indifference of r." (See the proof of 30.1 at the end of §30.) ▮

We now combine the four steps to obtain the G3 Density Theorem (33.1). This is solely a matter of general topology.

Proof of 33.1. With Step A, we have constructed a locally finite countable covering of $\mathscr{G}_2^r(a)$ by open sets N_c, and obtained in Step B the decomposition

$$\mathscr{G}_3^r(a) = \bigcap_{b \in \mathbf{Z}^+} \mathscr{G}_3^r(a, b)$$

with

$$\mathscr{G}_3^r(a, b) = \bigcup_{c \in \mathbf{Z}^+} \bigcap_{i,j=1}^{k_c} \mathscr{G}_3^r(a, b, c; i, j)$$

By Step C, $\mathscr{G}_3^r(a, b, c; i, j)$ is open, thus also the finite intersection over $i, j = 1, \ldots, k_c$, and the (countable) union over $c \in \mathbf{Z}^+$, so $\mathscr{G}_3^r(a, b)$ is open. As $\mathscr{G}_3^r(a, \infty, c; i, j)$ is dense in N_c, so is $\mathscr{G}_3^r(a, b, c; i, j)$, and also $\mathscr{G}_3^r(a, b)$. Thus $\mathscr{G}_3^r(a, b)$ is open and dense in $\mathscr{G}_2^r(a)$, and therefore in $\Gamma^r(\tau_X)$ as well. Thus $\mathscr{G}_3^r(X) = \bigcap_{a,b \in \mathbf{Z}^+} \mathscr{G}_3^r(a, b)$ is residual. ▮

Appendix A

THE WHITNEY EXTENSION THEOREM

by

JOEL ROBBIN

The proof given below is essentially Whitney's original proof (Whitney [*1*]) transcribed to our notation. We are grateful to Elias Stein for making his proof available to us, and for valuable conversations.

WHITNEY EXTENSION THEOREM. Let $\mathbf{F}$ be a Banach space, $A \subset \mathbf{R}^n$ a closed subset, and $f\colon A \to \mathbf{F}$.

(I) **f extends to a C^r ($r \geqslant 0$) function $F\colon \mathbf{R}^n \to \mathbf{F}$ provided that there exist $f_0, f_1, \ldots, f_r$ with $f_0 = f$, $f_k\colon A \to L_s^k(\mathbf{R}^n, \mathbf{F})$ ($k = 0, 1, \ldots, r$), and for $k = 0, 1, \ldots, r$, the condition (W_k) below is satisfied:**

(W_k) **If $R_k\colon A \times A \to L_s^k(\mathbf{R}^n, \mathbf{F})$ is defined by**

$$f_k(\mathbf{y}) = \sum_{i \leqslant r-k} \frac{f_{k+i}(\mathbf{x})}{i!}(\mathbf{y} - \mathbf{x})^i + R_k(\mathbf{x}, \mathbf{y})$$

for $\mathbf{x}, \mathbf{y} \in A$, then for each $\mathbf{x}_0 \in A$,

$$\frac{|R_k(\mathbf{x}_1, \mathbf{x}_2)\|}{\|\mathbf{x}_1 - \mathbf{x}_2\|^{r-k}} \to 0$$

as $\mathbf{x}_1$, $\mathbf{x}_2 \to \mathbf{x}_0$ in A, i.e., for every $\epsilon > 0$ there exists $\delta > 0$ such that for all $\mathbf{x}_1, \mathbf{x}_2 \in A$,

$$\|R_k(\mathbf{x}_1, \mathbf{x}_2)\| < \epsilon \, \|\mathbf{x}_1 - \mathbf{x}_2\|^{r-k}$$

whenever $\|\mathbf{x}_1 - \mathbf{x}_0\|, \|\mathbf{x}_2 - \mathbf{x}_0\| < \delta$.

(II) f extends to a C^∞ function $F\colon R^n \to F$, provided that there exist functions $f_0, f_1, f_2, \ldots$ such that (W_k) holds for each $k = 0, 1, 2, \ldots$.

(III) In (I) or (II), the extension F of f may be chosen so that $D^kF|A = f_k$ for all appropriate k.

Before giving the proof we give an example to show that the conditions (W_k) cannot be weakened to:

(W_k') For each $\mathbf{x} \in A$,

$$\|R_k(\mathbf{x}, \mathbf{y})\| \,/\, \|\mathbf{x} - \mathbf{y}\|^{r-k} \to 0$$

as $\mathbf{y} \to \mathbf{x}$ in A.

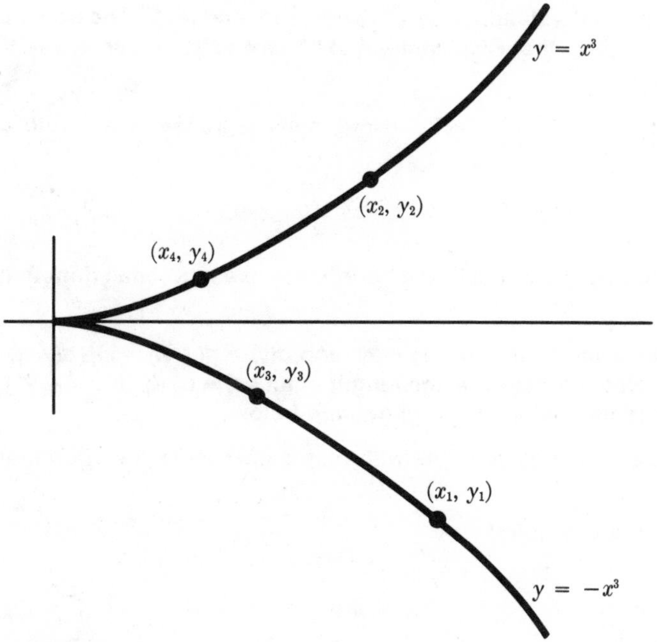

Figure A-1

Take $n = r = 1$ and $\boldsymbol{F} = \boldsymbol{R}$. Construct two sequences of real numbers $\{x_n\}$ and $\{y_n\}$ so that (see Figure A-1),

(i) $x_n \downarrow 0$ as $n \to \infty$;

(ii) $y_n / x_n^2 \to 0$ as $n \to \infty$;

(iii) $(y_{n+1} - y_n)/(x_{n+1} - x_n) = (-1)^n$.

Such a sequence may be constructed by taking (x_1, y_1) on the curve $y=-x^3$, $x>0$; (x_2, y_2) the intersection of the curve $y=x^3$, $x>0$ and the line through (x_1, y_1) with slope -1; (x_3, y_3) the intersection of the curve $y=-x^3$, $x>0$ and the line through (x_2, y_2) with slope -1, etc. Take $A=\{0\} \cup \{x_1, x_2, \ldots\}$. Let $f(0)=f_0(0)=0$, $f(x_n)=f_0(x_n)=y_n$, and $f_1 \equiv 0$. Since the x_n are isolated, (W_0') and (W_1') hold vacuously for $x=x_n$. $R_0(0, x_n)=y_n$ and $R_1(0, x_n)=0'$, hence (W_0') and (W_1') hold for $x=0$. However, f has no C^1 extension because of (iii) above.

We remark that the proof of the extension theorem in case $n=1$, $r<\infty$, and $\boldsymbol{F}=\boldsymbol{R}$ is simple: in that case the complement of A is a disjoint union of open intervals, and on each such interval F can be a polynomial so chosen that it has the appropriate derivatives at the end points. This seems to be the motivation for Whitney's proof which we give below.

We assume that $A \subset U$ where U is an open ball of diameter 1. We extend f to $F\colon U \to F$ satisfying the conclusion of the theorem. The general case follows from this special case by a straightforward partition of unity argument.

We will cover $U \setminus A$ with an infinite collection of cubes K_j such that the size of K_j is roughly proportional to its distance from A.

NOTATION. Let T_1 and T_2 be real-valued terms of variables v and let $C(v)$ be some condition on the variables v. We write "$T_1 \prec T_2$ for all v such that $C(v)$" instead of "There exists a positive real number M, such that $T_1 \leqslant MT_2$ for all v, such that $C(v)$."

We write $T_1 \approx T_2$ as short for $T_1 \prec T_2$ and $T_2 \prec T_1$. (Note that $\prec$ is transitive and reflexive and hence that $\approx$ is an equivalence relation.)

Let $\lambda = \dfrac{1}{4\sqrt{n}}$.

For any closed cube K (with edges parallel to the coordinate axes), K^λ shall denote the $1+\lambda$ dilation of K about its center.

Let $d(\mathbf{x}, \mathbf{y})$ be the usual metric on $\boldsymbol{R}^n$, $d(\mathbf{x}, \mathbf{y}) = \|\mathbf{y}-\mathbf{x}\|$; and $d(\mathbf{y}) = d(\mathbf{y}, A) = \inf\{d(\mathbf{y}, \mathbf{x}) \mid \mathbf{x} \in A\}$, K_j, $j=1, 2, \ldots$, the sequence of closed cubes defined below, e_j the length of an edge of K_j, $d_j = d(A, K_j)$, i.e., $d_j = \inf\{d(\mathbf{x}, \mathbf{y}) \mid \mathbf{x} \in A, \mathbf{y} \in K_j\}$, and N the integer (depending only on n) defined below.

We construct the sequence K_j of closed cubes with edges parallel to the coordinate axes and satisfying the following properties:

(1.1) The interiors of the K_j are disjoint;

(1.2) $U \setminus A \subset \bigcup_j K_j$;

(1.3) $e_j \approx d_j$ for all $j=1, 2, 3, \ldots$;

(1.4) $e_j \approx d(\mathbf{y})$ for all $\mathbf{y} \in K_j^\lambda$, and all $j=1, 2, \ldots$;

(1.5) $e_j \approx d(\mathbf{z})$ for all $\mathbf{z} \in U \setminus A$ such that the ball with center $\mathbf{z}$ and radius $\frac{1}{8}d(\mathbf{z})$ intersects K_j^λ;

(1.6) Each point of $U \setminus A$ has a neighborhood intersecting at most N of the K_j^λ.

Divide $\boldsymbol{R}^n$ into cubes of unit edge. Accept all cubes which intersect $U \setminus A$ and are distance $\geqslant \frac{1}{2}$ from A. Bisect each of the rejected cubes into 2^n parts and accept all those cubes which intersect $U \setminus A$ and are distance $\geq \frac{1}{4}$ from A. Repeat indefinitely to get the sequence $\{K_j\}$.

Properties (1.1) and (1.2) are immediate. To prove (1.3) we show

$$\frac{1}{2} e_j \leq d_j \leq (1 + 2\sqrt{n})e_j \qquad \text{for all } j$$

That $\frac{1}{2} e_j \leq d_j$ is immediate from the definition. Let $e_j = 2^{-k}$. For $k = 0$, we have $d_j \leq 1$, since the diameter of U is 1. For $k > 0$, K_j is one of the 2^n cubes of a cube K^* and K^* was rejected. Then $e^* = 2e_j = 2^{-k+1}$ and

$$d^* = d(A, K^*) < 2^{-k} = e_j$$

It follows from the triangle inequality and the fact that the diameter of a cube is $(n)^{1/2}$ times the length of its edge that

$$d_j \leq (1 + 2(n)^{1/2})e_j \qquad \text{for all } j$$

This completes (1.3).

To prove (1.4) we show that

$$\frac{1}{4} e_j \leq d_j(\mathbf{y}) \leq (4 + \lambda)\sqrt{n}\, e_j$$

whenever $\mathbf{y} \in K_j^\lambda$. Choose $\mathbf{y} \in K_j^\lambda$. Let $\mathbf{p}_j \in K_j$ satisfy $d(\mathbf{y}, K_j) = d(\mathbf{y}, \mathbf{p}_j)$. Then $d(\mathbf{y}, \mathbf{p}_j) \leq \lambda\sqrt{n}e_j = \frac{1}{4} e_j$. By (1.3), $\frac{1}{2}e_j \leq d_j \leq d(\mathbf{p}_j) \leq d(\mathbf{y}) + d(\mathbf{y}, \mathbf{p}_j)$. Hence $\frac{1}{4}e_j \leq d(\mathbf{y})$.

Now let $\mathbf{q}_j \in K_j$ satisfy $d(\mathbf{q}_j) = d_j$. Then by (1.3) and geometric considerations,

$$d(\mathbf{y}) \leq d(\mathbf{y}, \mathbf{q}_j) + d(\mathbf{q}_j) \leq \sqrt{n}\,(1 + \lambda)e_j + (1 + 2\sqrt{n})e_j$$

Hence $d(\mathbf{y}) \leq (4 + \lambda)\sqrt{n}\, e_j$. This completes (1.4).

Now, for (1.5), let $a = \frac{1}{4}$, $b = (4 + \lambda)\sqrt{n}$, and $\mathbf{y} \in$ the ball of radius $\frac{1}{2}ad(\mathbf{z}) = \frac{1}{8}d(\mathbf{z})$ and center $\mathbf{z}$, and $\mathbf{y} \in K_j^\lambda$. By (1.4) $ae_j \leq d(\mathbf{y}) \leq be_j$. Since

$$d(\mathbf{y}) \leq d(\mathbf{y}, \mathbf{z}) + d(\mathbf{z}) \quad \text{and} \quad d(\mathbf{z}) \leq d(\mathbf{y}, \mathbf{z}) + d(\mathbf{y})$$

we have

$$\frac{a}{2}\, e_j \leq d(\mathbf{z}) \leq \left(b + \frac{a}{2}\right)e_j$$

This proves (1.5).

Now we prove (1.6). From (1.5) it follows that there are constants p and q, depending only on n, such that for every $\mathbf{z} \in U \setminus A$, the K_j^λ intersecting the ball about $\mathbf{z}$ with radius $\frac{1}{8}d(\mathbf{z})$ are contained in a ball of radius $pd(\mathbf{z})$ about $\mathbf{z}$ and have edge at most $q\, d(\mathbf{z})$. Let N be the maximum number of cubes with edge $\geq q/p$ that fit in the unit ball.

Already N depends only on n, and, at most, N of the K_j^λ intersect the ball of radius $\frac{1}{8}d(z)$ and center z. This completes (1.6).

Now we construct a partition of unity on $U \setminus A$.

Let Q be the unit cube centered at the origin. Let η be a C^∞ function defined on $\boldsymbol{R}^n$ such that

$$\eta(\mathbf{y}) = \begin{cases} 1 & \text{for } \mathbf{y} \in Q \\ 0 & \text{for } \mathbf{y} \notin Q^\lambda \end{cases}$$

and $0 \leqslant \eta \leqslant 1$. Define

$$\eta_j(\mathbf{y}) = \eta\left(\frac{\mathbf{y} - \mathbf{c}_j}{e_j}\right)$$

when $\mathbf{c}_j$ is the center of K_j (recall e_j is the length of an edge of K_j) and

$$\sigma(\mathbf{y}) = \sum_j \eta_j(\mathbf{y})$$

Then,

(2.1) $$1 \leqslant \sigma(\mathbf{y}) \leqslant N \qquad \text{for all } \mathbf{y} \in U \setminus A.$$

Clearly for each $k = 0, 1, 2, \ldots$

$$D^k\eta_j(\mathbf{y}) \prec e_j^{-k} \qquad \text{for all } \mathbf{y} \in U \setminus A$$

and hence, by (1.4) and (1.6) for each $k = 0, 1, \ldots, r$,

(2.2) $$D^k\eta_j(\mathbf{y}) \prec d(\mathbf{y})^{-k} \qquad \text{for all } \mathbf{y} \in U \setminus A$$

and

$$D^k\sigma(\mathbf{y}) \prec d(\mathbf{y})^{-k} \qquad \text{for all } \mathbf{y} \in U \setminus A$$

Define

$$\varphi_j(\mathbf{y}) = \frac{\eta_j(\mathbf{y})}{\sigma(\mathbf{y})}$$

Then each φ_j is C^∞ and is supported on K_j^λ.

The following two properties are immediate:

(3.1) $$0 \leqslant \varphi_j(\mathbf{y}) \leqslant 1 \qquad \text{for all } \mathbf{y} \in U \setminus A;$$

(3.2) $$\sum_j \varphi_j(\mathbf{y}) = 1 \qquad \text{for all } \mathbf{y} \in U \setminus A.$$

By (1.6), we find:

(3.3) Every point of $U \setminus A$ has a neighborhood on which all but at most N of the φ_j vanish identically.

From (2.1), (2.2), (2.3), and the formula for differentiating a quotient, we have, for each $k = 0, 1, 2, \ldots, r$:

(3.4) $D^k\varphi_j(\mathbf{y}) \prec d(\mathbf{y})^{-k}$ **for all** $y \in U \setminus A$, **i.e., there are constants** M_k **such that**

$$D^k\varphi_j(\mathbf{y}) \leqslant M_k d(\mathbf{y})^{-k}$$

There is a constant α **and points** $x_j \in A$ **such that**

$$d(\mathbf{x}_j, \mathbf{y}) \leqslant \alpha d(\mathbf{y}) \qquad \text{whenever } \varphi_j(\mathbf{y}) \neq 0 \tag{3.5}$$

This follows from (1.3) and (1.4).

We now prove the Whitney Extension Theorem for the case $r < \infty$. Note that the proof uses only properties (3.1)–(3.5); it makes no new use of the fact that $\mathbf{R}^n$ is finite dimensional. Hence the problem of generalizing this case to the infinite-dimensional case reduces to proving analogies of (3.1)–(3.5).

For x $\in A$ **and y** $\in \mathbf{R}^n$ **define**

$$P(\mathbf{x}, \mathbf{y}) = \sum_{i=0}^{r} \frac{f_i(\mathbf{x})}{i!} (\mathbf{y} - \mathbf{x})^i \tag{4.1}$$

and for $k = 0, 1, \ldots, r$:

$$P_k(\mathbf{x}, \mathbf{y}) = \sum_{i \leqslant r-k} \frac{f_{k+i}(\mathbf{x})}{i!} (\mathbf{y} - \mathbf{x})^i \tag{4.2}$$

Then $P_0 = P$, and P_{k+1} is the derivative (with respect to **y**) of P_k.

For x, x′ $\in A$, **define** $R_k(x, x')$ **by**

$$f_k(\mathbf{x}, \mathbf{x}') = P_k(\mathbf{x}, \mathbf{x}') + R_k(\mathbf{x}, \mathbf{x}') \tag{4.3}$$

Define F $(= F^{(r)})$ **by**

$$F(y) = \begin{cases} f(\mathbf{y}) & \mathbf{y} \in A; \\ \sum_j \varphi_j(\mathbf{y}) P(\mathbf{x}_j, \mathbf{y}), & \mathbf{y} \in U \setminus A \end{cases} \tag{4.4}$$

By the converse of Taylor's Theorem (13.1), F is C^r on the interior of A. Clearer F is C^∞ on $U \setminus A$. Let ∂A denote the boundary of A (i.e., ∂A is the intersection of A with the closure of $U \setminus A$). We need only show that $D^k = f_k$ $(k = 0, 1, \ldots, r)$ on ∂A and that $D^r F$ is continuous on ∂A.

The difficulty in the proof is caused by the following. $D^k F(\mathbf{y})$ is expressed as a sum containing terms

$$D^{k-m}\varphi_j(\mathbf{y})\, P_m(\mathbf{x}_j, \mathbf{y})$$

where $\varphi_j(\mathbf{y}) \neq 0$. Even if **y** is close to some $\mathbf{x}_0 \in A$, it could be closer to A and hence the bound given by (3.4) is large. We circumvent this difficulty by choosing a point $\mathbf{x}^* \in A$ so that $d(\mathbf{x}^*, \mathbf{y})$ is roughly the same as $d(\mathbf{y})$ and hence, by (3.5), x_j is close to x^* (see Figure A-2). With this motivational remark in mind, we proceed.

For x, $\mathbf{x}^*$ ∈ A and y ∈ R^n,

$$\text{(5.1)} \quad P_k(\mathbf{x}, \mathbf{y}) = P_k(\mathbf{x}^*, \mathbf{y}) + \sum_{q \le r-k} \frac{R_{k+q}(\mathbf{x}^*, \mathbf{x})}{q!} (\mathbf{y} - \mathbf{x})^q$$

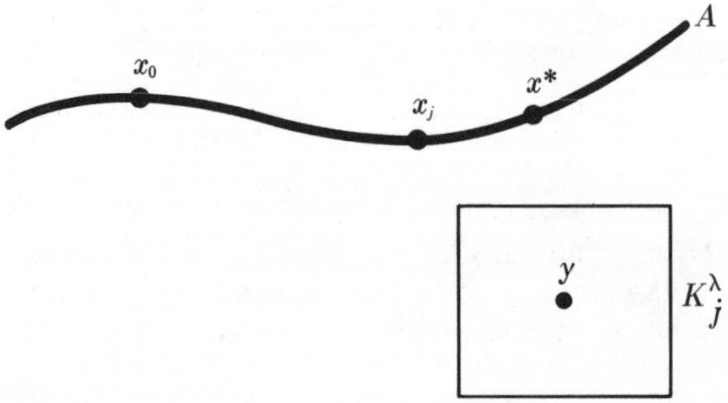

Figure A-2

To prove (5.1) use (4.2), (4.3), the fact that the $f_k(x^*)$ are multilinear maps, and the analog of the binomial theorem.

Now, fix $\mathbf{x}_0 \in \partial A$.

(5.2) For all $\eta > 0$, there exists $\delta > 0$ such that for all $\mathbf{y} \in U \setminus A$ and all $\mathbf{x}, \mathbf{x}^* \in A$ we have

$$\|P_k(\mathbf{x}, \mathbf{y}) - P_k(\mathbf{x}^*, \mathbf{y})\| \le \eta d(\mathbf{y})^{r-k} \le \eta \|\mathbf{y} - \mathbf{x}_0\|^{r-k}$$

whenever (with α as in (3.5))

$$(\ddagger) \qquad \begin{cases} \|\mathbf{y} - \mathbf{x}\| < \alpha d(\mathbf{y}) \\ \|\mathbf{y} - \mathbf{x}^*\| < \alpha d(\mathbf{y}) \\ \|\mathbf{y} - \mathbf{x}_0\| < \delta \end{cases}$$

Proof. $d(\mathbf{y}) \le \|\mathbf{y} - \mathbf{x}_0\|$; thus by making **y** close to $\mathbf{x}_0$ we can make any **x** and $\mathbf{x}^*$ satisfying (‡) close to $\mathbf{x}_0$. Choose $\eta > 0$. Define $\eta' > 0$ as below. By (W_{k+q}) and the above remark there is a $\delta > 0$, so that

$$\|R_{k+q}(\mathbf{x}^*, \mathbf{x})\| \le \eta' \|\mathbf{x}^* - \mathbf{x}\|^{r-k-q}$$
$$\le \eta'(2\alpha d(\mathbf{y}))^{r-k-q}$$

whenever (‡), and hence

$$\|R_{k+q}(\mathbf{x}^*, \mathbf{x})(\mathbf{y} - \mathbf{x})^q\| \le \eta'(2\alpha d(\mathbf{y}))^{r-k}$$

By (5.1)

$$\|P_k(\mathbf{x}, \mathbf{y}) - P_k(\mathbf{x}^*, \mathbf{y})\| \le \sum_{q \le r-k} \|R_{k+q}(\mathbf{x}^*, \mathbf{x})(\mathbf{y} - \mathbf{x})^q\|$$

Hence, take $\eta' = \eta/(2\alpha)^{r-k}(r-k)$ when $r \ne k$; $\eta' = \eta$ for $r = k$. This proves (5.2). ∎

(5.3) For every $\eta > 0$ there is a $\delta > 0$ such that for all $\mathbf{x}^* \in A$ and $\mathbf{y} \in U \setminus A$ we have

$$\|D^k F(\mathbf{y}) - P_k(\mathbf{x}^*, \mathbf{y})\| \leq \eta d(\mathbf{y})^{r-k}$$
$$\leq \eta \|\mathbf{y} - \mathbf{x}_0\|^{r-k}$$

whenever

(‡‡)
$$\begin{cases} \|\mathbf{y} - \mathbf{x}^*\| < \alpha d(\mathbf{y}) \\ \|\mathbf{y} - \mathbf{x}_0\| < \delta \end{cases}$$

Proof. Let

$$S_{jk}(\mathbf{x}^*, \mathbf{y}) = P_k(\mathbf{x}_j, \mathbf{y}) - P_k(\mathbf{x}^*, \mathbf{y})$$

Then

$$F(\mathbf{y}) - P(\mathbf{x}^*, \mathbf{y}) = \sum_j \varphi_j(\mathbf{y}) S_{j_0}(\mathbf{x}^*, \mathbf{y})$$

and hence

(*)
$$D^k F(\mathbf{y}) - P_k(\mathbf{x}^*, \mathbf{y}) = \sum_j \sum_{i \leq k} \binom{k}{i} D^{k-i} \varphi_j(\mathbf{y}) S_{ji}(\mathbf{x}^*, \mathbf{y})$$

Choose $\eta > 0$. Define $\eta' > 0$ as below. Take $\delta > 0$ as in (5.2) (reading η' for η). Let $\mathbf{y}, \mathbf{x}^*$ satisfy (‡‡). By (3.5) $\|\mathbf{y} - \mathbf{x}_j\| \leq \alpha d(\mathbf{y})$, if $\varphi_j(\mathbf{y}) \neq 0$, and hence by (5.2)

$$\|S_{ji}(\mathbf{y}, \mathbf{x}^*)\| \leq \eta' d(\mathbf{y})^{r-i}$$

Hence by (3.4), if $\varphi_j(y) \neq \mathbf{0}$ and (‡‡)

$$\|D^{k-i} \varphi_j(\mathbf{y}) S_{ji}(\mathbf{y}, \mathbf{x}^*)\| \leq \eta' M_{k-i} d(\mathbf{y})^{-r-k}$$

Since at most N nonzero terms appear in (*) by (3.3), we have a constant M depending only on $M_1, \ldots, M_k$ and k so that

$$\|D^k F(\mathbf{y}) - P_k(\mathbf{x}^*, \mathbf{y})\| \leq \eta' M d(\mathbf{y})^{r-k}$$

Take $\eta = \eta'/M$; this proves (5.3). ▮

(5.4) For every $\eta > 0$ there exists $\delta > 0$ such that for all $\mathbf{y} \in U \setminus A$ and $\mathbf{x}^* \in A$ we have

$$\|P_k(\mathbf{x}^*, \mathbf{y}) - P_k(\mathbf{x}_0, \mathbf{y})\| < \eta \|\mathbf{y} - \mathbf{x}_0\|^{r-k}$$

whenever

(‡‡)
$$\|\mathbf{y} - \mathbf{x}^*\| < \alpha d(\mathbf{y})$$
$$\|\mathbf{y} - \mathbf{x}_0\| < \delta$$

Proof. By (5.1)

$$P_k(\mathbf{x}_0, \mathbf{y}) - P_k(\mathbf{x}^*, \mathbf{y}) = \sum_{q \leq r-k} \frac{R_{k+q}(\mathbf{x}^*, \mathbf{x}_0)}{q!} (\mathbf{y} - \mathbf{x})^q$$

and by the triangle inequality, (‡‡) implies

$$\|\mathbf{x}^* - \mathbf{x}_0\| \leq (1 + \alpha)\|\mathbf{y} - \mathbf{x}_0\|$$

Now use the same argument as in (5.2). ▮

(5.5) $D^k F(\mathbf{x}_0) = f_k(\mathbf{x}_0) \qquad k = 0, 1, \ldots, r.$

Proof. We proceed by induction on k. For $k = 0$, this is the definition. Assume $k < r$ and $D^k F(\mathbf{x}_0) = f_k(\mathbf{x}_0)$. We must show that for every $\epsilon > 0$ there exists $\delta > 0$ such that

(**) $$\|D^k F(\mathbf{y}) - f_k(\mathbf{x}_0) - f_{k+1}(\mathbf{x}_0)(\mathbf{y} - \mathbf{x}_0)\| < \epsilon\|\mathbf{y} - \mathbf{x}_0\|$$

whenever $\|\mathbf{y} - \mathbf{x}_0\| < \delta$.

Choose $\epsilon > 0$. Take $\eta = \epsilon/3$ in (5.3) and (5.4); get $\delta_1, \delta_2 > 0$.

Since

$$\|P_k(\mathbf{x}_0, \mathbf{y}) - f_k(\mathbf{x}_0) - f_{k+1}(\mathbf{x}_0)(\mathbf{y} - \mathbf{x}_0)\| \leq \sum_{2 \leq i \leq r-k} \frac{\|f_{k+i}(\mathbf{x}_0)\|}{i!} \|\mathbf{y} - \mathbf{x}_0\|^i$$

we may choose $\delta_3 > 0$ so small that

(***) $$\|P_k(\mathbf{x}_0, \mathbf{y}) - f_k(\mathbf{x}_0) - f_{k+1}(\mathbf{x}_0)(\mathbf{y} - \mathbf{x}_0)\| \leq \eta\|\mathbf{y} - \mathbf{x}_0\|$$

whenever $\|\mathbf{y} - \mathbf{x}_0\| < \delta_3$.

By (W_k) choose δ_4 so small that (**) holds when $\|\mathbf{y} - \mathbf{x}_0\| < \delta_4$ and $\mathbf{y} \in A$. Now take $\delta = \min(\delta_1, \delta_2, \delta_3, \delta_4, 1)$. Choose $\mathbf{y}$ with $\|\mathbf{y} - \mathbf{x}_0\| < \delta$. If $\mathbf{y} \in A$, we have completed the proof. If $\mathbf{y} \in U \setminus A$, choose $\mathbf{x}^* \in A$ with $\|\mathbf{y} - \mathbf{x}^*\| < \alpha d(\mathbf{y})$. Then add the inequalities (5.3), (5.4), and (***) and use the triangle inequality to get (**). (Since $\delta \leq 1$, $\|\mathbf{y} - \mathbf{x}_0\|^{r-k} \leq \|\mathbf{y} - \mathbf{x}_0\|$.) This completes (5.5). ▮

(5.6) $D^r F$ **is continuous at** x.

Proof. We must show that for every $\epsilon > 0$ there exists $\delta > 0$ such that

$$\|D^r F(\mathbf{y}) - f_r(\mathbf{x}_0)\| < \epsilon$$

whenever $\|\mathbf{y} - \mathbf{x}_0\| < \delta$. This follows from (5.3) and (5.4) by the same sort of argument used in (5.5). ▮

We have completed (I), the case $r < \infty$ of the Whitney Extension Theorem.

Now for (II), the case $r = \infty$. Below we will define a function $\gamma = \gamma(j)$ from positive integers to positive integers with the property that $\gamma(j) \to \infty$ as the support of φ_j approaches A, i.e., as $d_j \to 0$. For $p = 0, 1, 2, \dots, \mathbf{x} \in A$ and $\mathbf{y} \in \mathbf{R}^n$ define

$$P^p(\mathbf{x}, \mathbf{y}) = \sum_{i \leq p} \frac{f_i(\mathbf{x})}{i!} (\mathbf{y} - \mathbf{x})^i$$

We then define F by

$$F(\mathbf{y}) = \begin{cases} f(\mathbf{y}) & \text{for } \mathbf{y} \in A \\ \sum_j \varphi_j(\mathbf{y}) P^{\gamma(j)}(\mathbf{x}_j, \mathbf{y}) & \text{for } \mathbf{y} \in U \setminus A \end{cases}$$

Then as $\mathbf{y} \to \mathbf{x}_0 \in A$, $\gamma(j)$ becomes larger than any fixed k, so that $f_k(\mathbf{x}_j)$ appears in the sum; then $D^k F(\mathbf{x}_0)$ will turn out to be $f_k(\mathbf{x}_0)$. Care must be taken that $\gamma(j)$ is not too large.

Define for $p = 0, 1, 2, \dots$

$$F^p(\mathbf{y}) = \begin{cases} f(\mathbf{y}) & \text{for } \mathbf{y} \in A \\ \sum_j \varphi_j(\mathbf{y}) P^p(\mathbf{x}_j, \mathbf{y}) & \text{for } \mathbf{y} \in U \setminus A \end{cases}$$

(6.1) There exist positive real numbers B_q (independent of the choice of the particular function γ) such that if $k \leq p \leq q$ are integers and $\mathbf{y} \in U \setminus A$ satisfies $p \leq \gamma(j) \leq q$ whenever $\varphi_j(\mathbf{y}) \neq 0$, then

$$\|D^k F(\mathbf{y}) - D^k F^p(\mathbf{y})\| \leq B_q d(\mathbf{y})^{p-k}$$

Proof. For $\mathbf{y} \in U \setminus A$ define

$$W_j^p(\mathbf{y}) = P^{\gamma(j)}(\mathbf{x}_j, \mathbf{y}) - P^p(\mathbf{x}_j, \mathbf{y})$$

Let $\mathbf{y}$ satisfy the hypothesis. Then if $\varphi_j(\mathbf{y}) \neq 0$

$$W_j^p(\mathbf{y}) = \sum_{p \leq i \leq \gamma(j)} \frac{f_i(\mathbf{x}_j)}{i!} (\mathbf{y} - \mathbf{x}_j)^i$$

and if $m \leq p$,

(i) $D^m W_j^p(\mathbf{y}) = \sum_{p \leq i \leq \gamma(j)} \dfrac{f_i(\mathbf{x}_j)}{(i-m)!} (\mathbf{y} - \mathbf{x}_j)^{i-m}$

Also

$$F(\mathbf{y}) - F^p(\mathbf{y}) = \sum_j \varphi_j(\mathbf{y}) W_j^p(\mathbf{y})$$

Thus, if $\varphi_j(\mathbf{y}) \neq 0$,

(ii) $$D^k F(\mathbf{y}) - D^k F^p(\mathbf{y}) = \sum_j \sum_{m \leq k} \binom{m}{k} D^{k-m} \varphi_j(\mathbf{y})\, D^m W_j^p(\mathbf{y})$$

We assumed the diameter of U is $\leqslant 1$. Let

$$L_q = \sup\{\|f_i(\mathbf{x})\|: i = 0, \ldots, q, \mathbf{x} \in A\}$$

By (i) we see

$$\|D^m W_j^p(\mathbf{y})\| \leqslant \gamma(j) L_{\gamma(j)} \|\mathbf{y} - \mathbf{x}_j\|^{p-m} \leqslant q L_q \alpha^{p-m} d(\mathbf{y})^{p-m}$$

if $\varphi_j(\mathbf{y}) \neq 0$. (We have used (3.5).)

Also by (3.4)

$$\|D^{k-m} \varphi_j(\mathbf{y})\| \leqslant M_{k-m} d(\mathbf{y})^{m-k}$$

By (ii) and (3.3)

$$\|D^k F(\mathbf{y}) - D^k F^p(\mathbf{y})\| \leqslant \sum_j \sum_{m \leqslant k} \binom{k}{m} \|D^{k-m} \varphi_j(\mathbf{y})\| \; \|D^m W_j^p(\mathbf{y})\|$$

$$\leqslant \sum_{\varphi_j(y) \neq 0} \sum_{m \leqslant k} \binom{k}{m} M_{k-m} q L_q \alpha^{p-m} d(\mathbf{y})^{p-k}$$

$$\leqslant B_q \, d(\mathbf{y})^{p-k}$$

for suitable B_q. This completes (6.1). ∎

By (1.3) and (1.4) $d_j \approx d(\mathbf{y})$ for $\varphi_j(\mathbf{y}) \neq 0$, i.e., there are constants a and b with $ad_j \leqslant d(\mathbf{y}) \leqslant bd_j$ for $\varphi_j(\mathbf{y}) \neq 0$. Now define the sequence $\{\delta_m\}$ so,

(1) $b\delta_{m+1} < \delta_m$;

(2) $\delta_{m-1} < 1/B_m$.

Then $\delta_m \downarrow 0$ as $m \to \infty$.

Define $\gamma(j)$ by

(3) $\delta_{\gamma(j)+1} \leqslant d_j < \delta_{\gamma(j)}$

Now F is well-defined. As before F is C^∞ on $U \setminus A$ and on the interior of A with $D^k F(\mathbf{x}) = f_k(\mathbf{x})$, for $\mathbf{x}$ is the interior of A.

Fix $\mathbf{x}_0 \in \partial A$ and integer k.

(6.2) For every $\eta > 0$ there exists $\delta > 0$ and $p \geqslant k$ such that, for all $y \in U \setminus A$,

$$\|D^k F(y) - D^k F^p(y)\| \leqslant \eta d(y)$$

whenever $\|y - x_0\| < \delta$.

Proof. Choose $\eta > 0$. Choose p so that $p \geqslant k + 3$ and $\delta_p < \eta$. Choose $\delta > 0$ so that $\delta < \min(ad_{p+1}, \eta, 1)$. Choose $y \in U \setminus A$ with $\|y - x_0\| < \delta$. Let q satisfy $\delta_q \leqslant d(y) < \delta_{q-1}$.

Since $d_j \leqslant \delta_{\gamma(j)}$ we have, if $\varphi_j(\mathbf{y}) \neq 0$, $d(\mathbf{y}) \leqslant bd_j \leqslant b\delta_{\gamma(j)} < \delta_{\gamma(j)-1}$; and hence $\gamma(j) \leqslant q$.

Since, if $\varphi_j(\mathbf{y}) \neq 0$,

$$\delta_{\gamma(j)+1} \leqslant d_j \leqslant \frac{d(\mathbf{y})}{a} \leqslant \frac{\delta}{a} \leqslant \delta_{p+1}$$

we have $p \leqslant \gamma(j)$.

The hypothesis of (6.1) holds, so

$$\begin{aligned} \|D^kF(\mathbf{y}) - D^kF^p(\mathbf{y})\| &\leqslant B_q\, d(\mathbf{y})^{p-k} \\ &\leqslant B_q\, d(\mathbf{y})^3 \\ &\leqslant B_q\, \delta_{q-1}\, d(\mathbf{y})^2 \\ &\leqslant d(\mathbf{y})^2 \\ &\leqslant \eta\, d(\mathbf{y}) \end{aligned}$$

This completes (6.2). ∎

(6.3) $D^kF(\mathbf{x}_0) = f_k(\mathbf{x}_0)$

Proof. We proceed by induction on k. For $k = 0$, this is the definition. Assume $D^kF(\mathbf{x}_0) = f_k(\mathbf{x}_0)$. We must show that for every $\epsilon > 0$ there exists $\delta > 0$ such that

$$(*) \qquad \|D^kF(\mathbf{y}) - f_k(\mathbf{x}_0) = f_{k+1}(\mathbf{x}_0)(\mathbf{y} - \mathbf{x}_0)\| < \epsilon\|\mathbf{y} - \mathbf{x}_0\|$$

whenever $\|\mathbf{y} - \mathbf{x}_0\| < \delta$.

Choose $\epsilon > 0$. Let $\eta = \epsilon/2$. Take δ_1 and p as we did in (6.1). Take δ_2 small enough so that $(*)$ holds for $\|\mathbf{y} - \mathbf{x}_0\| < \delta_2$ and $\mathbf{y} \in A$. By the case $r < \infty$, $D^{k+1}F^p(\mathbf{x}_0) = f_{k+1}(\mathbf{x}_0)$. Therefore take $\delta_3 > 0$ so that

$$(**) \qquad \|D^kF^p(\mathbf{y}) - f_k(\mathbf{x}_0) - f_{k+1}(\mathbf{x}_0)(\mathbf{y} - \mathbf{x}_0)\| < \eta\|\mathbf{y} - \mathbf{x}_0\|$$

whenever $\|\mathbf{y} - \mathbf{x}_0\| < \delta_3$.

Take $\delta = \min(\delta_1, \delta_2, \delta_3)$. Take $\mathbf{y}$ with $\|\mathbf{y} - \mathbf{x}_0\| < \delta$. If $\mathbf{y} \in A$, we are done. If $\mathbf{y} \in U \setminus A$, $(*)$ follows from $(**)$, (6.1) and the triangle inequality. This completes the Whitney Extension Theorem. ∎

Appendix B

REAL SEMIALGEBRAIC SETS

by
JOEL ROBBIN

In this appendix we prove Theorems 30.5 and 30.6 of the text.

The Tarski-Seidenberg Theorem (30.5) may be obtained as an easy corollary of Theorem 9.2.19 in Robinson [*1;* p. 236]. We restate it in somewhat weaker form as follows.

B1. THEOREM. Let K be a nonempty consistent set of sentences in prenex normal form, formulated in a language L which includes function symbols. Let K^* be another set of sentences of L with $K \subset K^*$ and such that K^* is model consistent and model complete relative to K.

Then for each wff $Q^*(x_1, \ldots, x_n)$ (all free variables displayed) there is a quantifier free wff $Q(x_1, \ldots, x_n)$ such that for any $a_1, \ldots, a_n$ in a model M of K, $Q(a_1, \ldots, a_n)$ holds in M if and only if $Q^*(a_1, \ldots, a_n)$ holds in all extensions M^* of M which are models of K^*.

Now we take K to be the theory of ordered fields (formulated with function symbols so K consists only of universal sentences) and K^* to be the theory of real closed fields. Then K and K^* satisfy the hypothesis of Theorem B1 (see Robinson [*1;* p. 108, Theorem 4.3.5]) and K^* is model complete (*ibid.*, [*1;* p. 105, Theorem 4.2.27]). Taking $M = \mathbf{R}$ in Theorem B1 we get the following.

B2. TARSKI-SEIDENBERG THEOREM (ALGEBRAIC FORM). For each formula $Q^*(y_1, \ldots, y_m, x_1, \ldots, x_n)$ of K there is a quantifier free formula $Q(y_1, \ldots, y_m, x_1, \ldots, x_n)$ such that for $b_1, \ldots, b_m \in R$, R models the sentence

$$(x_1), \ldots, (x_n). \quad Q^*(b_1, \ldots, b_m, x_1, \ldots, x_n) \equiv Q(b_1, \ldots, b_m, x_1, \ldots, x_n)$$

Since a semialgebraic set is a set of the form

$$\{(a_1, \ldots, a_n) \in \boldsymbol{R}^n \mid \boldsymbol{R} \text{ models } Q(b_1, \ldots, b_m, a_1, \ldots, a_n)\}$$

we have this corollary.

B3. TARSKI-SEIDENBERG THEOREM (GEOMETRIC FORM). Every formula $Q^*(b_1, \ldots, b_m, x_1, \ldots, x_n)$ where $b_1, \ldots, b_m \in \boldsymbol{R}$ defines a semialgebraic set. In particular, the algebraic image of a semialgebraic set is semialgebraic.

Tarski's original proof of Theorem B2 appears in Tarski [*1*]. It is effective in the sense that a primitive recursive procedure for finding Q from Q^* is given. Tarski was interested in finding a decision procedure for high school algebra, i.e., the theory K^*; in fact, he first showed K is complete (completeness implies the existence of a decision procedure). Robinson's proof of Theorem B1 is noneffective because it makes heavy use of the Gödel Completeness Theorem. Mathematicians having no background in mathematical logic will find an analytic proof of Theorem B3 in Friedman [*1;* p. 218, pp. 225–235].

Theorem 30.6 says that a semialgebraic set is a finite union of submanifolds. We will show that this is an easy consequence of the fact that an algebraic variety is a finite union of submanifolds; this latter fact is proved in Whitney [*2;* Theorem 2].

In the first place the problem of showing that an arbitrary semialgebraic set A is a finite union of submanifolds reduces to the special case where A has the following form:

$$A = \{\mathbf{x} \in \boldsymbol{R}^n \mid P_1(\mathbf{x}), \ldots, P_k(\mathbf{x}) > 0; \quad Q_1(\mathbf{x}) = Q_2(\mathbf{x}) = \cdots = Q_l(\mathbf{x}) = 0\}$$

Here $P_1(\mathbf{x}), \ldots, P_k(\mathbf{x}), Q_1(\mathbf{x}), \ldots, Q_l(\mathbf{x})$ are polynomials in $x = (x_1, \ldots, x_n)$. Thus $A = U \cap V$ where

$$U = \{\mathbf{x} \in \boldsymbol{R}^n \mid P_1(\mathbf{x}), \ldots, P_k(\mathbf{x}) > 0\}$$

and

$$V = \{\mathbf{x} \in \boldsymbol{R}^n \mid Q_1(\mathbf{x}) = \cdots = Q_l(\mathbf{x}) = 0\}$$

Since U is obviously open, the problem reduces to showing that V is a finite union of manifolds. But

$$V = \{x \in \boldsymbol{R}^n \mid Q_1(x)^2 + \cdots + (Q_l(x))^2 = 0\}$$

Thus V is an algebraic variety and, by Whitney [2], is therefore a finite union of manifolds. This completes the proof of 30.6.

Appendix C

THE STABLE, CENTER-STABLE, CENTER, CENTER-UNSTABLE, AND UNSTABLE MANIFOLDS

by

AL KELLEY*

The Institute for Advanced Study, Princeton, and
the University of California, Santa Cruz

1. Introduction

Our purpose is to give a proof of the existence and smoothness of the invariant manifolds in the title for a system of ordinary differential equations defined in a neighborhood of a critical point, periodic orbit, or periodic surface. The literature on stable and unstable manifolds is extensive, although most of it does not concern smoothness. The center-stable, center, and center-unstable manifolds have occurred only recently in the work of Pliss (*5*)† and Kelley (*4*). The theorem of Pliss states (without going into detail) that the stability of the center-stable manifold is completely determined by the stability of the center manifold. Although Pliss only proved the theorem for systems of ordinary differential equations in a neighborhood of a critical point, the same theorem is true for systems in a neighborhood of a periodic orbit or periodic surface. A proof of this extension to Pliss' theorem will be published elsewhere. In (*4*) is found an elementary application of the concept of the center manifold to Hamiltonian systems of equations. Section 4 below is due to D. V. Anosov.

*Research supported in part by the National Academy of Sciences, and the National Science Foundation through grant GP-2439. Manuscript received June 17, 1966.

†References in parentheses refer to the bibliography at the end of this appendix.

2. Notation

The norm $|\cdot|$ will represent the euclidean norm on vectors and the operator norm on matrices, and $\langle\cdot,\cdot\rangle$ will represent the usual scalar product on pairs of vectors. If $F=F(p)$ is a smooth vector valued function of the vector p, then F_p will represent the Jacobian matrix of partial derivatives. D_p^ρ will designate the usual partial differential operator; $D_p^\rho=\partial^{|\rho|}/\partial_{p_1}^{\rho_1}\cdots\partial_{p_n}^{\rho_n}$ where $\rho=(\rho_1,\ldots,\rho_n)$ is an n-tuple of non-negative integers, $|\rho|=\rho_1+\cdots+\rho_n$, and $n=\dim p$. In the proof of Lemma 3 below it will be convenient to use the notation $\rho=\rho_1+\rho_2$ where $\rho_j(j=1,2)$ designates an n-tuple rather than a component of an n-tuple. The meaning will be clear from the context.

3. Invariant Manifolds

Consider the real, $C^k(1\leqslant k<\infty)$ system of ordinary differential equations

$$\begin{aligned}\dot\theta&=a+\widetilde\Theta(\theta,x,y,z)\\ \dot x&=Ax+\widetilde X(\theta,x,y,z)\\ \dot y&=By+\widetilde Y(\theta,x,y,z)\\ \dot z&=Cz+\widetilde Z(\theta,x,y,z)\end{aligned}\tag{1}$$

where A, B, and C are constant square matrices in real canonical form; A has eigenvalues with negative real parts; B has eigenvalues with zero real parts ($B\equiv 0$ is allowed); C has eigenvalues with positive real parts; θ, x, etc. are vectors; a is a constant vector; $\widetilde\Theta$, $\widetilde X$, $\widetilde Y$, $\widetilde Z$ are defined and C^k in

$$N_\delta=\{(\theta,x,y,z)\mid\theta\text{ arbitrary},\ |x|+|y|+|z|<\delta\}$$

and have multiple period ω in θ; $\widetilde\Theta$, $\widetilde X$, $\widetilde Y$, $\widetilde Z$, $(\widetilde X,\widetilde Y,\widetilde Z)_{(x,y,z)}\equiv 0$ when $(x,y,z)=0$.

Equation (1) represents a system of ordinary differential equations in a neighborhood of a critical point, periodic orbit, or periodic surface depending on whether θ is absent from (1), $\dim\theta=1$, or $\dim\theta>1$, respectively. In the last two cases the condition $a\neq 0$ would also hold, but for our purposes one need not assume anything about a except that it is constant.

THEOREM 1. For system (1) with $3\leqslant k<\infty$ there exists invariant manifolds

$$M^+=\{(\theta,x,y,z)\mid\theta\text{ arbitrary},\ |x|<\delta_1,\ y=v^+(\theta,x),\ z=w^+(\theta,x)\}$$

$$M^-=\{(\theta,x,y,z)\mid\theta\text{ arbitrary},\ x=u^-(\theta,z),\ y=v^-(\theta,z),\ |z|<\delta_1\}$$

where v^+, w^+, u^-, v^- are real vector-valued functions defined and C^{k-2} in some neighborhood N_{δ_1} for δ_1 sufficiently small; v^+, w^+, u^-, v^- have multiple period ω in θ; v^+, w^+, u^-, v^-, $(v^+,w^+,u^-,v^-)_{(x,z)}\equiv 0$ when $(x,z)=0$; M^+, M^- are (locally) unique.

For system in (1) with $2\leqslant k<\infty$ there exists invariant manifolds

$$M^{*+}=\{(\theta,x,y,z)\mid\theta\text{ arbitrary},\ |x|+|y|<\delta_1,\ z=w^{*+}(\theta,x,y)\}$$

$$M^{*}=\{(\theta,x,y,z)\mid\theta\text{ arbitrary},\ x=u^{*}(\theta,y),\ |y|<\delta_1,\ z=w^{*}(\theta,y)\}$$

$$M^{*-}=\{(\theta,x,y,z)\mid\theta\text{ arbitrary},\ x=u^{*-}(\theta,y,z),\ |y|+|z|<\delta_1\}$$

where w^{*+}, u^*, w^*, u^{*-} are real vector-valued functions defined and C^{k-1} in some neighborhood N_{δ_1} for δ_1 sufficiently small; w^{*+}, u^*, w^*, u^{*-} have multiple period ω in θ; w^{*+}, u^*, w^*, u^{*-}, $(w^{*+}, u^*, w^*, u^{*-})_{(x,y,z)} \equiv 0$ when $(x, y, z)=0$; (M^{*+}, M^*, M^{*-} need not be unique).

The invariant manifolds M^+, M^{*+}, M^*, M^{*-}, and M^- are called, respectively, the stable manifold, the center-stable manifold, the center manifold, the center-unstable manifold, the unstable manifold.

Proof. Introducing the scalar change of variables $(x, y, z) \to (\lambda x, \lambda y, \lambda z)$ and multiplying $\widetilde{\Theta}$, $\widetilde{X}$, $\widetilde{Y}$, and $\widetilde{Z}$ by $\varnothing(|x|^2 + |y|^2 + |z|^2 + K\lambda^2)$ where K is a sufficiently large positive constant and $\varnothing(r)$ is a C^∞ real valued function satisfying $\varnothing(r) \equiv 1$ for $0 \leqslant r \leqslant \frac{1}{2}$ and $\varnothing(r) \equiv 0$ for $1 \leqslant r < \infty$, we obtain

$$\begin{aligned} \dot{\theta} &= a + \Theta(\theta, x, y, z, \lambda) \\ \dot{x} &= Ax + X(\theta, x, y, z, \lambda) \\ \dot{y} &= By + Y(\theta, x, y, z, \lambda) \\ \dot{z} &= Cz + Z(\theta, x, y, z, \lambda) \end{aligned} \tag{2}$$

where

$$\Theta(\theta, x, y, z, \lambda) = \varnothing(|x|^2 + |y|^2 + |z|^2 + K\lambda^2)\widetilde{\Theta}(\theta, \lambda x, \lambda y, \lambda z)$$
$$X(\theta, x, y, z, \lambda) = \varnothing(|x|^2 + |y|^2 + |z|^2 + K\lambda^2)\lambda^{-1}\widetilde{X}(\theta, \lambda x, \lambda y, \lambda z)$$

and so on, and the following conditions hold.

(2-i) Θ, X, Y, and Z exist and are continuous for all $(\theta, x, y, z, \lambda)$ and for each λ fixed are C^k in (θ, x, y, z).

(2-ii) Θ, X, Y, and Z have multiple period ω in θ.

(2-iii) Θ, X, Y, Z, and $(X, Y, Z)_{(x,y,z)} \equiv 0$ when $(x, y, z) = 0$.

(2-iv) Θ, X, Y, $Z \equiv 0$ for $|x|^2 + |y|^2 + |z|^2 \geqslant 1$.

(2-v) $D^\rho_{(\theta,x,y,z)}(\Theta, X, Y, Z) \to 0$ uniformly in (θ, x, y, z) as $\lambda \to 0$ for $0 \leqslant |\rho| \leqslant k$. If $\lambda \neq 0$, then systems (1) and (2) are locally (near $\{(\theta, x, y, z) \mid \theta \text{ arbitrary}, (x, y, z) = 0\}$) related by a scalar change of variables. Therefore it is sufficient to prove Theorem 1 for system (2). More precisely, however, we will prove Theorem 2, which will imply Theorem 1.

THEOREM 2. For system (2) with $3 \leqslant k < \infty$ there exists invariant manifolds

$$M^+_\lambda = \{(\theta, x, y, z) \mid \theta \text{ arbitrary}, |x| < 1, y = v^+(\theta, x, \lambda), z = w^+(\theta, x, \lambda), |\lambda| < \delta\}$$
$$M^-_\lambda = \{(\theta, x, y, z) \mid \theta \text{ arbitrary}, x = u^-(\theta, z, \lambda), y = v^-(\theta, z, \lambda), |z| < 1, |\lambda| < \delta\}$$

where the following conditions hold.

(3-i) v^+, w^+, u^-, and v^- are real vector-valued functions defined and continuous in

$$N^\delta_1 = \{(\theta, x, z, \lambda) \mid \theta \text{ arbitrary}, |x| + |z| < 1, |\lambda| < \delta\}$$

for some $\delta > 0$ sufficiently small, and for each λ fixed, these functions are C^{k-2} in (θ, x, z).

(3-ii) v^+, w^+, u^-, and v^- have multiple period ω in θ.

(3-iii) v^+, w^+, u^-, v^-, and $(v^+, w^+, u^-, v^-)_{(x,z)} \equiv 0$ when $(x, z) = 0$.

For system (2) with $2 \leqslant k < \infty$ there exists invariant manifolds

$$M_\lambda^{*+} = \{(\theta, x, y, z) \mid (\theta, x, y) \text{ arbitrary}, z = w^{*+}(\theta, x, y, \lambda), |\lambda| < \delta\}$$
$$M_\lambda^{*} = \{(\theta, x, y, z) \mid (\theta, y) \text{ arbitrary}, x = u^*(\theta, y, \lambda), z = w^*(\theta, y, \lambda), |\lambda| < \delta\}$$
$$M_\lambda^{*-} = \{(\theta, x, y, z) \mid (\theta, y, z) \text{ arbitrary}, x = u^{*-}(\theta, y, z, \lambda), |\lambda| < \delta\}$$

where the following conditions hold.

(3-iv) w^{*+}, u^*, w^*, and u^{*-} are real vector-valued functions defined and continuous in

$$N^\delta = \{(\theta, x, y, z, \lambda) \mid (\theta, x, y, z) \text{ arbitrary}, |\lambda| < \delta\}$$

for some $\delta > 0$ sufficiently small, and for each λ fixed these functions are C^{k-1} in (θ, x, y, z).

(3-v) w^{*+}, u^*, w^*, and u^{*-} have multiple period ω in θ.

(3-vi) w^{*+}, u^*, w^*, u^{*-}, $(w^{*+}, u^*, w^*, u^{*-})_{(x,y,z)} \equiv 0$ when $(x, y, z) = 0$. Moreover, M_λ^+, M_λ^- are (locally) unique (but M_λ^{*+}, M_λ^*, M_λ^{*-} need not be).

Proof of Theorem 2. Let (ψ, ξ, η, ζ) where $\psi = \psi(t) = \psi(t, \theta, x, y, z, \lambda)$, $\xi = \xi(t) = \xi(t, \theta, x, y, z, \lambda)$, etc., represent the unique solution of (2) with initial condition (θ, x, y, z) at $t = 0$. From (2-i, iv) the solution exists and is continuous for all $(t, \theta, x, y, z, \lambda)$ and for each λ fixed is C^k in (t, θ, x, y, z).

The functions v^+, w^+ which determine M_λ^+ will now be constructed as the unique solution to the differential-integral system

$$\begin{aligned} \dot{\theta} &= a + \Theta(\theta, x, v^+(\theta, x, \lambda), w^+(\theta, x, \lambda), \lambda) \\ \dot{x} &= Ax + X(\theta, x, v^+(\theta, x, \lambda), w^+(\theta, x, \lambda), \lambda) \end{aligned} \tag{3a}$$

$$\begin{aligned} v^+(\theta, x, \lambda) &= \int_{+\infty}^{0} e^{-B\sigma}\, Y(\psi^+, \xi^+, v^+(\psi^+, \xi^+, \lambda), w^+(\psi^+, \xi^+, \lambda), \lambda)\, d\sigma \\ w^+(\theta, x, \lambda) &= \int_{+\infty}^{0} e^{-C\sigma}\, Z(\psi^+, \xi^+, v^+(\psi^+, \xi^+, \lambda), w^+(\psi^+, \xi^+, \lambda), \lambda)\, d\sigma \end{aligned} \tag{3b}$$

where (ψ^+, ξ^+) with $\psi^+ = \psi^+(t) = \psi^+(t, \theta, x, v^+, w^+, \lambda)$, $\xi^+ = \xi^+(t) = \xi^+(t, \theta, x, v^+, w^+, \lambda)$ represents the unique solution to (3a) with initial condition (θ, x) at $t = 0$. To designate explicitly the *functional* dependence of the solution of (3a) on v^+, w^+, these functions are included in the arguments of ψ^+, ξ^+. In (3b) the functions ψ^+, ξ^+ occurring in the integrand are understood to be $\psi^+(\sigma) = \psi^+(\sigma, \theta, x, v^+, w^+, \lambda)$, $\xi^+(\sigma) = \xi^+(\sigma, \theta, x, v^+, w^+, \lambda)$. Assuming (3) has a unique solution (v^+, w^+), $v^+ = v^+(\theta, x, \lambda)$, $w^+ = w^+(\theta, x, \lambda)$, which satisfies conditions (3-i, ii, iii), we can easily show that M_λ^+ is an invariant manifold for system (2). Since (3a) is an autonomous system,

$$\psi^+(\sigma, \psi^+(t, \theta, x, v^+, w^+, \lambda), \xi^+(t, \theta, x, v^+, w^+, \lambda), \lambda) = \psi^+(t + \sigma, \theta, x, v^+, w^+, \lambda)$$
$$\xi^+(\sigma, \psi^+(t, \theta, x, v^+, w^+, \lambda), \xi^+(t, \theta, x, v^+, w^+, \lambda), v^+, w^+, \lambda) = \xi^+(t + \sigma, \theta, x, v^+, w^+, \lambda)$$

Replacing (θ, x) in (3b) by $(\psi^+(t), \xi^+(t))$, we have

$$v^+(\psi^+(t), \xi^+(t), \lambda) = \int_{+\infty}^{0} e^{-B\sigma} Y(\psi^+(t+\sigma), \dots)\, d\sigma$$

$$= \int_{+\infty}^{t} e^{-B(\tau - t)} Y(\psi^+(\tau), \dots)\, d\tau$$

$$w^+(\psi^+(t), \xi^+(t), \lambda) = \int_{+\infty}^{0} e^{-C\sigma} Z(\psi^+(t+\sigma), \dots)\, d\sigma$$

$$= \int_{+\infty}^{t} e^{-C(\tau - t)} Z(\psi^+(\tau), \dots)\, d\tau$$

Let $v^+(t) = v^+(\psi^+(t), \xi^+(t), \lambda)$, $w^+(t) = w^+(\psi^+(t), \xi^+(t), \lambda)$; then a direct calculation shows

$$\frac{d}{dt} v^+(t) = Bv^+(t) + Y(\psi^+(t), \xi^+(t), v^+(t), w^+(t), \lambda)$$

$$\frac{d}{dt} w^+(t) = Cw^+(t) + Z(\psi^+(t), \xi^+(t), v^+(t), w^+(t), \lambda)$$

Because solutions of (2) are unique,

$$\psi(t, \theta, x, v^+(\theta, x, \lambda), w^+(\theta, x, \lambda), \lambda) = \psi^+(t, \theta, x, v^+, w^+, \lambda)$$

$$\xi(t, \theta, x, v^+(\theta, x, \lambda), w^+(\theta, x, \lambda), \lambda) = \xi^+(t, \theta, x, v^+, w^+, \lambda)$$

$$\eta(t, \theta, x, v^+(\theta, x, \lambda), w^+(\theta, x, \lambda), \lambda) = v^+(\psi^+(t, \theta, x, v^+, w^+, \lambda), \xi^+(t, \theta, x, v^+, w^+, \lambda), \lambda)$$

$$\zeta(t, \theta, x, v^+(\theta, x, \lambda), w^+(\theta, x, \lambda), \lambda) = w^+(\psi^+(t, \theta, x, v^+, w^+, \lambda), \xi^+(t, \theta, x, v^+, w^+, \lambda), \lambda)$$

and M_λ^+ is an invariant manifold for (2).

To solve (3) inequalities involving the matrices A, B, and C are basic.

LEMMA 1. There exists $\mu > 0$, $\gamma \geq 0$, $\frac{1}{2}\mu > \gamma$, such that for all x, y, z,

$$\begin{aligned} \langle Ax, x\rangle &\leq -2\mu\, |x|^2 \\ |\langle By, y\rangle| &\leq \gamma\, |y|^2 \\ \langle Cz, z\rangle &\geq 2\mu\, |z|^2 \end{aligned} \tag{4}$$

and these inequalities imply

$$\begin{aligned} |e^{At}| &\leq e^{-2\mu t} && (0 \leq t < \infty) \\ |e^{Bt}| &\leq e^{\gamma|t|} && (-\infty < t < \infty) \\ |e^{-Ct}| &\leq e^{-2\mu t} && (0 \leq t < \infty) \end{aligned} \tag{5}$$

Proof of Lemma 1. Inequality (4) is an immediate consequence of the assumption that A, B, and C are contraction, center, and expansion matrices, respectively, in real canonical form. The constant μ depends on the eigenvalues of A and C; in particular we may choose 3μ equal to the minimum of the absolute values of the real parts of the eigenvalues of A and C. Then (4) requires (with no loss of generality) that the "off-diagonalizable" terms in A and C are sufficiently small. When B is diagonalizable, then $\gamma = 0$; otherwise the "off-diagonalizable" terms of B can be assumed (with no loss of generality) sufficiently small such that (4) holds for any $\gamma > 0$ arbitrarily small but fixed. (See (*1*) page 341 for details.)

Let $\xi = \xi(t, x) = e^{At}x$, then $\dot{\xi} = A\xi$ implies

$$\frac{d}{dt}|\xi|^2 = \frac{d}{dt}\langle\xi, \xi\rangle = 2\langle A\xi, \xi\rangle \leqslant -4\mu\,|\xi|^2$$

from which it follows that $|e^{At}| \leqslant e^{-2\mu t}$ for $0 \leqslant t < \infty$. Similar arguments prove the remaining inequalities in equation (5). This completes the proof of Lemma 1.

We now develop a useful generalization of an inequality used by Hale [*3*].

LEMMA 2. Let a be a nonnegative constant, and let $b(t)$ be a continuous real-valued function defined on a finite or infinite interval I which contains the origin. If $\varphi(t)$ is a C^1 vector or matrix which satisfies

$$|\dot{\varphi}(t)| \leqslant a\,|\varphi(t)| + b(t) \qquad t \in \mathrm{I} \tag{6}$$

then

$$|\varphi(t)| \leqslant e^{a|t|}\left\{|\varphi(0)| + \left|\int_0^t e^{-a|\tau|}\, b(\tau)\; d\tau\right|\right\} \qquad t \in \mathrm{I}$$

Proof of Lemma 2. From (6) for $t \geqslant 0$

$$|\varphi(t)| - |\varphi(0)| \leqslant |\varphi(t) - \varphi(0)| = \left|\int_0^t \dot{\varphi}(\tau)\, d\tau\right| \leqslant \int_0^t |\dot{\varphi}(\tau)|\, d\tau \leqslant \int_0^t \{a|\varphi(\tau)| + b(\tau)\}\, d\tau$$

Therefore

$$|\varphi(t)| \leqslant |\varphi(0)| + \int_0^t \{a|\varphi(\tau)| + b(\tau)\}\, d\tau \tag{7}$$

Consider the scalar function $\psi(t)$ defined by

$$\dot{\psi}(t) = a\psi(t) + b(t) \qquad \psi(0) = |\varphi(0)|$$

Thus

$$\psi(t) = |\varphi(0)| + \int_0^t \{a\psi(\tau) + b(\tau)\}\, d\tau \tag{8}$$

Subtracting (8) from (7), we obtain

$$|\varphi(t)| - \psi(t) \leqslant \int_0^t a\{|\varphi(\tau)| - \psi(\tau)\}\, d\tau$$

and it now follows from the Gronwall inequality ([*1*] Problem 1, Ch. 1) that for $t \geqslant 0$, $t \in \mathrm{I}$,

$$|\varphi(t)| \leqslant \psi(t) = e^{at}\{|\varphi(0)| + \int_0^t e^{-a\tau} b(\tau)\, d\tau\}$$

The proof for $t < 0$ is similar. This completes the proof of Lemma 2.

We now proceed to solve (3) by means of a contraction mapping in a Banach space. For l, m positive integers define

$$\mathscr{X}^l_m = \{\chi = \chi(\theta, x) \text{ satisfying } (9\text{-i}, \ldots, \text{v})\}$$

(9-i) χ is a real vector-valued function defined and C^l for all θ and $|x| < 1$.

(9-ii) $\dim \chi = m$.

(9-iii) χ has multiple period ω in θ.

(9-iv) χ, $\chi_x \equiv 0$ when $x = 0$.

(9-v) $\|\chi\| = \max\limits_{0 \leq |\rho| \leq l} \sup\limits_{\theta} \sup\limits_{|x|<1} |D^{\rho}_{(\theta,x)}\chi(\theta, x)| < \infty$.

With the norm $\|\cdot\|$ given in (9-v), $\mathscr{X}^l_m$ is a Banach space. Define $\tilde{\mathscr{X}}^l_m$ to be the closed unit ball in $\mathscr{X}^l_m$.

Let $\mathscr{X}^l_y = \mathscr{X}^l_{\dim y}$, etc. For $v \in \tilde{\mathscr{X}}^{k-1}_y$, $w \in \tilde{\mathscr{X}}^{k-1}_z$, $2 \leq k < \infty$, consider the system

$$\begin{aligned} \dot{\theta} &= a + \Theta(\theta, x, v(\theta, x), w(\theta, x), \lambda) \\ \dot{x} &= Ax + X(\theta, x, v(\theta, x), w(\theta, x), \lambda) \end{aligned} \tag{10}$$

where $(\psi^{(v,w)}, \xi^{(v,w)})$,

$$\begin{aligned} \psi^{(v,w)} &= \psi = \psi(t) = \psi(t, \theta, x, v, w, \lambda) \\ \xi^{(v,w)} &= \xi = \xi(t) = \xi(t, \theta, x, v, w, \lambda) \end{aligned} \tag{11}$$

represents the unique solution of (10) with initial condition (θ, x) at $t = 0$.

LEMMA 3. For $0 \leq t < \infty$, all θ, $|x| < 1$, $v \in \tilde{\mathscr{X}}^{k-1}_y$, $w \in \tilde{\mathscr{X}}^{k-1}_z$, $|\lambda| < \delta_0$ with $\delta_0 > 0$ chosen sufficiently small, the solution (ψ, ξ) of (10) (given explicitly in (11)) exists and satisfies

(11-i) $|\xi(t)| \leq e^{-\mu t}|x|$

(11-ii) $|D^{\rho}_{(\theta,x)}\psi(t)| \leq \alpha(t)e^{\beta(\lambda)t}$ $\quad (1 \leq |\rho| \leq k-1)$

(11-iii) $|D^{\rho}_{(\theta,x)}\xi(t)| \leq \alpha(t)e^{(-\mu+\beta(\lambda))t}$ $\quad (1 \leq |\rho| \leq k-1)$

where $\alpha(t)$ is a polynomial in t with positive coefficients, $\beta(\lambda) \geq 0$ is continuous in λ, $\beta(\lambda) \to 0$ as $\lambda \to 0$; these inequalities are uniform in θ, $v \in \tilde{\mathscr{X}}^{k-1}_y$, $w \in \tilde{\mathscr{X}}^{k-1}_z$, and (11-ii, iii) hold uniformly in $|x| < 1$ also.

Proof of Lemma 3. The proof is accomplished in a finite number of steps wherein we find a succession of α's and β's. In (11-ii, iii) we take α and β to be the largest of the α's and β's constructed, respectively.

If $F = F(\theta, x)$ is any smooth vector-valued function of (θ, x), then

$$F(\theta, x') - F(\theta, x'') = \int_0^1 F_x(\theta, sx' + (1-s)x'')\, ds \cdot \{x' - x''\}$$

In particular if $F(\theta, 0) \equiv 0$, then

$$F(\theta, x) = \int_0^1 F_x(\theta, sx)\, ds \cdot x$$

Thus from (2-iii), (9-iv), for $v \in \tilde{\mathscr{X}}^1_y$, $w \in \tilde{\mathscr{X}}^1_z$, $|x| < 1$, we have

$$X(\theta, x, v(\theta, x), w(\theta, x), \lambda) = \int_0^1 \{X_x(\theta, sx, v(\theta, sx), w(\theta, sx), \lambda) + X_y(\theta, sx, \dots)v_x(\theta, sx) + X_z(\theta, sx, \dots)w_x(\theta, sx)\}\, ds \cdot x$$

Hence from (2-v)

$$|X(\theta, x, v(\theta, x), w(\theta, x), \lambda)| \leqslant \mu|x|, \quad (|x| < 1, |\lambda| < \delta_0) \tag{12}$$

for $\delta_0 > 0$ sufficiently small. From (4), (10), (11), and (12) with $|x| < 1$, $|\lambda| < \delta_0$,

$$\dot{\xi} = A\xi + X(\psi, \xi, v(\psi, \xi), w(\psi, \xi), \lambda)$$

$$\frac{d}{dt}|\xi|^2 = 2\langle A\xi, \xi\rangle + 2\langle X(\psi, \xi, \dots), \xi\rangle$$

$$\frac{d}{dt}|\xi|^2 \leqslant -4\mu|\xi|^2 + 2|X|\,|\xi| \leqslant -2\mu|\xi|^2$$

which implies inequality (11-i) and the existence of (ψ, ξ) as stated. From (10)

$$\begin{aligned} \dot{\psi}_{(\theta,x)} &= [\Theta_\theta + \Theta_y v_\theta + \Theta_z w_\theta]\psi_{(\theta,x)} + [\Theta_x + \Theta_y v_x + \Theta_z w_x]\xi_{(\theta,x)} \\ \dot{\xi}_{(\theta,x)} &= [A + X_x + X_y v_x + X_z w_x]\xi_{(\theta,x)} + [X_\theta + X_y v_\theta + X_z w_\theta]\psi_{(\theta,x)} \end{aligned} \tag{13}$$

where $\Theta_\theta = \Theta_\theta(\psi, \xi, v(\psi, \xi), w(\psi, \xi), \lambda)$, etc. Since the matrix (in (13))

$$A' = A + X_x + X_y v_x + X_z w_x \to A$$

as $\lambda \to 0$, it follows from (4) for $|\lambda| < \delta_0$, δ_0 restricted further if necessary,

$$\langle A'p, p\rangle \leqslant -\mu|p|^2 \tag{14}$$

for all real vectors p, $\dim p = \dim x$. The procedure used to obtain (12) also yields

$$|X_\theta + X_y v_\theta + X_z w_\theta| \leqslant \beta_1(\lambda)|\xi| \leqslant \beta_1(\lambda)e^{-\mu t} \tag{15}$$

for $|x| < 1$ where $X_\theta = X_\theta(\psi, \xi, \dots)$, etc.; $\beta_1(\lambda) \geqslant 0$, $\beta_1(\lambda) \to 0$ as $\lambda \to 0$. From (2-v), (13), (14), (15),

$$\begin{aligned} &|\dot{\psi}_{(\theta,x)}| \leqslant \beta_2(\lambda)|\psi_{(\theta,x)}| + \beta_2(\lambda)|\xi_{(\theta,x)}| \\ &\frac{d}{dt}|\xi_{(\theta,x)}|^2 \leqslant -2\mu|\xi_{(\theta,x)}|^2 + 2\beta_2(\lambda)e^{-\mu t}|\psi_{(\theta,x)}|\,|\xi_{(\theta,x)}| \\ &|\psi_{(\theta,x)}(0)| = |\xi_{(\theta,x)}(0)| = 1,\ |x| < 1,\ |\lambda| < \delta_0 \end{aligned} \tag{16}$$

where $\beta_2(\lambda) \geq 0$, $\beta_2(\lambda) \to 0$ as $\lambda \to 0$. From Lemma 2 for $0 \leq t < \infty$,

$$|\psi_{(\theta,x)}(t)| \leq e^{\beta_2(\lambda)t} \{1 + \textstyle\int_0^t e^{-\beta_2(\lambda)\tau} |\xi_{(\theta,x)}(\tau)| \, d\tau\} \tag{17}$$

so that

$$\frac{d}{dt} |\xi_{(\theta,x)}|^2 \leq -2\mu |\xi_{(\theta,x)}|^2 + 2\beta_2(\lambda) e^{-\mu t} e^{\beta_2(\lambda)t} \left\{1 + \int_0^t e^{-\beta_2(\lambda)\tau} |\xi_{(\theta,x)}(\tau)| \, d\tau\right\} |\xi_{(\theta,x)}| \tag{18}$$

By restricting δ_0 further if necessary, we may assume $\beta_2(\lambda) < \mu$ for $|\lambda| \leq \delta_0$ so that near $t=0$, $|\xi_{(\theta,x)}(t)|$ is a decreasing function of t; $|\xi_{(\theta,x)}(t)| \leq 1$ for $0 \leq t < \epsilon$, $\epsilon > 0$ sufficiently small. Now compare (18) with the real scalar equation

$$\frac{d}{dt} f^2 = -2\mu f^2 + 2\beta_2(\lambda) e^{(-\mu+\beta_2(\lambda))t} \left\{1 + \int_0^t e^{-\beta_2(\lambda)\tau} 2 d\tau\right\} f \tag{19}$$

with the initial condition $f(0) = 1$. As long as $|f(t)| \leq 2$ holds, it follows that

$$|\xi_{(\theta,x)}(t)| \leq f(t) \tag{20}$$

From (19)

$$\dot{f} = -\mu f + \beta_2(\lambda) e^{(-\mu+\beta_2(\lambda))t} \left\{1 + \int_0^t e^{-\beta_2(\lambda)\tau} 2d\tau\right\}$$

Since $f(0) = 1$, the inequality $\dot{f} \geq -\mu f$ implies $f(t) > 0$ for $0 \leq t < \infty$. Thus

$$\dot{f} \leq (-\mu + \beta_2(\lambda)) f + \beta_2(\lambda) e^{(-\mu+\beta_2(\lambda))t} \{1 + 2t\}$$

$$f(t) \leq \{1 + \beta_2(\lambda)(t + t^2)\} e^{(-\mu+\beta_2(\lambda))t}$$

and by restricting δ_0 further if necessary, we have $|f(t)| \leq 2$ for $0 \leq t < \infty$ so that (20) holds for all $0 \leq t < \infty$. Hence we have proved (11-iii) for $|\rho| = 1$. The crude inequality $|\xi_{(\theta,x)}(t)| \leq 2$ in (17) yields

$$|\psi_{(\theta,x)}(t)| \leq e^{\beta_2(\lambda)t} \left\{1 + \int_0^t e^{-\beta_2(\lambda)\tau} 2d\tau\right\} \leq \{1 + 2t\} e^{\beta_2(\lambda)t}$$

so that (11-ii) holds for $|\rho| = 1$. We now proceed inductively. Let $D^{\rho}_{(\theta,x)}\psi = \psi_\rho$, $D^{\rho}_{(\theta,x)}\xi = \xi_\rho$, and consider the case $\rho = \rho_1 + \rho_2$, $|\rho_1| = |\rho_2| = 1$, $|\rho| = 2$. Assuming $k \geq 3$ (otherwise we are done), we have from (10)

$$\begin{aligned} \dot{\psi}_\rho &= [\Theta_\theta + \Theta_y v_\theta + \Theta_z w_\theta]\psi_\rho + [\Theta_x + \Theta_y v_x + \Theta_z w_x]\xi_\rho + \Theta_{\theta\theta}\psi_{\rho_2}\psi_{\rho_1} + \cdots \\ \dot{\xi}_\rho &= [A + X_x + X_y v_x + X_z w_x]\xi_\rho + [X_\theta + X_y v_\theta + X_z w_\theta]\psi_\rho + X_{x\theta}\psi_{\rho_2}\xi_{\rho_1} + \cdots \end{aligned} \tag{21}$$

The notation $\Theta_{\theta\theta}\psi_{\rho_2}\psi_{\rho_1}$, etc. is defined by writing out (21) in complete detail. Since (11-ii, iii) hold for $|\rho_1| = |\rho_2| = 1$, we obtain from (21)

$$|\dot{\psi}_\rho| \leq \beta_3(\lambda)|\psi_\rho| + \beta_3(\lambda)|\xi_\rho| + \beta_3(\lambda)\alpha_1(t) e^{\beta_3(\lambda)t}$$

$$\frac{d}{dt} |\xi_\rho|^2 \leq -2\mu|\xi_\rho|^2 + 2\beta_3(\lambda) e^{-\mu t}|\psi_\rho| \, |\xi_\rho| + 2\beta_3(\lambda)\alpha_1(t) e^{(-\mu+\beta_2(\lambda))t}|\xi_\rho| \qquad |\psi_\rho(0)| = |\xi_\rho(0)| = 0 \tag{22}$$

where $\alpha_1(t)$ is a polynomial in t with positive coefficients and $\beta_3(\lambda) \geq \beta_2(\lambda) \geq 0$, $\beta_3(\lambda) \to 0$ as $\lambda \to 0$. From Lemma 2

$$|\psi_\rho(t)| \leq \beta_3(\lambda) e^{\beta_3(\lambda)t} \int_0^t e^{-\beta_3(\lambda)\tau} \{|\xi_\rho(\tau)| + \alpha_1(\tau) e^{\beta_3(\lambda)\tau}\} \, d\tau$$

Since $|\xi_\rho(0)| = 0$, it follows that near $t = 0$

$$|\xi_\rho(t)| \leqslant 1 \tag{23}$$

and as long as this inequality holds, it follows that

$$|\psi_\rho(t)| \leqslant \beta_3(\lambda)\alpha_2(t)e^{\beta_3(\lambda)t} \tag{24}$$

where $\alpha_2(t) = \int_0^t\{1 + \alpha_1(\tau)\}\, d\tau$. Using inequality (24) in (22) we have

$$\frac{d}{dt}|\xi_\rho|^2 \leqslant -2\mu|\xi_\rho|^2 + 2[\beta_3(\lambda)]^2\alpha_2(t)e^{-\mu t}|\xi_\rho| + 2\beta_3(\lambda)\alpha_1(t)e^{(-\mu+\beta_3(\lambda))t}|\xi_\rho|$$

Comparing this differential inequality with the scalar equation

$$\frac{d}{dt} f^2 = -2\mu f^2 + 4\beta_4(\lambda)\alpha_3(t)e^{(-\mu+\beta_4(\lambda))t}f \quad f(0) = \frac{1}{2}$$

$$\dot{f} = -\mu f + 2\beta_4(\lambda)\alpha_3(t)e^{(-\mu+\beta_4(\lambda))t} \quad f(0) = \frac{1}{2}$$

where $\alpha_3(t)$ is a polynomial in t with positive coefficients, $\alpha_3(t) \geqslant \alpha_2(t), \alpha_1(t)$ for $0 \leqslant t < \infty$; $\beta_4(\lambda) \geqslant \beta_3(\lambda)$, $[\beta_3(\lambda)]^2 \geqslant 0$, $\beta_4(\lambda) \to 0$ as $\lambda \to 0$; it follows that

$$|\xi_\rho(t)| \leqslant f(t) \tag{25}$$

for $t \geqslant 0$ as long as $|\xi_\rho(t)| \leqslant 1$. Since

$$\dot{f} \geqslant -\mu f,\ f(0) = \frac{1}{2}$$

we have $f(t) > 0$ for $0 \leqslant t < \infty$, so that

$$\begin{aligned} \dot{f} &\leqslant (-\mu + \beta_4(\lambda))f + 2\beta_4(\lambda)\alpha_3(t)e^{(-\mu+\beta_4(\lambda))t} \\ f(t) &\leqslant e^{(-\mu+\beta_4(\lambda))t}\left\{\frac{1}{2} + \int_0^t 2\beta_4(\lambda)\alpha_3(\tau)\, d\tau\right\} \end{aligned} \tag{26}$$

Thus by restricting δ_0 further, if necessary, it follows that $f(t) \leqslant 1$ for $0 \leqslant t < \infty$ and hence (23), (24), and (25) are valid for all $0 \leqslant t < \infty$. Inequalities (24), (25), and (26) show that (11-ii, iii) hold for $1 \leqslant |\rho| \leqslant 2$. By continuing in this manner (a finite number of steps) one proves (11-ii, iii) valid for all $1 \leqslant |\rho| \leqslant k-1$. This completes the proof of Lemma 3. ∎

For $v \in \tilde{\mathscr{X}}_y^{k-1}$, $w \in \tilde{\mathscr{X}}_z^{k-1}$, define

$$(T_1v)(\theta, x) = \int_{+\infty}^0 e^{-B\sigma}\, Y^{(v,w)}\, d\sigma \tag{27a}$$

$$(T_2w)(\theta, x) = \int_{+\infty}^0 e^{-C\sigma}\, Z^{(v,w)}\, d\sigma \tag{27b}$$

where

$$Y^{(v,w)} = Y(\psi^{(v,w)}, \xi^{(v,w)}, v^{(v,w)}, w^{(v,w)}, \lambda)$$
$$Z^{(v,w)} = Z(\psi^{(v,w)}, \xi^{(v,w)}, v^{(v,w)}, w^{(v,w)}, \lambda)$$
$$v^{(v,w)} = v(\psi^{(v,w)}, \xi^{(v,w)})$$
$$w^{(v,w)} = w(\psi^{(v,w)}, \xi^{(v,w)})$$

and $(\psi^{(v,w)}, \xi^{(v,w)})$ is the solution of (10) which is given explicitly in (11).

For $(v, w) \in \tilde{\mathscr{X}}_y^{k-1} \times \tilde{\mathscr{X}}_z^{k-1}$ define

$$T(v, w) = (T_1 v, T_2 w)$$

LEMMA 4. For $2 \leqslant k < \infty$ and for $|\lambda| \leqslant \delta_1 \leqslant \delta_0$, $\delta_1 > 0$ sufficiently small, the transformation T maps $\tilde{\mathscr{X}}_y^{k-1} \times \tilde{\mathscr{X}}_z^{k-1}$ into itself and is a contraction in the C^{k-2} topology:

$$\|(v, w)\| = \max(\|v\|, \|w\|)$$

$$\|\cdot\| = \|\cdot\|_{k-2} = \max_{0 \leqslant |\rho| \leqslant k-2} \sup_{\theta} \sup_{|x|<1} |D^{\rho}_{(\theta,x)} \cdot |$$

Proof of Lemma 4. The fact that T maps $\tilde{\mathscr{X}}_y^{k-1} \times \tilde{\mathscr{X}}_z^{k-1}$ into itself for $|\lambda| \leqslant \delta_1$, δ_1 sufficiently small, is an immediate consequence of (2-iii, v), (5), and Lemma 3.

To show that T is a contraction in the C^{k-2} topology it is sufficient to show that T_1 is a contraction on $\tilde{\mathscr{X}}_y^{k-1}$ in the C^{k-2} topology uniformly in $w \in \tilde{\mathscr{X}}_z^{k-1}$, and similarly T_2 is a contraction on $\tilde{\mathscr{X}}_z^{k-1}$ in the C^{k-2} topology uniformly in $v \in \tilde{\mathscr{X}}_y^{k-1}$. We will give the argument for T_1; the argument for T_2 is completely analogous. To show T_1 a contraction it is sufficient to show uniformly in θ, $|x| < 1$, $|\lambda| \leqslant \delta_1$, $w \in \tilde{\mathscr{X}}_z^{k-1}$, $0 \leqslant |\rho| \leqslant k-2$, that the inequality

$$|D^{\rho}_{(\theta,x)}(T_1 v^1 - T_1 v^2)| \leqslant \frac{1}{2} \|v^1 - v^2\| \tag{28}$$

holds for $v^1, v^2 \in \tilde{\mathscr{X}}_y^{k-1}$.

Let $(\psi^j, \xi^j) = (\psi^{(v^j,w)}, \xi^{(v^j,w)})$, $(j = 1, 2)$, and let $Y^j = Y^{(v^j,w)} = Y(\psi^j, \xi^j, \ldots)$, $(j = 1, 2)$. To prove (28) we will show that uniformly in θ, $|x| < 1$, $|\lambda| \leqslant \delta_1$, $w \in \tilde{\mathscr{X}}_z^{k-1}$, $0 \leqslant |\rho| \leqslant k-2$, the inequalities

$$\begin{aligned} |D^{\rho}_{(\theta,x)}(\psi^1 - \psi^2)| &\leqslant \alpha(t) e^{\beta(\lambda)t} \|v^1 - v^2\| \\ |D^{\rho}_{(\theta,x)}(\xi^1 - \xi^2)| &\leqslant \alpha(t) e^{(-\mu+\beta(\lambda))t} \|v^1 - v^2\| \end{aligned} \tag{29}$$

hold where $\alpha(t)$ is a polynomial in t with positive coefficients, $\beta(\lambda) \geqslant 0$ is continuous in $|\lambda| \leqslant \delta_1$, $\beta(\lambda) \to 0$ as $\lambda \to 0$. If we suppose (29) valid, then by restricting δ_1 to be sufficiently small, inequality (28) is immediate. One computes from (27)

$$D^{\rho}_{(\theta,x)}(T_1 v^1 - T_1 v^2) = \int_{+\infty}^{0} e^{-B\sigma} D^{\rho}_{(\theta,x)}(Y^1 - Y^2)\, d\sigma$$

and then uses (2-iii, v), (5), Lemma 3, (29) to verify that the interchange of differentiation and integration is valid and that (28) holds. The Mean Value Theorem as presented at the beginning of the proof of Lemma 3 is used repeatedly.

Hence it remains to prove (29). From (10)

$$\frac{d}{dt}(\psi^1 - \psi^2) = \Theta^1 - \Theta^2$$
$$\frac{d}{dt}(\xi^1 - \xi^2) = A(\xi^1 - \xi^2) + X^1 - X^2 \tag{30}$$

where $\Theta^1 = \Theta(\psi^1, \xi^1, v^1(\psi^1, \xi^1), w(\psi^1, \xi^1), \lambda)$, etc. Thus

$$\left|\frac{d}{dt}(\psi^1 - \psi^2)\right| \leq |\Theta^1 - \Theta^2|$$
$$\frac{d}{dt}|\xi^1 - \xi^2|^2 = 2\langle A(\xi^1 - \xi^2), \xi^1 - \xi^2\rangle + 2\langle X^1 - X^2, \xi^1 - \xi^2\rangle$$

and from inequality (4)

$$\frac{d}{dt}|\xi^1 - \xi^2|^2 \leq -4\mu|\xi^1 - \xi^2|^2 + 2|X^1 - X^2|\cdot|\xi^1 - \xi^2|$$

Using the Mean Value Theorem, we obtain

$$|\Theta^1 - \Theta^2| \leq \beta_1(\lambda)\{|\psi^1 - \psi^2| + |\xi^1 - \xi^2| + |v^1(\psi^1, \xi^1) - v^2(\psi^2, \xi^2)| + |w(\psi^1, \xi^1) - w(\psi^2, \xi^2)|\}$$

where $\beta_1(\lambda) \geq 0$, $\beta_1(\lambda) \to 0$ as $\lambda \to 0$. Since

$$v^1(\psi^1, \xi^1) - v^2(\psi^2, \xi^2) = v^1(\psi^1, \xi^1) - v^1(\psi^2, \xi^2) + v^1(\psi^2, \xi^2) - v^2(\psi^2, \xi^2)$$

and $v^1 \in \tilde{\mathscr{X}}_y^{k-1}$, $w \in \tilde{\mathscr{X}}_z^{k-1}$; we have

$$|v^1(\psi^1, \xi^1) - v^2(\psi^2, \xi^2)| \leq |\psi^1 - \psi^2| + |\xi^1 - \xi^2| + \|v^1 - v^2\|$$
$$|w(\psi^1, \xi^1) - w(\psi^2, \xi^2)| \leq |\psi^1 - \psi^2| + |\xi^1 - \xi^2| \tag{31}$$

Thus

$$|\Theta^1 - \Theta^2| \leq \beta_2(\lambda)\{|\psi^1 - \psi^2| + |\xi^1 - \xi^2| + \|v^1 - v^2\|\}$$

where $\beta_2(\lambda) = 3\beta_1(\lambda) \geq 0$, $\beta_2(\lambda) \to 0$ as $\lambda \to 0$. By using the properties of (2-iii, v) and applying the Mean Value Theorem, we obtain

$$|X^1 - X^2| \leq \beta_3(\lambda)\{|\xi^1| + |\xi^2|\}\cdot\{|\psi^1 - \psi^2| + |\xi^1 - \xi^2| + |v^1(\psi^1, \xi^1) - v^2(\psi^2, \xi^2)| + |w(\psi^1, \xi^1) - w(\psi^2, \xi^2)|\} \tag{32}$$

where $\beta_3(\lambda) \geq 0$, $\beta_3(\lambda) \to 0$ as $\lambda \to 0$. From (11-i) for $|x| < 1$

$$|\xi^1(t)| + |\xi^2(t)| \leq 2e^{-\mu t} \tag{33}$$

so that (31) and (33) in (32) yields

$$|X^1 - X^2| \leq \beta_4(\lambda)e^{-\mu t}\{|\psi^1 - \psi^2| + |\xi^1 - \xi^2| + \|v^1 - v^2\|\}$$

where $\beta_4(\lambda) \geq \beta_3(\lambda) + \beta_2(\lambda) \geq 0$, $\beta_4(\lambda) \to 0$ as $\lambda \to 0$. By restricting δ_1 to be sufficiently small, we may assume $\beta_4(\lambda) \leq \mu$ for $|\lambda| \leq \delta_1$; then from (30) we finally obtain

$$\left|\frac{d}{dt}(\psi^1 - \psi^2)\right| \leq \beta_4(\lambda)\{|\psi^1 - \psi^2| + |\xi^1 - \xi^2| + \|v^1 - v^2\|\} \tag{34a}$$

$$\frac{d}{dt}|\xi^1-\xi^2|^2 \leqslant -2\mu|\xi^1-\xi^2|^2+2\beta_4(\lambda)e^{-\mu t}\{|\psi^1-\psi^2|+\|v^1-v^2\|\}\cdot|\xi^1-\xi^2| \tag{34b}$$

Since $\psi^1(0)-\psi^2(0)=0$, we have from (34a) and Lemma 2 for $t \geqslant 0$

$$|\psi^1(t)-\psi^2(t)| \leqslant \beta_4(\lambda)e^{\beta_4(\lambda)t}\int_0^t e^{-\beta_4(\lambda)\tau}\{|\xi^1(\tau)-\xi^2(\tau)|+\|v^1-v^2\|\}\,d\tau$$

Since $\xi^1(0)-\xi^2(0)=0$, the inequality

$$|\xi^1(t)-\xi^2(t)| \leqslant \|v^1-v^2\| \tag{35}$$

is valid in some neighborhood of $t=0$, and as long as (35) remains valid ($t \geqslant 0$),

$$|\psi^1(t)-\psi^2(t)| \leqslant 2\beta_4(\lambda)te^{\beta_4(\lambda)t}\,\|v^1-v^2\| \tag{36}$$

Using (36) in (34b) we obtain

$$\frac{d}{dt}|\xi^1-\xi^2|^2 \leqslant -2\mu|\xi^1-\xi^2|^2+2\beta_4(\lambda)\alpha_1(t)e^{(-\mu+\beta_4(\lambda))t}\|v^1-v^2\|\cdot|\xi^1-\xi^2| \tag{37}$$

where $\alpha_1(t)=1+2\beta_4(\lambda)t$. Comparing (37) with the scalar equation

$$\frac{d}{dt}f^2=-2\mu f^2+2\beta_4(\lambda)\alpha_1(t)e^{(-\mu+\beta_4(\lambda))t}\|v^1-v^2\|\cdot f \tag{38}$$

with $f(0)=\frac{1}{2}\|v^1-v^2\|>0$, we see that

$$|\xi^1(t)-\xi^2(t)| \leqslant f(t) \tag{39}$$

holds as long as (35) remains valid. From (38)

$$\dot f=-\mu f+\beta_4(\lambda)\alpha_1(t)e^{(-\mu+\beta_4(\lambda))t}\|v^1-v^2\|$$

and since for $0 \leqslant t < \infty$

$$\dot f \geqslant -\mu f, \qquad f(0)>0$$

is valid, it follows that $f(t)>0$ for $0 \leqslant t < \infty$ and, therefore,

$$\dot f \leqslant (-\mu+\beta_4(\lambda))f+\beta_4(\lambda)\alpha_1(t)e^{(-\mu+\beta_4(\lambda))t}\|v^1-v^2\|$$

$$f(t) \leqslant e^{(-\mu+\beta_4(\lambda))t}\left\{\frac{1}{2}\|v^1-v^2\|+\int_0^t\beta_4(\lambda)\alpha_1(\tau)d\tau\|v^1-v^2\|\right\}$$

$$f(t) \leqslant \left\{\frac{1}{2}+\beta_4(\lambda)\alpha_2(t)\right\}e^{(-\mu+\beta_4(\lambda))t}\|v^1-v^2\|$$

where $\alpha_2(t)=\int_0^t\alpha_1(\tau)\,d\tau$. Therefore by restricting δ_1 further if necessary, we have for $|\lambda| \leqslant \delta_1$ that

$$f(t) \leqslant \|v^1-v^2\|$$

holds for all $0 \leqslant t < \infty$. Thus (35), (36), (37), and (39) are valid for all $0 \leqslant t < \infty$ and (29) is proved for the case $|\rho|=0$.

Assuming that $k \geqslant 3$ (otherwise we are finished), we now want to show that (29) is valid for $|\rho| = 1$. Let $D^{\rho}_{(\theta,x)}\psi^1 = \psi^1_\rho$, etc. Then from (10),

$$\frac{d}{dt}(\psi^1_\rho - \psi^2_\rho) = \Theta^1_\theta\psi^1_\rho - \Theta^2_\theta\psi^2_\rho + \Theta^1_x\xi^1_\rho - \Theta^2_x\xi^2_\rho + \cdots$$

$$\frac{d}{dt}(\xi^1_\rho - \xi^2_\rho) = A(\xi^1_\rho - \xi^2_\rho) + X^1_\theta\psi^1_\rho - X^2_\theta\psi^2_\rho + \cdots$$

and by means of (2-iii, v), Lemma 1, Lemma 3, and inequality (29) for the case $|\rho| = 0$, and the Mean Value Theorem one achieves

$$\left|\frac{d}{dt}(\psi^1_\rho - \psi^2_\rho)\right| \leqslant \beta_5(\lambda)\,\{|\psi^1_\rho - \psi^2_\rho| + |\xi^1_\rho - \xi^2_\rho|\} + \beta_5(\lambda)\alpha_3(t)e^{\beta_5(\lambda)t}\|v^1 - v^2\|$$

$$\frac{d}{dt}|\xi^1_\rho - \xi^2_\rho|^2 \leqslant -2\mu|\xi^1 - \xi^2|^2 + 2\beta_5(\lambda)\alpha_3(t)e^{(-\mu+\beta_5(\lambda))t}\,\{|\psi^1_\rho - \psi^2_\rho| + \|v^1 - v^2\|\}\cdot|\xi^1 - \xi^2|$$

where $\alpha_3(t)$ is a polynomial in t with positive coefficients, $\beta_5(\lambda) \geqslant 0$, $\beta_5(\lambda) \to 0$ as $\lambda \to 0$. By restricting δ_1 further if necessary, one now readily establishes that (29) is valid for all $|\rho| \leqslant 1$. In an analogous manner one proceeds inductively (a finite number of steps) to establish (29) for all $0 \leqslant |\rho| \leqslant k-2$. This completes the proof of Lemma 4.

The fixed point of the transformation T is designated $v^+ = v^+(\theta, x, \lambda)$, $w^+ = w^+(\theta, x, \lambda)$, and these functions define the stable manifold M^+_λ. The unstable manifold M^-_λ is constructed in an analogous manner.

The function $w^{*+} = w^{*+}(\theta, x, y, \lambda)$ which defines the center-stable manifold M^{*+}_λ is taken to be the unique solution to the differential-integral system

$$\begin{aligned}\dot\theta &= a + \Theta(\theta, x, y, w^{*+}(\theta, x, y, \lambda), \lambda)\\ \dot x &= Ax + X(\theta, x, y, w^{*+}(\theta, x, y, \lambda), \lambda) \qquad (40a)\\ \dot y &= By + Y(\theta, x, y, w^{*+}(\theta, x, y, \lambda), \lambda)\end{aligned}$$

$$w^{*+}(\theta, x, y, \lambda) = \int_{+\infty}^{0} e^{-C\sigma}Z(\psi^{*+}, \xi^{*+}, \eta^{*+}, w^{*+}(\psi^{*+}, \xi^{*+}, \eta^{*+}, \lambda), \lambda)\,d\sigma \qquad (40b)$$

where $\psi^{*+} = \psi^{*+}(t) = \psi^{*+}(t, \theta, x, y, w^{*+}, \lambda)$, $\xi^{*+} = \cdots, \eta^{*+} = \cdots$ represents the unique solution of (40a) with initial condition (θ, x, y) at $t = 0$. This system is also solved by iteration, but with the following modification. For l, m positive integers define

$$\mathscr{X}^l_m = \{\chi = \chi(\theta, x, y) \text{ satisfying } (41\text{-i}, \ldots, \text{v})\}$$

(41-i) χ is a real vector-valued function defined and C^l for all (θ, x, y).

(41-ii) $\dim \chi = m$.

(41-iii) χ has multiple period ω in θ.

(41-iv) $\chi, \chi_{(x,y)} \equiv 0$ when $(x, y) = 0$.

(41-v) $\|\chi\| = \max\limits_{0 \leqslant |\rho| \leqslant l}\ \sup\limits_{(\theta,x,y)} |D^{\rho}_{(\theta,x,y)}\chi(\theta, x, y)| < \infty$.

With the norm in (41-v), $\mathscr{X}^l_m$ is a Banach space. Define $\tilde{\mathscr{X}}^l_m$ to be the closed unit ball in $\mathscr{X}^l_m$. For conciseness let $\tilde{\mathscr{X}}^l_z = \tilde{\mathscr{X}}^l_{\dim z}$. Now, for $w \in \tilde{\mathscr{X}}^k_z$ consider the system

$$\begin{aligned} \theta &= a + \Theta(\theta, x, y, w(\theta, x, y), \lambda) \\ \dot{x} &= Ax + X(\theta, x, y, w(\theta, x, y), \lambda) \qquad (42) \\ \dot{y} &= By + Y(\theta, x, y, w(\theta, x, y), \lambda) \end{aligned}$$

Let $\psi^w = \psi(t) = \psi(t, \theta, x, w, \lambda)$, $\xi^w = \cdots$, $\eta^w = \cdots$ represent the unique solution of (42) with initial condition (θ, x, y) at $t = 0$. Now define the transformation T acting on $\tilde{\mathscr{X}}^k_z$ as follows. For $w \in \tilde{\mathscr{X}}^k_z$,

$$(Tw)(\theta, x, y) = \int_{+\infty}^{0} e^{-C\sigma} Z(\psi^w, \xi^w, \eta^w, w(\psi^w, \xi^w, \eta^w), \lambda)\, d\sigma$$

Corresponding to Lemma 4, we can now prove

LEMMA 5. For $1 \leq k < \infty$ and $|\lambda| \leq \delta_2$, $\delta_2 > 0$ sufficiently small, the transformation T maps $\tilde{\mathscr{X}}^k_z$ into itself and is a contraction in the C^{k-1} topology:

$$\|\cdot\| = \|\cdot\|_{k-1} = \max_{0 \leq |\rho| \leq k-1} \sup_{(\theta, x, y)} |D^{\rho}_{(\theta, x, y)} \cdot |$$

The proof of Lemma 5 is analogous to the proof of Lemma 4. In fact, the details are even easier to carry out. The function $w^{*+} = w^{*+}(\theta, x, y, \lambda)$ is the unique fixed point of T.

The proof of the existence and smoothness of the center-unstable manifold is similar to that for the center-stable manifold. Once we have both M^{*+}_λ and M^{*-}_λ, then

$$M^*_\lambda = M^{*+}_\lambda \cap M^{*-}_\lambda$$

However, we can also construct the center manifold M^*_λ directly by constructing the functions $u^* = u^*(\theta, y, \lambda)$, $w^* = w^*(\theta, y, \lambda)$ as the unique solution of the following differential-integral system;

$$\begin{aligned} \dot{\theta} &= a + \Theta(\theta, u^*(\theta, y, \lambda), y, w^*(\theta, y, \lambda), \lambda) \\ u^*(\theta, y, \lambda) &= \int_{+\infty}^{0} e^{-A\sigma} X(\psi^*, u^*(\psi^*, \eta^*, \lambda), \eta^*, w^*(\psi^*, \eta^*, \lambda), \lambda)\, d\sigma \qquad (43a) \\ \dot{y} &= By + Y(\theta, u^*(\theta, y, \lambda), y, w^*(\theta, y, \lambda), \lambda) \\ w^*(\theta, y, \lambda) &= \int_{+\infty}^{0} e^{-C\sigma} Z(\psi^*, u^*(\psi^*, \eta^*, \lambda), \eta^*, w^*(\psi^*, \eta^*, \lambda), \lambda)\, d\sigma \qquad (43b) \end{aligned}$$

where $\psi^* = \psi^*(t) = \psi^*(t, \theta, u^*, y, w^*, \lambda)$, $\eta^* = \cdots$ represents the unique solution of equations (43a, b) with initial condition (θ, y) at $t = 0$. The procedure followed here is similar to the procedure used to solve (40).

If another invariant manifold

$$M'_\lambda = \{(\theta, x, y, z) \mid \theta \text{ arbitrary}, |x| < 1, y = v'(\theta, x, \lambda), z = w'(\theta, x, \lambda)\}$$

satisfies all the properties of M^+_λ, then M'_λ is composed of solutions of (2), which we designate ψ', ξ', $\eta' = v'(\psi', \xi', \lambda)$, $\zeta' = w'(\psi', \xi', \lambda)$. Since $|\xi'|$ goes exponentially to zero as $t \to 0$, so do $|v'(\psi', \xi', \lambda)|$ and $|w'(\psi', \xi', \lambda)|$. Therefore v', w' must satisfy (3); but since the solution of (3) is unique, $(v', w') = (v^+, w^+)$, and $M'_\lambda = M^+_\lambda$. A similar argument shows that M^-_λ is also unique. An example of nonuniqueness for the center manifold is given in Section 4 below, and this same counter-example can be used to show nonuniqueness for the center-stable and center-unstable manifolds also. This completes the proof of Theorems 1 and 2.

Let us point out what should already be obvious. Namely, the reason that the center-stable manifold has one more derivative than the stable manifold is because the factor $e^{-C\sigma}$ occurring in the integrand in (40b) is an exponentially converging factor, whereas the factor $e^{-B\sigma}$ occurring in the integrand in (27a) is not (see (5)). However, all the manifolds have one more derivative. This will be discussed in Section 5 below.

4. Nonuniqueness of the Center Manifold

Consider the pair of real scalar equations

$$\begin{aligned} \dot{x} &= -x \\ \dot{y} &= y^2 \end{aligned} \tag{44}$$

Dividing $\dot{x}$ by $\dot{y}$ we obtain

$$\frac{dx}{dy} = -\frac{x}{y^2}$$

which can be integrated to yield

$$x = ce^{y^{-1}}$$

where c is the constant of integration. This gives us the following phase portrait in the (y, x) plane for system (44), Figure C-1.

Let

$$u(y, c) = \begin{cases} ce^{y^{-1}} & \text{for } y < 0 \\ 0 & \text{for } y \geqslant 0 \end{cases}$$

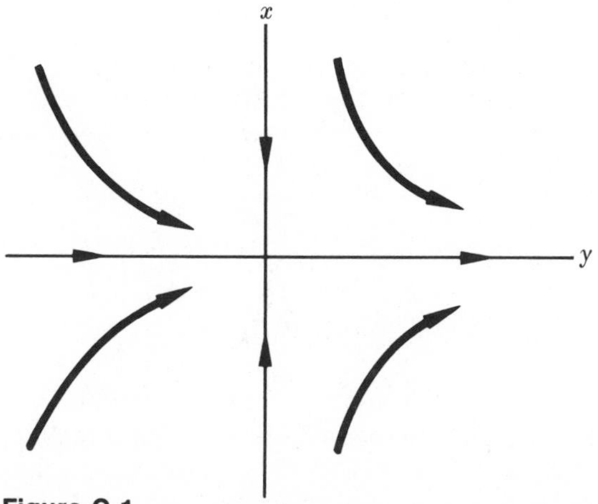

Figure C-1

Clearly $u(0, c) = u_y(0, c) = 0$, so that

$$M(c) = \{(x, y) \mid x = u(y, c),\ y \text{ arbitrary}\}$$

is a center manifold for each real constant c. By adding the scalar equation $\dot{z} = z$ to equation (44) we see that the center-stable and center-unstable manifolds are also nonunique. If, however, the center-stable manifold is stable (the origin is (Liapounov) stable with respect to the center manifold), then it is not difficult to show that the center-stable manifold is unique. With respect to $-t$ the same is true of the center-unstable manifold. If both the center-stable and center-unstable manifolds are unique, then the center manifold is also unique.

5. Additional Smoothness

In our construction of M_λ^+ and M_λ^- the procedure was to construct a mapping T on the closed unit ball $\tilde{\mathscr{X}}^{k-1}$ of the appropriate Banach space with a C^{k-1} topology. Then we proved

$$T\colon \tilde{\mathscr{X}}^{k-1} \to \tilde{\mathscr{X}}^{k-1}$$

and T is a contraction in the C^{k-2} topology. Thus the fixed point, say p, of T has $k-2$ derivatives. But also p is the limit in the C^{k-2} topology of elements in $\tilde{\mathscr{X}}^{k-1}$. Thus the $(k-2)$-th derivatives of p are uniformly Lipschitzian. Using this fact and the proof method of Theorem 4.2 on page 333 of [*1*], one can show that for λ sufficiently small $p \in C^{k-1}$, and even more, $p \in \tilde{\mathscr{X}}^{k-1}$. (The details of this program are quite laborious so we do not present them here.) Thus the manifolds $M_\lambda^+, M_\lambda^- \in C^{k-1}$ where system (2) is C^k, $2 \leqslant k < \infty$. An analogous argument shows that $M_\lambda^{*+}, M_\lambda^{*}, M_\lambda^{*-} \in C^k$ where system (2) is C^k, $1 \leqslant k < \infty$.

When the y equation in (1) is absent, then $M^+ = M^{*+}$, $M^- = M^{*-}$. Therefore in this case M^+, M^- are as differentiable as system (1). This fact will be used in Section 7 below.

Finally, we remark that multiple periodicity in θ for system (1) is not essential in the proof of Theorem 1. Rather, one needs only to be able to put the original system in a form similar to (2), but without multiple periodicity in θ. Of course, the invariant manifolds also will not exhibit multiple periodicity in θ.

6. Perturbation Theory for M^{*+}, M^*, M^{*-}

For simplicity we will not discuss the perturbation theory of M^+, M^- in the general case. But notice that when the center equation (y equation) is absent from (1), then $M^{*+} = M^+$, $M^{*-} = M^-$, so that the results of this section apply to M^+, M^- in that special case.

Consider the real C^k, $1 \leqslant k < \infty$ system of ordinary differential equations

$$\begin{aligned}
\dot{\theta} &= a + \tilde{\Theta}(\theta, x, y, z, \epsilon)\\
\dot{x} &= Ax + \tilde{X}(\theta, x, y, z, \epsilon)\\
\dot{y} &= By + \tilde{Y}(\theta, x, y, z, \epsilon)\\
\dot{z} &= Cz + \tilde{Z}(\theta, x, y, z, \epsilon)
\end{aligned} \tag{45}$$

where a, A, B, and C are as in (1); θ, x, etc. are vectors; ϵ is a real (perturbation) scalar; $\tilde{\Theta}, \tilde{X}, \tilde{Y}, \tilde{Z}$ are defined, and C^k in

$$N_\delta = \{(\theta, x, y, z, \epsilon) \mid \theta \text{ arbitrary},\ |x| + |y| + |z| + |\epsilon| < \delta\}$$

for some δ positive and have multiple period ω in θ; $\widetilde{\Theta}$, $\widetilde{X}$, $\widetilde{Y}$, $\widetilde{Z}$, $(\widetilde{X}, \widetilde{Y}, \widetilde{Z})_{(x,y,z)} \equiv 0$ when $(x, y, z, \epsilon)=0$. Thus when $\epsilon = 0$, (45) reduces to a system of the form (1).

THEOREM 3. For system (45) there exists invariant manifolds

$$M^{*+} = \{(\theta, x, y, z) \mid \theta \text{ arbitrary}, |x| + |y| + |\epsilon| < \delta_1, z = w^{*+}(\theta, x, y, \epsilon)\}$$
$$M^{*} = \{(\theta, x, y, z) \mid \theta \text{ arbitrary}, x = u^{*}(\theta, y, \epsilon), |y| + |\epsilon| < \delta_1, z = w^{*}(\theta, y, \epsilon)\}$$
$$M^{*-} = \{(\theta, x, y, z) \mid \theta \text{ arbitrary}, x = u^{*-}(\theta, y, z, \epsilon), |y| + |z| + |\epsilon| < \delta_1\}$$

where w^{*+}, u^{*}, w^{*}, u^{*-} are real vector-valued functions defined and C^k in some neighborhood N_{δ_1} for δ_1 sufficiently small; w^{*+}, u^{*}, w^{*}, u^{*-} have multiple period ω in θ; w^{*+}, u^{*}, w^{*}, u^{*-}, $(w^{*+}, u^{*}, w^{*}, u^{*-})_{(x,y,z)} \equiv 0$ when $(x, y, z, \epsilon) = 0$.

The proof of this theorem is essentially a copy of the proof of Theorem 1. One merely introduces a scalar change of variables

$$(x, y, z, \epsilon) \to (\lambda x, \lambda y, \lambda z, \lambda^2 \epsilon)$$

and then changes the system outside a neighborhood of the (x, y, z, ϵ) origin similar, as in the proof of Theorem 1. The essential property of the transformed system will be the analogue of (2–v), namely,

$$D^{\rho}_{(\theta,x,y,z,\epsilon)}(\Theta, X, Y, Z) \to 0$$

uniformly in $(\theta, x, y, z, \epsilon)$ as $\lambda \to 0$ for $0 \leqslant |\rho| \leqslant k$, where analogous to the procedure in the proof of Theorem 1,

$$\Theta(\theta, x, y, z, \epsilon, \lambda) = \varnothing(|x|^2 + |y|^2 + |z|^2 + \epsilon^2 + K\lambda^2)\widetilde{\Theta}(\theta, \lambda x, \lambda y, \lambda z, \lambda^2 \epsilon)$$

and so on. With this property there is no difficulty in solving the appropriate differential-integral system for w^{*+}, etc., provided λ is sufficiently small.

If there is no center equation (y equation) in (45) then $M^{*+} = M^{+}$, $M^{*-} = M^{-}$. Since we have not defined M^{+}, M^{-} in the general perturbation case, we can take this as a definition. Also, with no center equation in (45) the center manifold

$$M^{*} = \{(\theta, x, z) \mid \theta \text{ arbitrary}, x = u^{*}(\theta, \epsilon), z = w^{*}(\theta, \epsilon), |\epsilon| \leqslant \delta_1\}$$

is the same as what is known as the periodic surface. There is an extensive literature concerning this invariant manifold. See for example (2), (6). As a corollary to Theorem 3 we have that the periodic surface is as differentiable as the system of differential equations.

7. Perturbation Theory without Center

In this section we want to discuss how M^{+}, M^{-} vary with respect to the perturbing function. Consider the real C^k, $1 \leqslant k < \infty$, system of ordinary differential equations

$$\begin{aligned} \dot{\theta} &= a + \Theta(\theta, x, y) + \epsilon\hat{\Theta}(\theta, x, y) \\ \dot{x} &= Ax + X(\theta, x, y) + \epsilon\hat{X}(\theta, x, y) \\ \dot{y} &= By + Y(\theta, x, y) + \epsilon\hat{Y}(\theta, x, y) \end{aligned} \tag{46}$$

where A, B are constant matrices in real canonical form; A has eigenvalues with negative real parts; B has eigenvalues with positive real parts; θ, x, etc. are vectors; a is a constant vector; ϵ is a perturbation parameter; Θ, $\hat{\Theta}$, X, $\hat{X}$, Y, $\hat{Y}$ are defined and C^k in

$$N_\delta = \{(\theta, x, y) \mid \theta \text{ arbitrary}, |x| + |y| < \delta\}$$

and have multiple period ω in θ; Θ, X, Y, $(X, Y)_{(x,y)} \equiv 0$ when $(x, y) = 0$.

Let P (for perturbation) represent the triple $(\hat{\Theta}, \hat{X}, \hat{Y})$. From Theorem 4 we know that locally (for (x, y, ϵ) sufficiently small) there exists stable and unstable manifolds $M^\pm = M^\pm(P, \epsilon)$. Since $M^\pm(P, 0)$ are independent of P, let $M^\pm(P, 0) = M_0^\pm$. Define $\mathscr{X}^{k,l}$ to be the set of all triples $P = (\hat{\Theta}, \hat{X}, \hat{Y})$ which are defined and C^k in N_δ, have multiple period ω in θ, and satisfy

$$\max_{0 \leq |p| \leq l} \sup_\theta \sup_{|x|+|y|<\delta} |D^p_{(\theta,x,y)} P| \leq 1$$

where $l \leq k$ is a positive integer. For $P \in \mathscr{X}^{k,l}$ let

$$M^+(P, \epsilon) = \{(\theta, x, y) \mid \theta \text{ arbitrary}, y = v^+(\theta, x, P, \epsilon)\}$$

where P in the argument of v^+ denotes a functional dependence.

THEOREM 4. Uniformly in $P \in \mathscr{X}^{k,l}$, v^+ is defined and C^k on

$$N^{\delta_0} = \{(\theta, x, \epsilon) \mid \theta \text{ arbitrary}, |x| < \delta_0, |\epsilon| < \delta_0\}$$

where δ_0 is a sufficiently small positive constant which is independent of P. Moreover

$$\max_{0 \leq |p| \leq l} \sup_\theta \sup_{|x|<\delta_0} |D^p_{(\theta,x)}(v^+(\theta, x, P, \epsilon) - v^+(\theta, x))| \to 0$$

as $\epsilon \to 0$ uniformly in $P \in \mathscr{X}^{k,l}$, where $v^+(\theta, x) \overset{\text{def}}{=} v^+(\theta, x, P, 0)$.

The proof of Theorem 4 is also essentially the same as the proof of Theorem 1. After introducing a scalar change of variables and changing the system outside a neighborhood of the origin, the assertions are readily proved. But the assertions are logically equivalent for both the original system (46) and the transformed system. A similar theorem holds for M^-.

Since A, B in (46) have eigenvalues with nonzero real parts, $M^* = M^+ \cap M^-$.

THEOREM 5. M^+, M^- have the following characterization for ϵ sufficiently small:

$$M^+ = \{(\theta, x, y) \mid (\psi, \xi, \eta) \to M^* \quad \text{as } t \to +\infty\}$$

$$M^- = \{(\theta, x, y) \mid (\psi, \xi, \eta) \to M^* \quad \text{as } t \to -\infty\}$$

where $\psi = \psi(t, \theta, x, y, \epsilon)$, $\xi = \cdots$, $\eta = \cdots$ represents the unique solution of (46) with initial condition (θ, x, y) at $t = 0$.

Proof. It is sufficient to prove this theorem for a system which has been transformed from (46). Let

$$\begin{aligned} \dot{\theta} &= a + \Theta(\theta, x, y, \epsilon) \\ \dot{x} &= Ax + X(\theta, x, y, \epsilon) \\ \dot{y} &= By + Y(\theta, x, y, \epsilon) \end{aligned} \tag{47}$$

be a transformed system. If we introduce the change of variables

$$p = x - u^-(\theta, y, \epsilon) \qquad q = y - v^+(\theta, x, \epsilon) \tag{48}$$

then in these new coordinates (47) has the form

$$\begin{aligned} \dot\theta &= a + \widetilde{\Theta}(\theta, p, q, \epsilon) \\ \dot p &= Ap + P(\theta, p, q, \epsilon) \\ \dot q &= Bq + Q(\theta, p, q, \epsilon) \end{aligned} \tag{49}$$

where

$$\begin{aligned} |P(\theta, p, q, \epsilon)| &\leqslant \mu|p| \\ |Q(\theta, p, q, \epsilon)| &\leqslant \mu|q| \end{aligned} \tag{50}$$

and μ is the positive constant given in (5). (B in (49) is C in (5).) Let us compute P, for example, to see that inequality (50) is true. From (48)

$$\begin{aligned} \dot p = \dot x - \dot v^- &= Ax + X - v_{\bar\theta}^-\{a + \Theta\} - v_{\bar x}^-\{Ax + X\} \\ &= Ax - v_{\bar\theta}^-\{a + \Theta(\theta, v^-, y, \epsilon)\} - v_{\bar x}^-\{Ax + X(\theta, v^-, y, \epsilon)\} + X(\theta, p + v^-, y, \epsilon\} + v_{\bar\theta}^-\{\Theta(\theta, v^-, y, \epsilon) - \Theta(\theta, p + v^-, y, \epsilon)\} \\ &\quad + v_{\bar x}^-\{X(\theta, v^-, y, \epsilon) - X(\theta, p + v^-, y, \epsilon)\} \\ &= Ax - Av^- - X(\theta, v^-, y, \epsilon) + X(\theta, p + v^-, y, \epsilon) + v_{\bar\theta}^-\{\Theta(\theta, v^-, y, \epsilon) - \Theta(\theta, p + v^-, y, \epsilon)\} + v_{\bar x}^-\{X(\theta, v^-, y, \epsilon) \\ &\quad - X(\theta, p + v^-, y, \epsilon)\} \\ &= Ap + P(\theta, p, q, \epsilon) \end{aligned}$$

Thus we see that $P \in C^{k-1}$ and that P satisfies (50), provided Θ, X, Y have sufficiently small first-order derivatives. From (5), (49), and (50),

$$\begin{aligned} \frac{d}{dt}|p|^2 &= 2\langle Ap, p\rangle + 2\langle P, p\rangle \\ &\leqslant -4\mu|p|^2 + 2\mu|p|^2 \\ &\leqslant -2\mu\,|p|^2 \\ \frac{d}{dt}|q|^2 &= 2\langle Bq, q\rangle + 2\langle Q, q\rangle \\ &\geqslant 4\mu|q|^2 - 2\mu|q|^2 \\ &\geqslant 2\mu|q|^2 \end{aligned}$$

Our theorem follows immediately from these differential inequalities.

Finally we state a theorem which is closely related to Theorem 4. We want to show that $M^+(P, \epsilon) \to M^+(P_0, \epsilon)$ in the C^{l-1} topology as $P \to P_0$ in the C^l topology, where ϵ is small but fixed. A similar statement will hold relative to M^-.

THEOREM 6. For $P, P_0 \in \mathscr{X}^{k,l}$ if $P \to P_0$ in the C^l topology,

$$\max_{0\leq|\rho|\leq l} \sup_{\theta} \sup_{|x|+|y|<\delta} |D^{\rho}_{(\theta,x,y)}(P - P_0)| \to 0$$

then $v^+(\theta, x, P, \epsilon) \to v^+(\theta, x, P_0, \epsilon)$ in the C^{l-1} topology:

$$\max_{0\leq|\rho|\leq l-1} \sup_{\theta} \sup_{|x|<\delta_0} |D^{\rho}_{(\theta,x)}\{v^+(\theta, x, P, \epsilon) - v^+(\theta, x, P_0, \epsilon)\}| \to 0$$

The proof of Theorem 6 is obtained by introducing the change of variables (48) relative to P_0:

$$p = x - u^-(\theta, y, P_0, \epsilon)$$

$$q = y - v^+(\theta, x, P_0, \epsilon)$$

System (49) will now only be C^{k-1}, but otherwise Theorem 6 reduces to Theorem 4 with only minor modifications.

BIBLIOGRAPHY

(1) E. Coddington and N. Levinson, *Theory of Ordinary Differential Equations,* McGraw-Hill, New York, 1955.

(2) S. P. Diliberto, *Perturbation theorems for periodic surfaces,* Rend. Circ. Mat. (Palmero), **9** (1960), 1–35, and **10** (1961), 1–51.

(3) J. Hale, *Integral manifolds of perturbed differential systems,* Ann. Math., **73** (1961), 496–531.

(4) A. Kelley, *The center manifold and integral manifolds for Hamiltonian systems,* Notices Amer. Math. Soc., **12** (1965), 143–144.

(5) V. A. Pliss, *Principle reduction in the theory of the stability of motion* (Russian), Izv. Akad. Nauk S.S.S.R., Mat. Ser. **28** (1964), 1297–1324.

(6) R. J. Sacker, *A new approach to the perturbation theory of invariant surfaces,* Comm. Pure Appl. Math., **18** (1965), 717–732.

BIBLIOGRAPHY

ABRAHAM, R.

[1] *Transversality in manifolds of mappings,* Bull. Amer. Math. Soc., **69** (1963), 470–474.

[2] *Lectures of Smale on Differential Topology,* Columbia University, New York, 1962.

[3] *Generic Properties of Riemannian Metrics* (to appear).

ABRAHAM, R. and MARSDEN, J.

[1] *Foundations of Mechanics,* Benjamin, New York, 1967.

BROWN, A.

[1] *Functional dependence,* Trans. Amer. Math. Soc., **38** (1935), 379–394.

CHEVALLEY, C.

[1] *Theory of Lie Groups,* Princeton Univ. Press, Princeton, New Jersey, 1946.

DIEUDONNE, J.

[1] *Foundations of Modern Analysis,* Academic Press, New York, 1960.

EILENBERG, S. and CARTAN, H.

[1] *Local Categories and Functors,* Int. Symp. on Algebraic Topology, Mexico City, 1958, 16–23.

FRIEDMAN, A.

[1] *Generalized Functions and Partial Differential Equations,* Prentice Hall, Englewood Cliffs, New Jersey, 1963.

GLAESER, G.

[1] *Étude de quelques algèbres Tayloriennes,* J. Anal. Math., **11** (1958), 1–118.

HARTMAN, P.

[1] *Ordinary Differential Equations,* Wiley, New York, 1964.

HOCKING, J. and YOUNG, G.

[1] *Topology,* Addison-Wesley, Reading, Massachusetts, 1961.

KELLEY, J.

[1] *General Topology,* Van Nostrand, Princeton, New Jersey, 1955.

KNESER, M.

[1] *Abhängigkeit von funktionen,* Math. Z., **54** (1951), 34–51.

KUPKA, I.

[1] *Contribution à la théorie des champs génériques,* Contributions to Differential Equations, **2** (1963), 457–484; **3** (1964), 411–420.

LANG, S.

[1] *Introduction to Differentiable Manifolds,* Interscience, New York, 1962.

LEVINE, H.

[1] *Singularities of Differentiable Mappings,* Mathematisches Institut der Universitat Bonn, Bonn, 1959.

MARCINKIEWICZ, J. and ZYGMUND, A.

[1] *On the differentiability of functions and summability of trigonometric series,* Fund. Math., **26** (1936), 1–43.

METIVIER, M.

[1] *Valeurs critiques des applications différentiables,* Anais de Acad. Brazileina de Ciencias, **36** (1964), 383–397.

MILNOR, J.

[1] *Topology from a Differentiable Viewpoint,* Univ. of Virginia Press, Charlottesville, Virginia, 1966.

MORSE, A. P.

[1] *The behavior of a function on its critical set,* Ann. Math., **40** (1939), 62–70.

NEMITSKII, V.

[1] *Some modern problems in the qualitative theory of ordinary differential equations,* Russian Math. Surveys, **20** (1965), 1–34.

PEIXOTO, M.

[1] *Qualitative theory of differential equations and structural stability* (to appear).

[2] *On an approximation theorem of Kupka and Smale* (to appear).

PONTRIAGIN, L.

[1] *Ordinary Differential Equations,* Addison-Wesley, Reading, Massachusetts, 1962.

ROBINSON, A.

[1] *Introduction to Model Theory and the Metamathematics of Algebra,* North Holland, Amsterdam, 1963.

SEIDENBERG, A.

[1] *A new decision procedure for elementary algebra,* Ann. Math., **60** (1954), 365–374.

SMALE, S.

[1] *Stable manifolds for differential equations and diffeomorphisms,* Topologia Differenziale, C.I.M.E. (I), Edizioni Cremonese, Rome, 1962.

[2] *An infinite dimensional version of Sard's theorem,* Amer. J. Math., **87** (1965), 861–866.

STERNBERG, S.

[1] *Lectures on Differential Geometry,* Prentice-Hall, Englewood Cliffs, New Jersey, 1964.

TARSKI, A.

[1] *A Decision Procedure for Elementary Algebra and Geometry,* University of California Press, Berkeley, California, 1951.

THOM, R.

[1] *Quelques propriétes globales des variétés différentiables,* Comm. Math. Helv., **28** (1954), 17–86.

[2] *Un lemma sur les applications différentiables,* Bol. Soc. Mat. Mex. (2), **1** (1956), 59–71.

[3] *The Work of Stephen Smale,* Proceedings of the International Congress of Mathematicians, 1966 (to appear).

WHITNEY, H.

[1] *Analytic extensions of differentiable functions defined on closed sets,* Trans. Amer. Math. Soc., **36** (1934), 369–387.

[2] *Elementary structure of real algebraic varieties,* Ann. Math., **66** (1957), 545–556.

INDEX